Understanding and Teaching
Elementary School Mathematics

Understanding and Teaching
Elementary School Mathematics

by David Rappaport
Professor of Education
Illinois Teachers College – Chicago (North)

John Wiley & Sons, Inc. *New York London Sydney*

Library of Congress Catalog Card Number: 66-10587
Printed in the United States of America

To my wife Ayala

Preface

Ever since the Soviet Union launched the first satellite in 1957 many American leaders have been alarmed by the mathematics curriculum of the public schools. They consider the mathematics program inadequate to meet the needs of the world today. Although leaders in mathematics education had been advocating changes in the mathematics curriculum, their pleas did not receive wide public support. Now many school administrators who had previously been apathetic to change are eager to join the bandwagon for a new and modern mathematics program.

There appears to be general agreement that the mathematics curricuium has to be upgraded, and such changes have already been effected. What was formerly taught in college is now being taught in many high schools. Many topics formerly taught in high school are now introduced in junior high school. In fact the trend for change has even reached first grade in elementary school. Recognition of the need for a radical change in the mathematics curriculum, however, has not produced agreement on exactly what changes should be made or how they should be introduced.

School administrators were, and are, faced with some dilemmas. Should the traditional program be kept without change until experimental studies indicate that the "new" mathematics is superior to the old and that it is appropriate for elementary school children? Should the traditional program be discarded completely and replaced by "modern" mathematics? Should changes be introduced gradually and, if so, how, when, and how much? If new programs are to be introduced, which ones? Should it be the SMSG, the Madison project, the Maryland project, the Ball State program, the Greater Cleveland program, the University of Illinois program, the Mathematics Workshop for Children, the Suppes material, or any of a host of other programs?

The content of the new mathematics program is not the only problem facing schools today. Are the teachers ready and qualified to teach the "new" mathematics? If teachers are not ready now for the "new" mathematics, can they be trained while they are teaching this unfamiliar material? Or should the school wait until they have competent teachers?

Some administrators have been reluctant to introduce the new programs in their schools. Others have selected teachers to attend institutes that train teachers for the new programs. But some administrators have been overzealous for change and have imposed a "modern" mathematics curriculum on unwilling and unprepared teachers. They have considered change synonymous with improvement.

Teacher education institutions, in response to wide demand, are offering courses that emphasize both the new content and the new teaching methods to in-service as well as pre-service teachers. What is generally lacking is a balance between the "new" and the "old."

It is the aim of this book to present both new and traditional material. It is assumed that most traditional mathematics is good mathematics and that much of the new mathematics should be incorporated into all schools. This book attempts to present the content and the methods of teaching mathematics to children and to help teachers who fear the "new" mathematics because they do not understand it. Often the traditional mathematics that has been included is also presented from the "new" point of view. Both old and new content is based on sound pedagogical and psychological principles, which should satisfy the "traditionalists" who seek improved teaching methods and the "modernists" who emphasize new content as well as good teaching methods.

Although the new elementary school mathematics program calls for topics in algebra, geometry, set concepts, and logical implications, the bulk of the mathematics program is still arithmetic. The concepts basic to arithmetic, however, are also basic to algebra, and the emphasis on principles will help children to understand mathematics.

I am most grateful to Dr. Roy Dubisch of the University of Washington for his comments and suggestions, to Miss Dolores Kenders and Mrs. Roberta Schaefer for typing the manuscript, and above all to the students in my methods classes who challenged me at all times to make mathematics meaningful to them.

David Rappaport

Contents

Chapter 1 *Basic Principles*

1.1 MATHEMATICS IN TODAY'S SCHOOLS

Some form of mathematics has been used by man from the very beginning of his existence. He learned to count and to measure. But he also had to invent a language by which to communicate his ideas of quantity to other men. As civilization became more complex, mathematics became more important to man's existence. It is self-evident that advances in science and technology would not have been possible without the development of mathematics. Mathematics has not only achieved a prominent position in the development of civilization but it has also been an indispensable instrument in its development.

The schools have responded to the mathematical needs of society by giving a prominent place to arithmetic in the elementary school curriculum. But in doing so the impression has often been given that arithmetic is not really mathematics, or that it is lowly mathematics. Examine the titles of textbooks. *Arithmetic Grades 1 to 6, Mathematics Grade 8, Seeing through Arithmetic, Seeing through Mathematics* are a few titles of recent textbooks. This distinction between arithmetic and mathematics gives the impression that arithmetic is for children whereas mathematics is for adults. Most people will say that they learned arithmetic in elementary school and mathematics in high school. This kind of distinction is generally not made for science. One studies elementary science in elementary school and advanced science in high school or in college, but at all levels it is called science. This attitude toward arithmetic is not shared by the mathematicians. In their opinion arithmetic is not only mathematics; it is also important mathematics. The renowned mathematician K. F. Gauss (1777–1855) assigned the greatest importance to arithmetic when he said:

Mathematics is Queen of the Sciences and Arithmetic the Queen of Mathematics. She often condescends to render service to astronomy and other natural sciences, but under all circumstances the first place is her due.*

Many teachers and school administrators consider arithmetic to be a tool subject. In their view the main reason for teaching arithmetic is social utility. It is necessary for the solution of practical problems of everyday life or as an important tool for the solution of problems in science and technology. Thus there is the impression that mathematics deals with theory whereas arithmetic deals with practical applications. This utilitarian interpretation of arithmetic has resulted in an overemphasis on the learning of skills and processes and a neglect of the meanings in arithmetic.

An opposing view considers the study of arithmetic as a study of number theory. According to this interpretation arithmetic is a branch of mathematics that is highly advanced and a challenge to the most mature. Although the child's first experience with mathematics is through arithmetic, he learns only the elementary concepts of arithmetic in elementary school. He may continue to study arithmetic throughout his educational career.

This second view of arithmetic was its original meaning, according to Dantzig, who wrote:

The Greek word *arithmos* meant number, and *arithmetica* was the theory of numbers even as late as the seventeenth century. What we call arithmetic today was *logistica* to the Greeks, and in the Middle Ages was called, as we saw, algorism.†

1.2 THE CHANGING ELEMENTARY SCHOOL MATHEMATICS CURRICULUM

For many years mathematics was taught in a traditional program: arithmetic in the first eight grades, algebra in grades 9 and 11, geometry in grades 10 and 11, and trigonometry in grade 12. The grammar school program was devoted only to arithmetic; the other mathematical subjects were taught in high school. The arithmetic program was divided into two parts: in the first six grades the children were taught the fundamental processes of addition, subtraction, multiplication, and division,

*Quoted by Eric Temple Bell, *Mathematics Queen and Servant of Science*. New York: McGraw-Hill Book Company, 1951. p. 1.

†Tobias Dantzig, *Number, The Language of Science*, New York: The Macmillan Company, 1954. p. 37.

with integers, fractions, and decimals; in grades 7 and 8 they learned to apply their computational skills to social, useful, or practical situations. The topics generally covered in the last two years of elementary school were areas, volumes, surfaces, percentages, taxes, commissions, insurance, installment buying, and interest. Paul Rosenbloom characterized this mathematics curriculum as appropriate to the conditions of 1910 when the majority of the pupils left school before high school, and when the majority of the adults were unskilled laborers.*

Many organizations, groups, and individuals have been working since 1957 to change the mathematics curriculum. They have accepted the challenge to prepare children mathematically for the conditions that they face today and also for conditions that they will face in the second half of the twentieth century. Remarkable progress has been made in these efforts. The programs that have already been initiated indicate the trends for the future. In some areas the mathematics curriculum of the elementary school is a completely new one that bears very little resemblance to the traditional program.

Although many schools have experimented with new mathematics programs, most schools are still teaching the same old curriculum in the same old ways. It takes a long time to modify an entrenched curriculum. Nevertheless a good beginning has been made despite the fact that new programs have, at times, been imposed upon reluctant teachers by school administrators eager to be the first to get on a bandwagon.

What is this new elementary school mathematics program? An examination of new textbooks, experimental studies, pamphlets, and enrichment material reveals such topics as sets, numeration systems other than the decimal system, modular numbers, number line, functions, slide rule, equations, sentences, logic, operation with sets, exponents, and geometry. It is no longer correct to think of elementary school mathematics as only arithmetic. Many authors of elementary school textbooks, although the titles of the books are generally arithmetic, now include topics in algebra, geometry, sets, and numeration systems. Some of the notable departures from the traditional mathematics program are described in this chapter.

The Hawley and Suppes Geometry Material.† These two books for grades 1, 2, and 3 teach children to make geometry constructions with straightedge and compass. The constructions included are: drawing

*Paul C. Rosenbloom, "Mathematics K-14," *Educational Leadership*, March 1962. pp. 359–363.

†Newton Hawley and Patrick Suppes. *Geometry for Primary Grades*, Books 1 and 2. San Francisco: Holden-Day, 1960, 1961. 126 pages each.

line segments, bisecting an angle, drawing perpendicular lines, reproducing given angles and triangles, drawing polygons, circles, equilateral triangles, bisecting a line segment, and constructing squares, rectangles, and similar triangles. In addition to the constructions the children learn the appropriate vocabulary of geometry such as length, segment, arc, diameter, similar, perpendicular, square, isosceles, equilateral, diagonal, quadrilateral, pentagon, hexagon, and perpendicular bisector. The children are also exposed to some propositions of geometry. One may assume that this material is for a select group of gifted children. The authors, however, state that this material was not intended for gifted children but, rather, for all children.

*The University of Illinois Arithmetic Project.** The material developed by David Page uses the number line and frames to develop an understanding of whole numbers, fractions, negative numbers, the commutative law for addition and multiplication, the associative law for addition and multiplication, the distributive law, exponents, equations, and functions. Another unit is based on a square array of numbers from 1 to 100. The aim is to develop mathematical reasoning. Page does not specify the grade level for this material. The teacher who knows the abilities of the children will decide what material to use and in which grade to teach the various units. Page merely mentions that the project material has been used successfully from the first grade and up.

Frames, introduced by Max Beberman at the University of Illinois, are now widely used by program directors, textbook writers, and teachers. A frame in the form of a geometric design is used as a placeholder for a numeral. A square, rectangle, circle, triangle, pentagon, or any simple closed curve may be used. In the example $\square + 6 = 13$, the $\square$ is a placeholder for the numeral 7. We could express the same thought by using other frames such as:

$$\square + 6 = 13$$
$$\triangle + 6 = 13$$
$$\bigcirc + 6 = 13$$
$$⬠ + 6 = 13$$

The Madison Project.† This material developed by Davis includes algebra and some coordinate geometry for children in the fourth,

*David A. Page, *Number Lines, Functions, and Fundamental Topics.* Urbana, Illinois: University of Illinois Arithmetic Project, 1961. 192 pp.

†Robert B. Davis, *Discovery in Algebra.* Reading, Mass.: Addison Wesley, 1960. 234 pp.

fifth, and sixth grades. Some children may begin this work as early as the third grade; others may have to wait until the seventh or even the eighth grade. All children, according to Davis, can learn this new mathematics.

This project contains material on sentences, simple equations, quadratic equations, graphs, signed numbers, inequalities, matrix games, identities, simultaneous equations, postulates, and logical implication. The children use frames in learning the basic concepts of mathematics.

*School Mathematics Study Group (SMSG).** This group of university professors, college teachers, high school teachers of mathematics, and elementary school teachers is supported by the National Science Foundation. They were divided into writing panels and have developed a number of units in all phases of mathematics ranging from the fourth grade in the elementary school through the twelfth grade in high school. It is the most comprehensive effort to create a sequential mathematics program in grades K-12. Whereas other groups have developed a few innovations and have introduced a few new concepts, either as enrichment or as part of the regular program, SMSG material is a radical departure from the traditional mathematics curriculum.

The fourth, fifth, and sixth grade material, for example, contains such topics as sets, operation with sets, numbers and numerals, the number line, numeration systems, the nature and properties of addition, subtraction, multiplication and division, geometry based on the set concept, prime numbers, and exponents. Throughout all the units the basic concepts of mathematics are developed, and arithmetic, algebra, and geometry are presented as related mathematics unified through the concept of sets.

1.3 LEARNING THEORIES

There have been two general theories of learning that have influenced the educational practices of the American Schools since 1900. Although each of these schools of thought has several variations, they, nevertheless, stand out as two distinct theories of learning. The first of them is connectionism, or bond psychology, and the second is gestalt psychology.

Bond Psychology. The general premise of this educational psychology as developed by Edward L. Thorndike, its chief spokesman for more than thirty years, is that learning takes place through the

*School Mathematics Study Group, *Mathematics for the Elementary School.* New Haven, Conn.: Yale University Press, 1961. 925 pp.

establishing of a bond, or connection, between a stimulus and a response. A complicated process is broken up into a number of simple steps, each of which constitutes a bond. These bonds are strengthened by repeated use. Several laws were stated to explain the development of bonds; among the most important were the laws of frequency, recency, and effect. Thus bonds were stronger when used more frequently or established more recently and when the effect was pleasanter.

The teacher's task is to divide knowledge into minute quantities that constitute the bonds the child must establish. The teacher determines the bonds to be formed, when they should be formed, and how they should be formed. Since bonds that are established must be strengthened by use, mathematics teachers resorted to drill and more drill as the dominant technique in teaching. It was assumed that the child who made the correct response, that is, derived the correct answer, understood the process. Too often teachers considered it unnecessary to offer any explanations in their teaching and merely showed children how to perform the process.

Thorndike offered teachers the following seven golden rules to help them establish bonds in a correct way:*

1. Consider the situation the pupil faces.
2. Consider the response you wish to connect with it.
3. Form the bond; do not expect it to come by a miracle.
4. Other things being equal, form no bonds that will have to be broken.
5. Other things being equal, do not form two or three bonds when one will serve.
6. Other things being equal, form bonds in the way that they are required later to act.
7. Favor, therefore, the situations which life itself will offer and the responses which life itself will demand.

Although this may be somewhat of an oversimplification, bond psychology emphasized the atomization of knowledge into small steps that the teacher showed children; and it held that learning took place when bonds were established, that bonds were strengthened by drill, that crutches were to be avoided, since it was wrong to establish a bond that would later have to be broken, and that a child who learned the parts was supposed to have learned the whole process.

Gestalt Psychology. Learning, according to gestalt psychology, takes place through analysis, structure, restructure, patterns, and reorganization of a situation. The child begins with the whole and

*Edward L. Thorndike, *The Psychology of Arithmetic*. New York: The Macmillan Company, 1922. p. 101.

breaks it up into parts. He then relates the parts to the whole and the whole to the parts. Every time there is a new analysis of the situation there is a better understanding because the relationship between the whole and the parts becomes clearer. Learning is a continual reorganization of knowledge. According to gestalt psychology, a child may learn a series of steps without understanding the process as a whole. Whereas bond psychology emphasizes drill, gestalt psychology relies on insight. The child who is exposed to a particular situation analyzes it and discovers the meaning or the pattern or structure. He may make the discovery suddenly, in a moment of insight. Once the basic meaning is understood, it is not necessary to resort to drill to strengthen the so-called bond. The child who discovers relationships himself will remember the facts longer and will apply this knowledge more readily to new situations. It is the contention of gestalt psychologists that drill often prevents insight.

1.4 EDUCATIONAL PRINCIPLES

Leading educators emphasize the teaching of mathematics for understanding rather than for the sole purpose of learning computational skills. Although it is expected that children should be able to compute and to derive the correct answers when required in practical situations, it is important for children to learn mathematics as mathematics. There are basic meanings in mathematics which should be understood. There is a rationale to mathematics.

The child understands the meanings best when he makes his own discoveries. Instead of showing children the "what" and the "how," teachers should conduct the mathematics classes in such a way that children will develop insight and will see the relationships that constitute the basic concepts in mathematics. The child who discovers the relationships will also be able to explain the "why."

In order to help the child discover the important generalizations there should be sufficient manipulative devices that each child can use. These are concrete aids such as number blocks, abaci, fraction kits, counting frames, placeholder charts, and number lines that the child can use when he finds it necessary.

The child should proceed from the concrete to the abstract. Some children may substitute pictures for concrete objects. At a certain period in his development the child will discard concrete devices and substitute semiconcrete devices such as lines or circles. He may learn to add 5 and 3 by making 5 marks (/////) and then 3 marks (///) and then count to find the sum 8. At the highest level the child discards all manipulative devices and achieves the required results by operating with the abstract symbols.

Although the advocates of bond psychology frowned upon the use of semiconcrete devices because they were crutches, modern educators support the use of crutches because they help the child see relationships. The former follow Thorndike's dictum that no bond should be established that will later have to be broken. The latter support the view that insight often results from the use of crutches and that crutches will be discarded by most children themselves because understanding will make the use of a crutch unnecessary. As the child proceeds from the concrete to the abstract he discards manipulative devices, but these aids should be available to the child when he finds it necessary to use them. Forcing children to avoid all use of concrete aids will make many children insecure and often will lead to frustration.

Children should be challenged, motivated, and stimulated to develop their fullest capacities. The mathematics curriculum should be a challenge to all children at their own level. Children should be encouraged to discover more and more generalizations. This means that each child should be accepted as he is and should be given the opportunity to continue his development from his own level of learning.

1.5 PSYCHOLOGICAL PRINCIPLES

Children differ in their abilities to learn. Students in education classes are continually reminded that they must provide for individual differences. This advice is generously given, but the means of accomplishing the goal is a continual challenge to teachers. If it is true that children vary in ability, the same assignment should not be given to all children. Since some learn rapidly, others slowly, pupils should be encouraged to learn at their own rate. To pressure children to learn at a faster rate than they can may frustrate them. To allow children to work at a slower rate than their abilities indicate is doing those children a disservice.

Children who learn at a slower rate than others should be given more time. They should be allowed to work at the tasks that they can perform successfully. This means, of course, easier exercises. These children should also be provided with the necessary manipulative devices that will help them think through a situation. Once the necessary techniques are learned, or the required meanings are understood, the child is able to proceed to more difficult exercises or to more complex situations.

The faster learner should be encouraged by the teacher to proceed at his own rate. He should be motivated to tackle more difficult exercises. Such a child seldom resorts to manipulative aids because he is capable of thinking on the abstract level. This child should discover more generalizations. The faster learners should be provided with enrichment material which will be a continual challenge to them.

Mathematics readiness is just as important as reading readiness. Every child who is ready for new material should be given the opportunity to learn the new. This means that the mathematics curriculum should be varied enough to provide all children the opportunities to learn at their own rate. It also means that all children should work at tasks that are meaningful to them.

1.6 LEVELS OF LEARNING

In order to promote discovery in the classroom so that children will better understand the basic meanings and concepts in arithmetic and at the same time provide for individual differences, teachers must understand and recognize different levels of learning. Children should learn to find the answers to specific questions, to discover patterns or generalizations in the rationale of mathematics, and be able to explain the *why* of a process. These three levels of learning may be characterized as operation, generalization, and rationalization.

Operational Level. This is the first or simplest level of learning. At this level children resort to concrete or semiconcrete manipulative aids. The child who counts on his fingers when he is adding, or makes marks on a paper, is on the operational level of learning. When working with fractions, he usually needs circles that are divided into equal parts.

EXAMPLE 1

The children have learned about fractional units so that they know the meaning of $\frac{1}{2}$, $\frac{1}{3}$, $\frac{1}{4}$, $\frac{1}{6}$, $\frac{1}{8}$, and $\frac{1}{12}$. The children are then asked to express these fractional units in terms of other units. They will take their fractional units and make comparisons. They will thus learn that one-half is equal to two-fourths, three-sixths, four-eighths, or six-twelfths. They will also learn that one-third equals two-sixths, that three-fourths equals nine-twelfths, that five-sixths equals ten-twelfths, etc. Since they find their answers by using manipulative aids, they are at the operational level of learning.

EXAMPLE 2

The children are asked to find three-fourths of five-sixths. They may perform the following steps. They will first divide a rectangle into six equal parts and keep five of them. Then they may divide each of the sixths into four equal parts and keep three of them. They will conclude that the answer to the question is fifteen twenty-fourths. All multiplication of fractions is done by using the concrete devices. Again this is an operational level of learning.

EXAMPLE 3

The children are asked to add two odd integers. They add 5 and 3, 7 and 5, 9 and 3, 15 and 7, etc. They find the answers to the particular examples by performing the addition operation.

Generalization Level. When the children have done sufficient exercises of each of the three examples, they may discover some generalizations. In Example 1 they may discover that if they multiply the numerator and denominator of a fraction by the same number, they get equivalent fractions. In Example 2, they may discover that to multiply two fractions they may derive the correct answers by multiplying the numerators and the denominators of the original fractions. Once these generalizations are discovered the child no longer has to resort to concrete aids. He has found a tool that he may use. He is on the second, or generalization, level of learning. In Example 3, he may discover, or generalize, that the sum of two odd numbers is always an even number.

Rationalization Level. This is the highest level of learning. The teacher now asks the children to prove the generalization, or to explain why the generalization is true. This is often quite difficult. It may not be easy to prove these generalizations. Try to find the explanation or the proof for each of the three generalizations described on the preceding page. It is generally known that in multiplying two decimals, the number of decimal places in the answer is equal to the number of decimal places in the multiplicand added to the number of decimal places in the multiplier; but why?

The generalization is the rule. The rationalization is the explanation, based on definitions and postulates, of why the rule works. A child may add pairs of odd integers and find that their sum is always an even integer. Thus $7+3=10$, $9+5=14$, $11+15=26$. He generalizes that the sum of any two odd integers is an even integer. Why is this generalization true? He may learn to represent an even integer as $2n$ or $2m$ and an odd integer as $2n+1$ or $2m+1$. He may then reason that the sum of any two odd integers may be expressed as $(2n+1)+(2m+1)$ or $2n+2m+2$ or $2(n+m+1)$. Although $n+m+1$ may be either even or odd, $2(n+m+1)$ is always even. This is a rationalization, or a proof, of the generalization that the sum of two odd integers is an even integer.

The child may then ask what happens if he subtracts an odd integer from an odd integer. He finds that $9-3=6$, $17-5=12$, $23-15=8$ and generalizes that the difference of two odd integers is always even. Why is this true? He may use the same reasoning as above and write

$(2n+1)-(2m+1)=2n+1-2m-1$ or $2n-2m$ or $2(n-m)$. Again $n-m$ may be even or odd, but $2(n-m)$ is always even. We assume that n is greater than m. If m is greater than n, we merely write $2(m-n)$.

Experience may show that the square of an even number is always even and that the square of an odd number is always an odd number. These are generalizations. The proofs are rationalizations.

Suggestions to Teachers. It is quite evident that although all children will rely at first on concrete aids and that most children will make discoveries or generalizations, not all, in fact only a few, will be able to rationalize the generalizations. The teacher should not demand rationalizations from all children. The teacher must recognize each child's level of learning. The child who is on the operational level of learning should be allowed to use his manipulative devices. Such children should be challenged or motivated, but not required to discover generalizations. The bright or capable learners should be encouraged to rationalize or prove the generalizations. This is difficult for most children. In the same classroom will be found children at all three levels of learning.

1.7 THE TEACHER'S TASK AND CHALLENGE

The elementary school teacher is faced with the very difficult task of teaching mathematics in a meaningful way so that children learn the basic concepts in mathematics, of providing a classroom atmosphere that gives children an opportunity to discover these meanings themselves, and of providing for individual differences by challenging the very capable pupils and at the same time not frustrating the slower learners. These demands can be fulfilled by teachers who have mastered the subject matter, who know the capabilities of every child in the class, and who have an understanding of the psychology of learning. In effect the teacher must know how children learn, know the level of learning of each child, and he must know the mathematics so well that he can motivate each child to make the best use of his abilities.

1.8 SUMMARY

The rapid advances in the field of mathematics during the last fifty years together with the technological development in the same period have made great demands on the individual who has to adjust himself to the needs of the present and who has to prepare himself for the changes that will take place in the future. Recognizing these needs, educational leaders have taken a new look into the mathematics curriculum of the elementary school. Whereas in the past the elementary program was mainly arithmetic and its applications, the school program today includes algebra, geometry, and logical implication.

Parallel to the concern for the content of the elementary school mathematics program is the concern for the child as a learner. Greater efforts have been made to make mathematics meaningful so that the child always understands what he is doing. Greater emphasis is placed on concepts and principles than on computational skills.

Following the democratic principle that every child should be given the opportunity to develop to the best of his abilities, the school program attempts to challenge every pupil. Concrete manipulative devices are provided for those who need these aids, and at the same time pupils who are capable of working on the abstract level are presented with challenging situations.

The successful mathematics teacher must have a good knowledge of the subject matter, he must know each child in the class so that he can recognize each child's level of learning, and he must understand the psychology of learning so well that he can adjust the curriculum so that each pupil can progress according to his abilities. The teacher who has an understanding of subject, children, and educational psychology is the teacher who is best prepared to adjust the educational program to meet the needs of all children.

QUESTIONS FOR DISCUSSION

Discuss the following statements from the point of view of the educational and psychological principles presented in this chapter.

1. Children should never be allowed to count on their fingers.
2. Children should be taught only the computational skills. When they get older, they will learn the explanations for the processes.
3. Children should be taught only one method for getting an answer because they will become confused if exposed to several methods.
4. Anyone can teach arithmetic in the primary grades because the work on that level is very simple.
5. With inexpensive calculating machines easily available, skills in computation are no longer necessary.
6. Why must children understand the meanings in arithmetic? People drive automobiles without knowing how they work.
7. No drillmaster will ever be a good mathematics teacher.
8. Traditional mathematics was always useful and practical mathematics. The "new" mathematics is only a fad and will be discarded because it is purely abstract mathematics that has nothing to do with every day living.
9. A teacher should be unconcerned if children get the wrong answers as long as they understand the processes.

10. Algebra should not be taught in the elementary school because it is a difficult subject for young children.
11. The "new" mathematics should be taught only to the gifted children.
12. Children who have not learned the arithmetic facts should be given a large number of exercises, or drill material, until they master the facts.

SUGGESTED SUPPLEMENTARY READING

1. Adler, Irving, "Some Thoughts about Curriculum Revision," *The Mathematics Teacher,* November 1963. pp. 505–510.
2. Banks, J. Houston, *Learning and Teaching Arithmetic.* Boston: Allyn and Bacon, 1959. Chap. 1.
3. Brownell, William A., "Meaning and Skill—Maintaining the Balance," *The Arithmetic Teacher,* October 1956. pp. 129–136.
4. Bruner, Jerome S., "Needed: A Theory of Instruction," *Educational Leadership,* May 1963. pp. 523–532.
5. ———, "On Learning Mathematics," *The Mathematics Teacher,* December 1960. pp. 610–619.
6. Churchill, Eileen M., *Counting and Measuring.* Toronto: University of Toronto Press, 1961. Chap. 6.
7. Clark, John R., "Looking Ahead at Instruction in Arithmetic," *The Arithmetic Teacher,* December 1961. pp. 388–394.
8. Dantzig, Tobias, *Number, The Language of Science.* New York: The Macmillan Company, 1954. Chap. 3.
9. Diamond, R. J., "A Community Inspired by the New Mathematics Programs," *School Science and Mathematics,* November 1963. pp. 658–664.
10. Dicky, John W., "Arithmetic and Gestalt Psychology," *The Elementary School Journal,* September 1938. pp. 46–53.
11. Dienes, Z. P., *Building up Mathematics.* London: Hutchinson Educational, 1960. Chaps. 1 and 2.
12. Fehr, Howard F., "Modern Mathematics and Good Pedagogy," *The Arithmetic Teacher,* November 1963. pp. 402–411.
13. ———, "Theories of Learning Related to the Field of Mathematics," *The Learning of Mathematics, Its Theory and Practice,* Twenty-First Yearbook, The National Council of Teachers of Mathematics. Washington, D.C.: The National Council of Teachers of Mathematics, 1953. Chap. 1.
14. Gordon, Ira J., "Pressures and Concerns: Ends and Means," *Educational Leadership,* May 1963. pp. 545–553.
15. Harner, William A., "A Problem in Seventh-Grade Mathematics," *The Mathematics Teacher,* November 1962. pp. 549–552.
16. Hartung, Maurice L., "Basic and Superficial Ideas in Arithmetic," *The Arithmetic Teacher,* March 1959. pp. 65–70.
17. ———, "Mathematics in the Total School Program," *The Mathematics Teacher,* May 1958. pp. 336–343.
18. Hendrix, Gertrude, "Learning by Discovery," *The Mathematics Teacher,* May 1961. pp. 290–299.
19. Langer, Rudolph E., "To Hold as 'Twere, the Mirror up to Nature; to Show the Very Age and Body of the Time," *The Mathematics Teacher,* December 1959. pp. 594–599.

20. MacLane, Saunders, "The Reform Has Been Oversold," *NEA Journal,* November 1962. pp. 45–46.
21. McLellan, James A., and John Dewey, *The Psychology of Number,* New York: D. Appleton and Company, 1895.
22. Marks, John L., C. Richard Purdy, and Lucien B. Kinney, *Teaching Arithmetic for Understanding.* New York: McGraw-Hill Book Company, 1958. Chap. 1.
23. Phillips, Jo McKeeby, "One Classroom, with Arithmetic and Justice for All," *The Arithmetic Teacher,* October 1958. pp. 165–171.
24. Piaget, Jean, *The Child's Conception of Number.* New York: The Humanities Press, 1952.
25. Polya, George, "On Learning, Teaching, and Learning Teaching," *The American Mathematical Monthly,* June-July 1963. pp. 605–619.
26. Rappaport, David, "Mathematics – Logical, Psychological, Pedagogical," *The Arithmetic Teacher,* February 1962. pp. 67–71.
27. ———, "The Meanings Approach in Teaching Arithmetic," *Chicago Schools Journal,* January 1963. pp. 172–174.
28. ———, "Operation, Generalization, Rationalization," *The Elementary School Journal,* February 1963. pp. 286–290.
29. ———, "Understanding Meanings in Arithmetic," *The Arithmetic Teacher,* March 1958. pp. 96–99.
30. Rosenbloom, Paul, "Mathematics: K-14," *Educational Leadership,* March 1962. pp. 359–363.
31. Stone, Marshall H., "Fundamental Issues in the Teaching of Elementary School Mathematics," *The Arithmetic Teacher,* October 1959. pp. 177–179.
32. Thorndike, Edward L., *The Psychology of Arithmetic.* New York: The Macmillan Company, 1922.
33. Van Engen, Henry, "The Formation of Concepts," *The Learning of Mathematics, Its Theory and Practices,* Twenty-first Yearbook, The National Council of Teachers of Mathematics. Washington, D.C.: The National Council of Teachers of Mathematics, 1953. Chap. 3.
34. ———, "Twentieth Century Mathematics for the Elementary School," *The Arithmetic Teacher,* March 1959. pp. 71–76.

Chapter 2 *Number and Numeration Systems*

2.1 INTRODUCTION

The concept of number, generally associated with a child's first experience with arithmetic, is highly abstract and sophisticated. In this chapter we consider only the set of natural numbers, 1, 2, 3 . . . . In later chapters other kinds of number are discussed from the pedagogical point of view as well as the logical aspect. The child never sees a number. He sees a number of objects but not the number. We write a symbol that stands for a number, but the symbol is not the number. This distinction between number and numeral, the notation for number, is important to an understanding of the modern approach to number concepts. Number and enumeration are presented from the traditional and the modern point of view, but both are developed in a meaningful manner.

2.2 COUNTING

When man began to write a record of his history, he had already learned to count. He had developed names for sets of objects. The shepherd counted the number of his sheep. The watchman counted the number of enemy soldiers. As man counted the objects in a set, he developed two aspects of number. The first is the cardinal—the quantitative aspect or size of a set. We speak of the five fingers on the hand or the five toes on a foot. The second is the ordinal concept or the idea of position or order. We say that a person is the fourth in line. The number five may be used to describe the collection of five fingers on one hand or it may be used to describe the last finger counted in the sequence one, two, three, four, five. The first usage is the cardinal usage and the second is the ordinal.

The cardinal and ordinal aspects of number are interrelated. The two go hand in hand. As we count objects in a set one at a time, we single out the objects. This is the ordinal concept. When we stop counting and look upon the set as a whole, its totality, we develop the cardinal concept. Thus one can say that he has five objects when he counts one, two, three, four, five. On the other hand, an object cannot be fifth in a set unless there is a set of four that precedes it. We turn to a given page that comes after page 216, but it cannot be page 217 unless there are 216 pages that precede it. (We assume, of course, that no page has been torn out of the book.)

Man used his fingers to represent a number of objects. He would hold up the five fingers of one hand to represent five objects. He thus set up a *one-to-one correspondence* between his fingers and a set of objects. The shepherd may have put aside a pebble for each sheep that he counted. If he did, he set up a one-to-one correspondence between pebbles and sheep. At some time in his historical development man began to use tally lines, or other marks, to keep a record of the number of objects or to communicate this quantity to others.

2.3 CHILDREN LEARN THE NUMBER NAMES

Children should be taught to develop an understanding of numbers by means of concrete objects. As they play with blocks, they learn to count them. They thus learn the names for one, two, three, etc. They learn to associate a number with sets of objects that have the same number of elements. They are presented with a set of three blocks, three toy automobiles, three pencils, or any set of three objects. As the child experiences various sets of concrete objects, he learns to abstract the concept of number and to dissociate it from the objects themselves. Although the child sees four pencils, or four blocks, or four toys, he cannot see the number four. The more experiences a child has with different sets of concrete objects, the sooner he will reach the abstract level of his understanding.

The child begins with the concrete and arrives at the abstract level. He may sometimes be exposed to two intermediate steps in proceeding from the concrete to the abstract. Since concrete objects of various kinds are not always readily available, pictures of objects may be used instead. The child learns to identify a set of three birds, or three dogs, or three fruits, or three toys. Concrete objects are more effective than pictures of concrete objects because actual objects can be manipulated whereas pictures cannot. If the pictures are cut out, they can then be treated as concrete objects.

The child may also learn to use semiconcrete aids such as lines or circles. Thus the child may represent three as / / / or as 0 0 0. The child's development of number proceeds as follows: concrete ⟶ picture ⟶ semiconcrete ⟶ abstract. Not all children follow the same pattern. Some children need to spend a great deal of time with concrete objects, whereas others may need just a little experience with objects. Some children may need to experience all of the steps from concrete objects to pictures to semiconcrete objects and finally to the abstract concept. Other children may be able to develop the abstract concept with just a little exposure to concrete objects. The teacher who knows the children in the class can vary the activities according to the needs of the children.

Concrete manipulative devices in a classroom are necessary to meet the needs of the children. The teacher may construct such aids when necessary. If there are no blocks, toys, or other objects in sufficient number, the teacher can cut up squares out of construction paper of different colors. The hundred board, peg board, and counting frame can be used by children as concrete manipulative devices to learn about number.

Although rote counting may help children learn the number names in sequential order, this should not be overemphasized. The child who recites numbers 1 to 100 or 1000 may be merely vocalizing. His ability to utter the sounds is not always a sign that he understands what the numbers mean. The child should learn that a set of three and one more make a set of four. He should learn that five is one more than four, six is one more than five, nine is one more than eight, etc. Too often teachers as well as parents pressure children into recitation of numbers beyond the child's understanding. Rote counting may be harmful to the child's learning. Children should learn the numbers slowly but meaningfully. As the child manipulates concrete objects he learns the story about numbers, let us say the number eight. He learns that a set with eight elements can be formed by combining a set with five elements with a set with three elements, six and two, seven and one. The child who learns in this manner has a better understanding of number than the child who merely recites a sequence of names. Again it is necessary to stress that children learn at different rates.

The child must learn to identify a set of objects as a set of a certain size and he must also learn the proper number name associated with a given set.

Concrete Objects	Semiconcrete	Number Name
		one
		two
		three
		four
		five
		six
		seven
		eight
		nine
		ten

2.4 NUMBER AS A PROPERTY OF A SET

One of the most important concepts in the modern approach to the understanding of mathematics is the concept of set. A set is a collection of objects. We have a set of fingers, a set of dishes, a set of books, a set of furniture, etc. The elements of a set need not be alike. One may have a set that includes a cube, a ball and a bat. A set may be composed of a basketball team and its manager, or children in a classroom.

One of the things we can do with sets is to match, or pair, the elements of one set with the elements of a second set. When there is an exact matching of the elements of two sets, we say that there is a one-to-one correspondence between the two sets. There is a one-to-one correspondence between our set of hands and our set of feet. There is a one-to-one correspondence between the fingers on one hand and the toes on one foot.

Many sets may be matched in a one-to-one correspondence. The set of hands, the set of ears, the set of eyes, the set of feet that belong to one person may be matched in a one-to-one correspondence. We say that all of these sets have a common property, namely, they can be matched with each other. In Fig. 1 we have three sets that are made up of different kinds of elements, but all of the three sets have a common property, this is, they can be matched with each other. We notice that the elements in Fig. 1*a* match exactly the elements in Fig. 1*b*, and the elements in Fig. 1*b* match the elements in Fig. 1*c*. All three sets in Fig. 1, because they have the common property of matching each other, are assigned the same number. In this case the number is four. All other sets that match the sets in Fig. 1 have associated with them the same number, four.

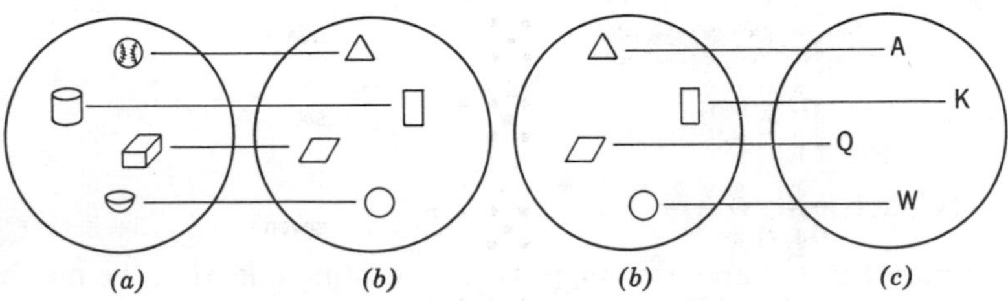

Fig. 1

To all the sets that match our set of hands we associate the number *two*. To all the sets that match the fingers on one hand we associate the number *five*. It is in this sense that we define number as the common property of a collection of sets that are in one-to-one correspondence. By matching the elements of various sets, the child learns about number as the property of a collection of matching sets, about one-to-one correspondence, and the number names associated with the different kinds of sets or groupings. He gets a better understanding of the real meaning of number.

What about sets that do not match? Suppose all of the elements of one set have been paired with the elements of a second set, and the second set contains some unmatched elements. The second set has more elements than the first set, and the first set has fewer elements than the second set. By matching the elements of various sets, children learn about more than and less than, greater and lesser. This can be refined a little more by having children match two sets whose difference is one. Thus they learn that five is one more than four, four is one more than three, three is one more than two, etc. Children learn that there is an order to numbers. They learn the sequential order of numbers and also the relation between numbers.

As children learn that one number is less than another, the question arises, "What number is less than one?" This question can be answered by confronting children with an empty set. The set that has just one element has one less element than a set with two elements and one more element than a set that has no elements. To all sets that are empty we associate the number zero. Figure 2 shows the place of zero in the sequence of numbers.

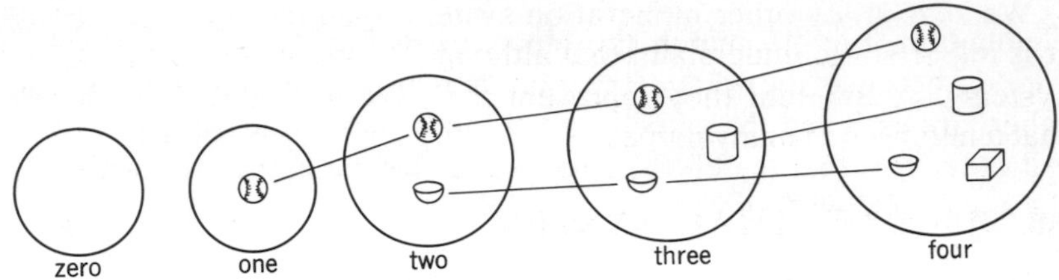

Fig. 2

2.5 NUMERALS

As man learned about number as representing quantity, the number of objects in a set or the number of elements in a set, he also developed a system of notation or a language of symbols with which to communicate his idea of quantity to others. The Egyptians, Greeks, Babylonians, Romans – all peoples – developed their own symbols for numbers. We call these symbols numerals. Numerals are names for numbers. We never see numbers because they are abstract concepts. We do see the numerals that stand for numbers. We perform operations with numbers, not numerals. Since one sees only the numerals, it becomes very easy to form the false conclusion that we add, subtract, or multiply numerals.

Numbers can be represented by different numerals. Just as the word for eight is different in French, English, Russian, Spanish, or Italian, the numerals for eight are different in various notation systems. Many people are familiar with Roman numerals as well as with the Hindu–Arabic we use. The following numbers are represented by both Roman and Hindu–Arabic numerals:

Number Names	Roman Numerals	Hindu-Arabic Numerals
one	I	1
two	II	2
three	III	3
four	IV	4
five	V	5
six	VI	6
ten	X	10
seventeen	XVII	17
thirty-two	XXXII	32
sixty-three	LXIII	63
one hundred twelve	CXII	112
three hundred fifty-eight	CCCLVIII	358
seven hundred eighty-one	DCCLXXXI	781
nineteen hundred sixty-three	MCMLXIII	1963

We shall study other numeration systems than those just presented. It is important to understand that although the numerals in the various systems are different they represent the same numbers. Thus we say that a number has many names.

2.6. THE DECIMAL SYSTEM

Our numeration system is based on the following ten symbols: 0, 1, 2, 3, 4, 5, 6, 7, 8, 9. With these symbols we can represent any number we want regardless of its size. This is possible because we have a place-value system. These symbols, or digits, indicate the number of units. The size or value of the units is determined by the position of the digits. The numeral 34 represents 3 units called tens and 4 units called ones. If we reverse the order of the digits and write 43, we represent 4 units of tens and 3 units of ones. The third position to the left is the hundreds place. The numeral 752 represents 7 units of hundreds, 5 units of tens, and 2 units of ones.

This system is a decimal system because it uses the idea of ten. It takes 10 ones to make 1 ten, 10 tens to make 1 hundred, 10 hundreds to make 1 thousand, etc. In representing numbers in a place-value system of notation it is necessary to have a symbol that shows an absence of units. Since zero is the number associated with the empty set, it has become customary to use the symbol for zero, or the numeral for zero, as the absence symbol. The phrase "zero as a placeholder" is used frequently. What is really meant is that the numeral for zero is used as a placeholder. The numeral 703 represents 7 units of hundreds, no units of tens, and 3 units of ones. If the zero were omitted, and 73 were written instead of 703, a different number would be indicated. Now we would have 7 tens instead of 7 hundreds. The peoples of ancient times by using an abacus did not need a zero because the rod or wire of the abacus acted as a placeholder. (See Fig. 3.)

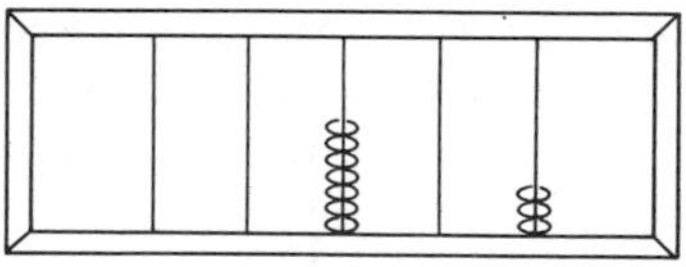

Fig. 3

It is true, of course, that every digit is a placeholder. Zero is not unique in this respect. From the pedagogical point of view, zero assumes an importance as a placeholder that is quite different from that of the other symbols. Because zero indicates an absence of units, children have a tendency to omit it when they write numerals. Since the other symbols indicate a definite number of units, children do not omit them.

The decimal notation system is an additive system. The numeral 746 can be axpressed as $7\times 100+4\times 10+6\times 1$. The digits 7, 4, and 6 are coefficients that indicate the number of units. The value of the units, determined by the position of the digits, can also be expressed as powers of 10. Thus the numeral 746 represents $7\times 10^2+4\times 10^1+6\times 10^0$.

The word units is generally considered to represent ones. We thus speak of the *units* column, the tens column, the hundreds column, etc. In this book a unit is anything that is repeated in measurement. We speak of 7 feet, 8 yards, 36 miles, 49 square feet, 40 cubic yards, and 100 cubic centimeters. In the decimal numeration system the different kinds of units are powers of 10. We have ones (10^0), tens (10^1), hundreds (10^2), thousands (10^3), etc. Each digit in the decimal numeral represents a number of units. The position of the digit indicates the kind of unit or power of 10.

2.7. TEACHING THE DECIMAL SYSTEM

Children first learn the symbols that are associated with the first nine numbers. They should recognize the sets of objects, the number associated with each set, and the numeral that represents each number. The sets of objects may be arranged in different ways, but the number and numerals remain the same. Figure 4 shows two different patterns for elements of a set together with the number and the numerals.

Elements of a Set	Word	Symbol	Elements of a Set
o	one	1	o
oo	two	2	o o
ooo	three	3	o o o
oooo	four	4	o o o o
ooooo	five	5	o o o o o
o o o o o o	six	6	o o o o o o
o o o o o o o	seven	7	o o o o o o o
o o o o o o o o	eight	8	o o o o o o o o
o o o o o o o o o	nine	9	o o o o o o o o o

Fig. 4

When children have learned to recognize the number associated with any set having one to nine elements, they are ready to form sets of ten elements. They may put ten things to one side and the other things a little to the right. Eleven corresponds to a set of ten and one more, twelve corresponds to a set of ten and two more, thirteen to ten and three, up to nineteen, which corresponds to ten and nine. If there are twenty or more objects children form sets of ten. They may have two sets of ten and two more, or two sets of ten and five more. The problem facing children is how to notate numbers corresponding to sets of more than nine elements. Just as a digit has been used to indicate the number of ones, a digit may be used to indicate the number of tens. The first column on the right is reserved for the ones, and the column to the left of it is reserved for the tens. A place-value chart or an abacus may be used to illustrate this. (See Fig. 5.)

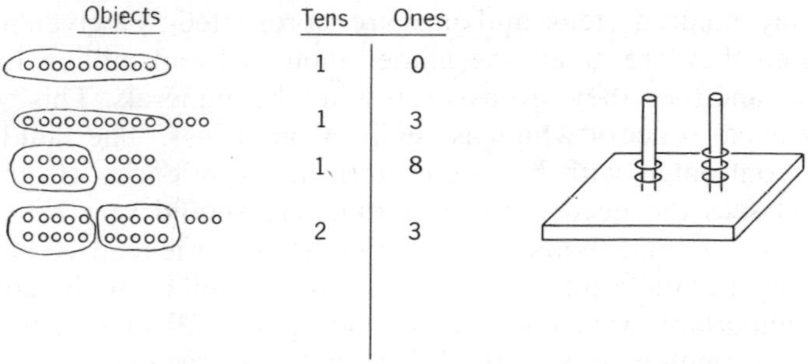

Objects	Tens	Ones
(oooooooooo)	1	0
(oooooooooo) ooo	1	3
(ooooo ooooo) oooo oooo	1	8
(ooooo ooooo) (ooooo ooooo) ooo	2	3

Fig. 5

It must be pointed out that although we may have more than nine objects, we cannot notate that number with a single digit in the decimal system. As soon as there are 10 ones, the symbol 1 is written in the tens column. If there are nineteen objects and one more is added the child should discover the way to notate the result by himself. He starts with 1 ten and 9 ones. When 1 one is added, he has 10 ones which make 1 ten. Now he has 2 tens which are called 20. In like manner the child should learn that 29 and 1 more make 30, 39 and 1 more make 40, 79 and 1 more make 80, etc. But 99 and 1 more creates a new situation. The numeral 99 represents 9 tens and 9 ones. Adding 1 makes 10 ones or 1 ten, but now there are 10 tens. A set of 10 tens makes a new unit. This unit, of course, is called hundred and is recorded in the third column to the left. We record 1 hundred as 100. The place-value chart is extended to include hundreds as well as tens and ones. Figure 6 indicates some numerals that represent numbers greater than a hundred. The place-value chart does not require any zeros. The zero or absence symbol is necessary as a placeholder when numbers are notated.

Numerals	Hundreds	Tens	Ones
35		3	5
50		5	0
137	1	3	7
259	2	5	9
403	4	0	3
680	6	8	0

Fig. 6

Children are often exposed to large numbers before they comprehend their meaning. Children are asked to read three- or four-place numerals and to identify the number of units of each kind. They have to state how many hundreds, tens, and ones are represented by a given numeral. Too often they are given the names thousand and million for given positions and then they are asked to read the numerals. This becomes a mechanical process which is really meaningless. The child should not be confronted with hundreds until he experiences 10 groups of tens and sees the need for a new unit. He should see the need for creating a new unit, thousand, when he has experienced 10 hundreds. In this manner the numerals come to have meaning for the child.

The important principle that should govern all class activities is that the curriculum should be differentiated according to the abilities of the children. Some children can grasp the meaning of 1 hundred as 10 tens or 1 thousand as 10 hundreds very quickly. These children should be given the opportunity to work with large numbers. Some children however, arrive at an understanding of numbers and numerals for those numbers at a much slower rate, and they should not be expected to work with larger number concepts until they are ready for it. To expose them to large numbers that they do not really understand will result in mechanical processes which will generally result in frustration or will develop in the child a negative attitude toward mathematics.

2.8 OTHER NUMERATION SYSTEMS

The principle of place value is not unique to the decimal system. The Mayans in Central America had developed a vigesimal system based on the idea of twenty. The Babylonians had developed the sexigesimal based on the idea of sixty. The only vestiges of that system in our present culture are the measurement of angles, in which 60 seconds equal 1 minute and 60 minutes equal 1 degree, and the measurement of time, in which 60 seconds equal 1 minute and 60 minutes equal 1 hour. We can apply the principle of place value to other bases like base five, base eight, base twelve, base three, base two. The base tells us how to group our objects. It indicates how many units of one kind are necessary in order to form a new unit. The exchange ratio differs with different bases, but the principle of exchange remains the same. The work "exchange" is intended to be picturesque. It is mental rather than physical. Just as we exchange 5 pennies for 1 nickel and 5 nickels for 1 quarter, we exchange mentally 5 ones for 1 five and 5 fives for 1 twenty-five.

Base Five. In the base five, five units are exchanged for a bigger unit. Five ones make 1 five, 5 fives make 1 twenty-five, etc. The numeral 34_{five} (read three four base five) represents 3 fives and 4 ones, or 19 in the decimal system. The numeral 423_{five} (read four two three base five) represents 4 twenty-fives, 2 fives, and 3 ones, or 113 in the decimal system. The digits in each position indicate the number of units, but the value of the unit is determined by the position. Each position represents a power of 5. Thus 3243_{five} represents $3 \times 5^3 + 2 \times 5^2 + 4 \times 5^1 + 3 \times 5^0$. Its equivalent in the base ten is 448. It is apparent that in our discussion of the base five, or other bases, we use the decimal number names. There is no twenty-five, as a number name, in the base five. The very word twenty implies 2 tens, which would not exist in the base five. We must also be careful in our reading of other base numerals not to read, for example, 34_{five} as thirty-four.

To express the decimal number 976 in the base five it is necessary to determine what kinds of units the base five has. By using the ratio of 5 to 1, we get the units 1, 5, 25, 625, 3125, etc. It is obvious that the largest base five unit in 976 is 625. Since there is only 1 such unit, we subtract 625 from 976. The remainder 351 contains 2 one hundred twenty-fives, or 250. Subtracting this from 351 leaves 101, which contains 4 twenty-fives and 1 one. The numeral 976_{ten} written in base five is 12401_{five}. These steps can be summarized as follows:

$$\begin{array}{rl} 976 & \\ \underline{-625} & 1 \times 625 \\ 351 & \\ \underline{-250} & 2 \times 125 \\ 101 & \\ \underline{-100} & 4 \times 25 \\ 1 & \\ \underline{-0} & 0 \times 5 \\ 1 & \\ \underline{-1} & 1 \times 1 \\ 0 & \end{array}$$

$$976_{\text{ten}} = 12401_{\text{five}}$$

Base five 5^4 5^3 5^2 5^1 5^0	to	*Base ten*
2 3 4	$2\times5^2+3\times5^1+4\times5^0$	= 69
3 0 1 2	$3\times5^3+0\times5^2+1\times5^1+2\times5^0$	= 382
4 3 0 3	$4\times5^3+3\times5^2+0\times5^1+3\times5^0$	= 578
2 2 0 3 4	$2\times5^4+2\times5^3+0\times5^2+3\times5^1+4\times5^0$	= 1519

Base ten	to	*Base five* 5^5 5^4 5^3 5^2 5^1 5^0
463	$3\times125+3\times25+2\times5+3\times1$	3 3 2 3
1597	$2\times625+2\times125+3\times25+4\times5+2\times1$	2 2 3 4 2
3785	$1\times3125+1\times625+0\times125+1\times25+2\times5+0\times1$	1 1 0 1 2 0

Base Eight. In this base we have the symbols 0, 1, 2, 3, 4, 5, 6, and 7. Now eight units are exchanged for a new unit. The numeral 34_{eight} represents 3 eights and 4 ones, or 28 in the base ten. The numeral 537_{eight} represents 5 sixty-fours, 3 eights, and 7 ones, or 351 in the base ten. Each position represents a unit that is a power of 8. Thus 3475_{eight} equals $3\times8^3+4\times8^2+7\times8^1+5\times8^0$, or 1853 in the decimal system.

To change from the base ten to the base eight it is necessary to determine first the kinds of units that exist in the base eight. These are ones, eights, sixty-fours, five hundred twelves, etc. The decimal number 976 contains 1 unit of 512. The remainder 464 contains 7 units of 64. The remainder 16 contains 2 units of 8 and no ones. The numeral 976_{ten} is equivalent to 1720_{eight}. This can be summarized as follows:

976	
−512	1×512
464	
−448	7×64
16	
−16	2×8
0	
−0	0×1

$976_{\text{ten}} = 1720_{\text{eight}}$

Base eight 8^4 8^3 8^2 8^1 8^0	to	*Base ten*
2 3 4	$2\times8^2+3\times8^1+8^0$	156
3 0 1 2	$3\times8^3+0\times8^2+1\times8^1+2\times8^0$	1546
4 3 0 3	$4\times8^3+3\times8^2+0\times8^1+3\times8^0$	2243
2 2 0 3 4	$2\times8^4+2\times8^3+0\times8^2+3\times8^1+4\times8^0$	9244

Base ten		to			*Base eight*		
			8^4	8^3	8^2	8^1	8^0
463	$7\times64+1\times8+7$				7	1	7
1597	$3\times512+0\times64+7\times8+5$			3	0	7	5
3785	$7\times512+3\times64+1\times8+1$			7	3	1	1

Base Twelve. In this duodecimal system we use the ten symbols of the decimal system and add two new symbols, *t* for ten and *e* for eleven. Now it takes 12 units to make 1 new unit. The numeral 34_{twelve} represents 3 twelves and 4 ones, or 40 in the decimal system. The numeral 537_{twelve} represents 5 units of 144, 3 units of 12, and 7 ones, or 763 in the base ten. Each duodecimal unit is a power of 12. The numeral 3475_{twelve} indicates $3\times12^3+4\times12^2+7\times12^1+5\times12^0$, or 5849 in the decimal system. To change from the base ten to the base twelve it is necessary to determine the kind of units in the base twelve, or the powers of 12. These units, with decimal number names, are 1, 12, 144, 1728, etc. The decimal number 976 contains 6 units of 144 plus 9 units of 12 plus 4 ones. The numeral 976_{ten} is equivalent to 694_{twelve}. This can be summarized as follows:

$$\begin{array}{rl} 976 & \\ -864 & 6\times144 \\ \hline 112 & \\ -108 & 9\times12 \\ \hline 4 & \\ -4 & 4\times1 \\ \hline 0 & \end{array}$$

$$976_{\text{ten}} = 694_{\text{twelve}}$$

Base Twelve				to	*Base Ten*
12^3	12^2	12^1	12^0		
	2	3	4	$2\times12^2+3\times12^1+4\times12^0$	328
3	0	1	2	$3\times12^3+0\times12^2+1\times12^1+2\times12^0$	5198
4	3	0	3	$4\times12^3+3\times12^2+0\times12^1+3\times12^0$	7347

Base ten		to	*Base twelve*			
			12^3	12^2	12^1	12^0
463	$3\times144+2\times12+7$			3	2	7
1597	$e\times144+1\times12+1$			*e*	1	1
3785	$2\times1728+2\times144+3\times12+5$		2	2	3	5

Base Three. The ternary system has just the symbols 0, 1, 2. The place values in this numeration system are powers of 3. Since it takes three units to make a new one, there is no digit representing any number greater than 2. The numeral 21_{three} represents 2 threes and 1 one, or 7 in the decimal system. The numeral 2112_{three} represents 2 twenty-sevens, 1 nine, 1 three, and 2 ones, or 68 in the base ten. To change from the decimal to the ternary system we must determine first the units in the base three. The decimal number 976 contains 1 (729), 1 (243), 0 (81), 0 (27), 0 (9), 1 (3), 1 (1). The numeral 976_{ten} is equivalent to 1100011_{three}. This can be summarized as follows:

976	
−729	1 × 729
247	
−243	1 × 243
4	
−0	0 × 81
4	
−0	0 × 27
4	
−0	0 × 9
4	
−3	1 × 3
1	
−1	1 × 1
0	

$$976_{ten} = 1100011_{three}$$

Base three to *Base ten*

3^4	3^3	3^2	3^1	3^0		
		2	2	1	$2\times 3^2+2\times 3^1+1\times 3^0$	25
	1	1	2	2	$1\times 3^3+1\times 3^2+2\times 3^1+2\times 3^0$	44
2	0	2	2	0	$2\times 3^4+0\times 3^3+2\times 3^2+2\times 3^1+0\times 3^0$	186

Base ten to *Base three*

		3^7	3^6	3^5	3^4	3^3	3^2	3^1	3^0
463	$1\times 243+2\times 81+2\times 27+0\times 9+1\times 3+1$				1	2	2	0	1	1
1597	$2\times 729+0\times 243+1\times 81+2\times 27+0\times 9+1\times 3+1$			2	0	1	2	0	1	1
3785	$1\times 2187+2\times 729+0\times 243+1\times 81+2\times 27+0\times 9+1\times 3+2$	1	2	0	1	2	0	1	2

Base Two. The binary system is the simplest numeration system because it has just two symbols, 0 and 1. This makes it effective for an electronic system in which the electric current is either on or off. The binary units, powers of 2, are 1, 2, 4, 8, 16, 32, 64, 128, 256, 512, 1024, etc. The numeral 1101_{two} represents $1\times 8+1\times 4+0\times 2+1\times 1$, or 13 in the decimal system. To change from the binary system to the decimal system we must determine the power of 2 place value and add those that have the 1 coefficient. To change from the decimal to the binary system it is necessary to establish the binary units and begin with the largest binary unit contained in the decimal number. The decimal number 976 is equal to $1\times512+1\times256+1\times128+1\times64+0\times32+1\times16+0\times8+0\times4+0\times2+0\times1$. Thus 976_{ten} is equivalent to 1111010000_{two}. This can be summarized as follows:

976	
−512	1×512
464	
−256	1×256
208	
−128	1×128
80	
−64	1×64
16	
−0	0×32
16	
−16	1×16
0	
0	0×8
0	
0	0×4
0	
0	0×2
0	
0	0×1

$976_{ten} = 1111010000_{two}$

Powers of 2: $2^0=1$, $2^1=2$, $2^2=4$, $2^3=8$, $2^4=16$, $2^5=32$, $2^6=64$, $2^7=128$, $2^8=256$, $2^9=512$, $2^{10}=1024$, $2^{11}=2048$.

Base ten to *Base two*

Base ten	2^{11}	2^{10}	2^9	2^8	2^7	2^6	2^5	2^4	2^3	2^2	2^1	2^0
463				1	1	1	0	0	1	1	1	1
1597		1	1	0	0	0	1	1	1	1	0	1
3785	1	1	1	0	1	1	0	0	1	0	0	1

Changing from Base Ten to Any Base. It is possible to change from base ten to any other number base by continual division and recording of the remainders. The remainders written in reverse order will yield the new numeral. Let us take the decimal 976 and convert it to the base five by continual division.

```
5)976
5)195   R 1
 5)39   R 0
  5)7   R 4
  5)1   R 2
    0   R 1
```

Since we want to convert the decimal number 976 to a base five numeral, we want to know how many fives we have in 976. By dividing by 5 we find that there are 195 fives and 1 one. The second division by 5 tells us how many second power of five we have. We find that there are exactly 39 (5^2) and no fives left over. The third division by 5 tells us how many third power of 5, namely, $7(5^3)$ and $4(5^2)$ remaining. The next division by 5 tells us how many fourth power of 5 we have. The quotient gives us that number, and the remainder 2 indicates that there are $2(5^3)$ remaining. We know that 2 is not enough to make another five grouping. Dividing by 5 gives the remainder 1. The remainders tell us how many of each power of 5 we have. Since each remainder in succession gives a higher power, we reverse the order and write 12401_{five}. We may do the same with any base.

8)976		12)976		3)976		2)976	
8)122	R 0	12)81	R 4	3)325	R 1	2)488	R 0
8)15	R 2	12)6	R 9	3)108	R 1	2)244	R 0
8)1	R 7	0	R 6	3)36	R 0	2)122	R 0
0	R 1			3)12	R 0	2)61	R 0
				3)4	R 0	2)30	R 1
				3)1	R 1	2)15	R 0
				0	R 1	2)7	R 1
						2)3	R 1
						2)1	R 1
						0	R 1

$$976_{ten} = 1720_{eight} = 694_{twelve} = 1100011_{three} = 1111010000_{two}$$

Dividing 976 by 8 gives us 122 groups of 8 and no ones remaining. Dividing 122 by 8 gives us 15 groups of 8 squared and a remainder of 2 eights. Dividing the 15 groups of 8 squared gives 1 group of 8 cubed and 7 groups of 8 squared remaining. Thus reversing the order of the remainders gives us 1 group of 8^3, 7 groups of 8^2, 2 groups of 8 and no ones. In like manner successive divisions by 12, 3, or 2 gives us the successive powers of 12, 3, and 2.

2.9 TEACHING OTHER NUMBER BASES

Number bases other than the base ten can be taught to children by relating them to practical concrete situations that children have experienced. But it must be understood that such concrete situations are limited and that one must develop concepts that go beyond the concrete level. Pennies, nickels, and quarters may be used for a game of coins that is based on the base five. Suppose that we have a number of pennies that we wish to exchange for the largest coins possible, using only pennies, nickels, and quarters. Let us say that we have 7 pennies. These would be represented by 1 nickel and 2 pennies, and could be written as 12 in the coin game. Eighteen pennies could be represented by 3 nickels and 3 pennies, and notated as 33. Thirty-two pennies could be exchanged for 1 quarter, 1 nickel, and 2 pennies, and notated as 112. Suppose we had 97 pennies. These could be exchanged for 3 quarters, 4 nickels, and 2 pennies, and this could be notated as 342. We have no coins to play this game with larger numbers because we do not have a coin equal to 5 quarters. Concrete realities prevent us from extending the practical situation, but the idea of the base five can be established beyond the practical game of coins. The 7 days of the week gives us an opportunity, though very limited, to establish the base seven.

The base twelve can be established in a concrete manner when children learn that 12 make 1 dozen and that 12 dozen make 1 gross. Again we are limited by concrete reality to only three-place numerals.* The base four can be developed by using the relation of 1 gallon equal to 4 quarts, and also the fact that 4 weeks make 1 lunar month. Once the idea of exchange is developed, the child can go beyond the concrete examples and operate on the abstract ideational level.

The binary system may be developed in a concrete way by using the relationship that 2 pints make 1 quart, 2 quarts make 1 half-gallon, and 2 half-gallons make 1 gallon. This can be extended even further by beginning with 2 half-pints equal to 1 pint. This can be used effectively only when the children have had experience with half-pints, pints, quarts, half-gallons, and gallons.

The abacus has been used extensively to develop the understanding of the decimal system. An abacus can be made for any base. These have already been manufactured by commercial companies, but they can also be constructed by the teacher or by children themselves. In constructing a base five abacus it is advisable to make the rods just the right length to hold only five cubes or cylinders. This restriction will bring out the need for an exchange for a new unit.

2.10 SUMMARY

The distinction between number and numeral is a very important one. Number is the abstract idea, relating to the size of a set. A numeral is a name for a number. It is the symbolic representation for a number. Numerals constitute the language by which man communicates his

*Although twelve gross is sometimes called a great gross, this term is unfamiliar to most people.

ideas about number. It is important for children to learn that a number has many names. The number concept is the same in all languages and in all bases, but the representation for number, namely, the numeral is different. Thus the number thirty-eight can be notated as 38_{ten}, 32_{twelve}, 46_{eight}, 123_{five}, 1102_{three}, 100110_{two}.

Children should be provided with concrete aids to help them learn about numbers. They match the elements of various sets. In doing this they learn the meaning of one-to-one correspondence, greater and lesser, and they learn to abstract the concept of number. Both cardinal and ordinal concepts of number should be emphasized.

EXERCISES

1. Write as Roman numerals:
   (*a*) 38 (*b*) 163 (*c*) 341 (*d*) 781 (*e*) 1496
2. Write as decimal numerals:
   (*a*) XXVIII (*b*) LXVI (*c*) CCLXXXVI (*d*) DCLXI
   (*e*) MDCCCLXXVII
3. What is the significance of the zero in 2035? What if the zero were omitted and the numeral 235 were written instead?
4. Change the following to the decimal system:
   (*a*) 342_{five} (*b*) 413_{eight} (*c*) $9e4_{twelve}$ (*d*) 531_{seven}
   (*e*) 20112_{three} (*f*) 3123_{four} (*g*) 11101011_{two}
5. Change the following decimal numbers to the indicated base:
   (*a*) 49 to base five
   (*b*) 321 to base eight
   (*c*) 943 to base twelve
   (*d*) 462 to base three
   (*e*) 973 to base two
6. Change from one base to another base by first converting to the base ten and then from base ten to the indicated base:
   (*a*) 376_{eight} to base twelve
   (*b*) 593_{twelve} to base five
   (*c*) 21121_{three} to base two
   (*d*) 4432_{five} to base eight
   (*e*) 1100011101_{two} to base twelve
7. Discuss the importance of distinguishing between number and numeral.
8. How would you develop the meaning of the cardinal concept of number?
9. How would you develop the understanding of the ordinal numbers?

SUGGESTED SUPPLEMENTARY READING

1. Banks, J. Houston, *Learning and Teaching Arithmetic*. Boston: Allyn and Bacon, 1959. Chaps. 2 and 3.

2. Bell, Clifford, Clela D. Hammond, and Robert B. Herrera, *Fundamentals of Arithmetic for Teachers.* New York: John Wiley and Sons, 1962. Chap. 2.
3. Botts, Truman, "Numbers, Sets, and Counting," *The Arithmetic Teacher,* pp. 281–286. October 1961.
4. Buckingham, Burdette R., *Elementary Arithmetic, Its Meaning and Practice.* Boston: Ginn and Company, 1953. Chap. 3.
5. Churchill, Eileen M., *Counting and Measuring.* Toronto: University of Toronto Press, 1961. Chaps. 2 and 3.
6. Clark, John R. "Number, Numeral, and Operation," *The Arithmetic Teacher,* pp. 222–225. May 1960.
7. Dantzig, Tobias, *Number, The Language of Science.* New York: The Macmillan Company, 1954. pp. 253–268.
8. Dienes, Z. P., *Building up Mathematics.* London: Hutchinson Educational, 1960. Chap. 3.
9. Dubisch, Roy, *The Nature of Number.* New York: The Ronald Press Company, 1952. Chaps. 1–5.
10. Galfo, Armand J., "When Does $2+2=10$?" *School Science and Mathematics,* pp. 653–657. November 1963.
11. Gibb, E. Glenadine, and Phillip S. Jones, "Number and Operation," *The Growth of Mathematical Ideas Grades K–12.* Twenty-fourth Yearbook, The National Council of Teachers of Mathematics. Washington, D.C.: The National Council of Teachers of Mathematics, 1959. pp. 7–64.
12. Hamilton, E. W., "Number System, Fad or Foundation?" *The Arithmetic Teacher,* May 1961. pp. 242–245.
13. Hudson, Charles, "Some Remarks on Teaching Different Bases," *School Science and Mathematics,* November 1963. pp. 649–652.
14. Larsen, Harold D., and H. Glenn Ludlow, *Arithmetic for Colleges.* New York: The Macmillan Company, 1963. Chap. 1.
15. Marks, John L., C. Richard Purdy, and Lucien B. Kinney, *Teaching Arithmetic for Understanding.* New York: McGraw-Hill Book Company, 1958. Chaps. 4 and 5.
16. Peters, Ann C., "The Number System and the Teacher," *The Arithmetic Teacher,* October 1957. pp. 155–160.
17. Stringfellow, Emma L., "Number Systems," *School Science and Mathematics,* October 1959. pp. 557–560.
18. Swain, Robert L., *Understanding Arithmetic.* New York: Rinehart and Company, 1957. Chaps. 1 and 2.
19. Willerding, Margaret F., "Other Number Systems–Aid to Understanding Mathematics." *The Arithmetic Teacher,* November 1961. pp. 350–356.

Chapter 3 *Addition*

3.1 OPERATIONS WITH SETS

In Chapter 2 we have discussed the concept of number as a property of a set. The set concept may be used to explain addition. A set is a collection of objects or a collection of elements. We can perform operations with sets.

A pair of braces { } is used to signify a set. Suppose we have a set $A = \{\ ,\ ,\ \}$ and a set $B = \{\ ,\ \}$. We notice that two elements in B are included in A. We say that B is a subset of A and indicate it in this manner, $B \subseteq A$. It is possible for two sets to have exactly the same elements. In that case the first set is a subset of the second set, and the second set is a subset of the first set. If all of the elements of set A are included in set B but set B has some elements that are not in set A, then set A is a proper subset of set B. If $A = \{1, 2, 3, 4, 5, 6\}$ and $B = \{3, 4, 5\}$, then $B \subset A$.

The letters of the word *tame* constitute a set $A = \{t, a, m, e\}$. The letters of the word *mate* constitute a set $B = \{m, a, t, e\}$. Since all of the elements of set A are included in B, we write $A \subseteq B$ and read it as A is included in B or A is a subset of B. Since all of the elements in set B are included in set A, we may write $B \subseteq A$ and read it as B is included in A or B is a subset of A. Since $A \subseteq B$ and $B \subseteq A$, we say $A = B$. Let set $C = \{m, a, t\}$ and set $D = \{a, t, e\}$. We note that all of the elements in C are included in A. Therefore we show this by $C \subseteq A$. Since all of the elements of A are not in C, we call set C a proper subset of set A and indicate it by $C \subset A$. The symbol $\subset$ is reserved for proper inclusion or *proper subset*. We also note that set $D \subset$ set A, that $C \subset B$, and that $D \subset B$.

Let $E = \{p, a, l, e\}$, $F = \{l, e, a, p\}$, $G = \{p, e, a, l\}$, $H = \{l, a, p\}$,

$I = \{p, a, l\}$, and $J = \{p, a\}$. We may express the following: $E \subseteq F$, $E \subseteq G$, $F \subseteq G$, $H \subset E$, $H \subset F$, $H \subset G$, $I \subset F$, $I \subset G$, $J \subset E$, $J \subset H$, $J \subset I$. Other conclusions, of course, may be formed. These are left to the reader.

In the foregoing examples we may state the same relationships in a different manner. If A is included in B, then B includes A. Similarly, if E is included in F, then F includes E. We use the symbol $\supseteq$ to express the idea "includes." We write $E \supseteq F$ or $F \supseteq E$, $H \supseteq I$ or $I \supseteq H$, etc. If C is a proper subset of A, then we say that A *properly includes* C. We use the symbol $\supset$ to show proper inclusion. Thus $B \supset C$, D $\supset C$, $E \supset H$, $E \supset I$, $I \supset J$. Other statements for *properly includes* are left to the reader.

Suppose we have set A = {[ball],[cylinder],[cube]} and set B = {[cylinder],[cube],⊖}. We may ask what elements are in both A and B. The answer is {[cylinder] [cube]}. We write it as follows: {[ball],[cylinder],[cube]} ∩ {[cylinder],[cube],⊖} = {[cylinder],[cube]}, or $A \cap B$, read as the intersection of A and B. Intersection of sets is an operation with sets that yields a new set that is composed of the elements that are common to both sets. We have defined the empty set as one that contains no elements. We indicate it with a pair of braces with nothing between them, { }. The empty set is also called the null set and is indicated by this symbol, ϕ. If two sets do not have any common elements their intersection is the empty set. Thus $\{3, 4, 5, 6\} \cap \{7, 8, 9\} = \{\ \}$.

We might have asked a different question regarding the following two sets, A = {[ball],[cylinder],[cube]} and B = { [cylinder],[cube],⊖, What set will contain the elements of both sets, if we agree not to repeat any element? An answer is the set {[ball],[cylinder],[cube],⊖ }. We call this the union of two sets and use this symbol ∪. $A \cup B$ is read as the union of A and B. The union of two sets is a third set that is composed of the elements in both sets. An example of the union of two sets is: $\{1, 2, 3, 4, 5, 6\} \cup \{4, 5, 6, 7, 8\}$. $= \{1, 2, 3, 4, 5, 6, 7, 8\}$.

An element x is in $A \cup B$ if, and only if, x is in A or x is in B (or both). In like manner we can define the intersection of two sets. An element x is in $A \cap B$ if, and only if, x is in A and x is in B. Two sets are disjoint if their intersection is an empty set.

Suppose we have the following sets: $A = \{1, 2, 3, 4, 5, 6\}$, $B = \{3, 4, 5, 6, 7, 8\}$, $C = \{9, 10, 11, 12\}$, $E = \{3, 4, 5\}$, and $F = \{7, 8, 9, 10\}$. We can show union of sets, intersection of sets, subsets, and disjoint sets. Here are a few conclusions:

1. $A \cap B = \{3, 4, 5, 6\}$
2. $B \cap F = \{7, 8\}$
3. $C \cap F = \{9, 10\}$
4. $E \subset A$

5. $E \subset B$
6. $A \cap C = \{\,\}$
7. $B \cap C = \{\,\}$
8. $E \cap F = \{\,\}$
9. $A \cup B = \{1, 2, 3, 4, 5, 6, 7, 8\}$
10. $C \cup F = \{7, 8, 9, 10, 11, 12\}$
11. $A \cup C = \{1, 2, 3, 4, 5, 6, 9, 10, 11, 12\}$
12. $E \cup F = \{3, 4, 5, 7, 8, 9, 10\}$

3.2 ADDITION AS AN OPERATION ASSOCIATED WITH THE UNION OF DISJOINT SETS

Children who have learned to operate with sets are ready to learn addition as an operation with numbers. They combine things to form a union of sets. They combine a set of 4 objects with a set of 3 objects to form a set of 7 objects. The sets may have like objects or unlike objects. The union of two sets is a set that contains all of the objects that are in the first set or in the second set.

The child has learned to associate a number with a set of elements. He associates the number three with a set containing 3 apples. He associates the number five with a set containing 5 apples. When the child combines the apples in the two sets, he forms 1 set of 8 apples. He may associate the sum of the two numbers with the union of the two sets. Thus $3+5=8$. It must be made clear that the 3, 5, and 8 have nothing to do with apples. Suppose the child has a set of 3 apples and a set of 5 bananas. The union of these two sets is 8 pieces of fruit. Again we have $3+5=8$. The union of a set of 3 nickels and 5 pennies forms a set of 8 coins. Again we have $3+5=8$.

Although there is a close association between the addition of numbers and the union of sets, great care must be taken to develop this association with the union of disjoint sets. If set $A = \{$ ⚾, ⛁, ⬠ $\}$ and set $B = \{$ ○, ▯, △, ▱ $\}$, A and B are disjoint sets. We may write $n(A)$ to represent the number of elements in A, and $n(B)$ to represent the number of elements in B. Here we can show that $n(A)+n(B) = n(A \cup B)$, where $n(A \cup B)$ is the number of elements in the union of A and B. We represent this as $3+4=7$. If set $A = \{$ ⚾, ⛁, ⬠ $\}$ and set $B = \{$ ○, ⛁, ⬠, △ $\}$, then $A \cup B = \{$ ⚾, ⛁, ⬠, ○, △ $\}$. In this case $n(A)+n(B) \neq n(A \cup B)$.

3.3 ADDITION AS A MAPPING PROCESS

In developing the concept of number as a property of a set it was necessary to match the elements of one set with the elements of a second set. Whenever the elements of one set are matched, or paired off, with the elements of a second set, we say that one set is mapped onto a second set. Mapping is the process of associating the elements of one set with the elements of another set. The following is an example of mapping; let set $A = \{1, 2, 3, 4\}$ and set $B = \{1, 4, 9, 16\}$. Since we can associate the 1 of set B with the 1 of set A, the 4 of B with the 2 of A, the 9 of B with the 3 of A, the 16 of B with the 4 of A, we say that set A has been mapped onto set B. This is an example of a one-to-one mapping. It is also possible to have a many-to-one mapping. Let set $A = \{-1, -2, -3, 1, 2, 3\}$ and set $B = \{1, 4, 9\}$. Since we can match the 1 of B with both -1 and 1 of A, the 4 of B with both the -2 and 2 of A, the 9 of B with both the -3 and 3 of A, we have a two-to-one mapping. This is shown in Fig. 7.

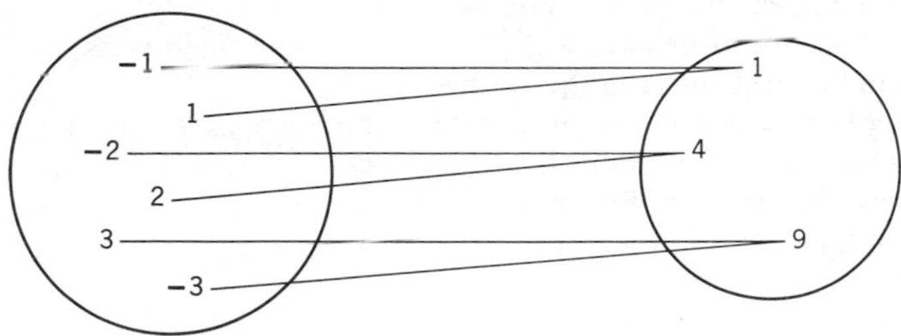

Fig. 7

We can also consider addition as a mapping process. We now consider set A as a set whose elements are number pairs $\{(3, 4), (2, 1), (4, 2), (5, 4)\}$ and set B as made up of single numbers $\{7, 3, 6, 9\}$. We can match each element of B with an element (number pair) of A in the following manner:

$$(3,4) \xrightarrow{+} 7$$

$$(2,1) \xrightarrow{+} 3$$

$$(4,2) \xrightarrow{+} 6$$

$$(5,4) \xrightarrow{+} 9$$

We can represent this mapping with diagrams as in Fig. 8.

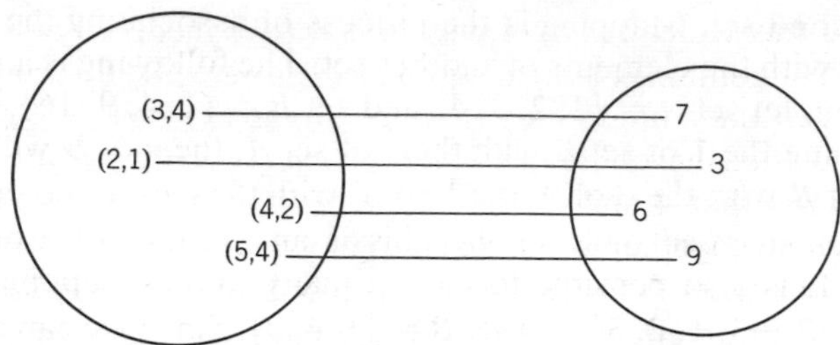

Fig. 8

Addition is also a many-to-one mapping, as can be seen in Fig. 9.

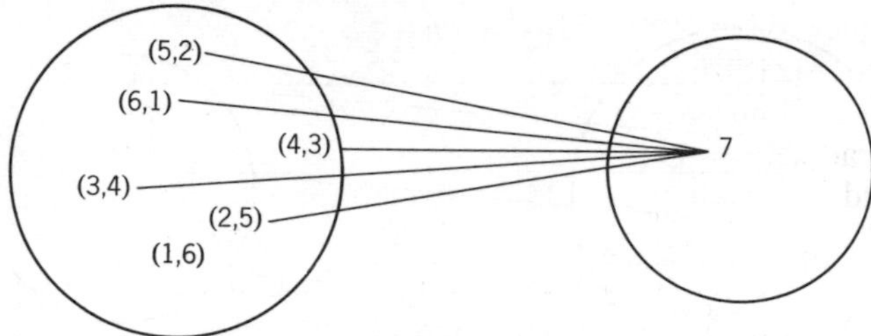

Fig. 9

3.4. THE BASIC ADDITION COMBINATIONS

Whether one considers addition as related to the union of disjoint sets or the mapping of one set onto another set, it is necessary to learn the sums of two 1-digit numbers* in order to perform the process called addition.† Mathematical addition is an operation, not a process. The process described in this section is really computation. In the past there was great emphasis on the computational skills. These were considered to be all important. The result was an overemphasis on computational skills. In contrast, the new approach to teaching elementary school mathematics emphasizes the understanding of the concept of numbers and operations with numbers; however, we

*Numbers do not have digits. Numerals do have digits. We use this phraseology, however, as a shorthand expression rather than "the sums of numbers represented by one-digit numerals."

†Process refers to the rules for obtaining answers to problems of addition. This is different from addition as an abstract operation.

should refrain from going to the opposite extreme of ignoring computational skills.

The child has to learn how many toys 4 toys and 3 toys will make altogether. He combines two sets into a single set and finds the number of elements in their union by counting. Suppose he counts 4 objects in a set and then he combines 3 more objects with the original set. He thus learns that 4 and 3 make 7. If he is asked often to find how many he has all together when he combines two sets, he will learn the basic addition facts.* Once he has learned these combinations he will respond automatically, and will not have to resort to counting.

How many addition combinations are there? In the traditional curriculum the child was expected to know 81 combinations from $1+1$ to $9+9$. The zero combinations were excluded because it was not considered proper to combine a set of 5 objects and a set of zero objects. In this view, zero is not a "proper" number but an indication of an absence of objects. This is, of course, a misconception of the number zero. In forming the union of two sets, one of the sets may be an empty set. Thus $5+0$ is just as proper as $5+4$. Since children in the first grade do respond to the union of a set with the empty set, they should learn all the addition combinations from $0+0$ to $9+9$. There are 100 combinations.

Combining sets of tens or hundreds is just like combining sets of ones. When the child has learned that 5 ones plus 3 ones form a set of 8 ones, he also learns that 5 tens and 3 tens form a set of 8 tens, or that 5 hundreds and 3 hundreds form a set of 8 hundreds.

The child learns the basic addition combinations in two stages. First he learns the addition of two addends whose sums are less than 10. Then he learns the addition of two addends whose sums are equal to, or greater than, 10. This is necessary because of our decimal notation system. Although we have the numbers ten, eleven, twelve, etc., in order to notate these numbers in the decimal system, we have to form sets of 10 and exchange them for new units. Thus 10 units of ones become 1 unit of tens and zero units of ones. Eleven units of ones become 1 unit of tens and 1 unit of ones. The 36 addition combinations whose sums are under 10 require thinking only about ones. The remaining 45 addition combinations whose sums are greater than 9 require thinking about a new unit, namely 10.

3.5 THE PROCESS OF EXCHANGE

It is important for children to learn that 10 units of one kind must be exchanged for 1 unit of the next higher size, since the largest single

*The basic addition facts are found by forming the union of two sets containing 0, 1, 2, . . . 9 elements.

digit in the decimal system is 9. In adding 8 ones and 5 ones the child learns by means of counting that the sum is 13 ones. However, it is not possible to notate that many ones in the decimal system. It becomes necessary to exchange 10 of the ones for 1 ten. We symbolize thirteen by the numeral 13, or 1 ten and 3 ones. The word *carry* should be eliminated from the mathematics vocabulary; it neither describes nor explains what is actually done. The idea of exchange enables children to understand addition in the decimal system, and it helps them learn addition in other numeration systems without too much difficulty.

To add 82 and 54 we think in this manner; a group of 2 ones and a group of 4 ones make a group of 6 ones, and a group of 8 tens and a group of 5 tens make a group of 13 tens. Since we have more than 9 tens, we have enough to make a new unit. We exchange 10 of the 13 tens for 1 hundred. We thus get the answer 136, or 1 hundred, 3 tens, and 6 ones. Once the concept of exchange is learned and fully understood, we can add any number of addends with any number of digits in each addend.

EXAMPLE:

```
 534      534      534      534
 252      252      252      252
 687      687      687      687
----        1       11       11
         ----     ----     ----
            3       73     1473
 (a)      (b)      (c)      (d)
```

Fig. 10

We begin with the ones column, Fig. 10*a*. Four ones plus 2 ones make 6 ones and 7 more ones make 13 ones. We exchange 10 of the ones for 1 ten, leaving 3 ones. We place the 1 ten in the tens column, Fig. 10*b*. We now add the number of tens. Three tens plus 5 tens make 8 tens, and 8 tens make 16 tens, and 1 ten make 17 tens. We exchange 10 tens for 1 hundred, leaving 7 tens. We place the 7 tens in the tens column and the 1 hundred in the hundreds column, Fig. 10*c*. Now we add the hundreds. Five hundreds plus 2 hundreds plus 6 hundreds plus 1 hundred make a group of 14 hundreds. We exchange 10 of the hundreds for 1 thousand, leaving 4 hundreds. We place the 1 thousand in the thousands column and the 4 hundreds in the hundreds column. The complete work is shown in Fig. 10*d*.

The place-value numeration system is based upon the concept of exchange of a number of units of one kind for one unit of another kind. This will be developed further in the examples of addition of numbers in other bases.

3.6 BASIC POSTULATES FOR ADDITION

As children learn the addition of numbers they should discover certain generalizations that are fundamental to arithmetic. They will need the help of the teacher in making these discoveries. Some children will do these very quickly by themselves, but other children will not see these generalizations readily. The teacher, by means of pointed questions, will help the children discover these relationships.

The Commutative Property. It will not take children long to discover that

$$5+3=3+5, \quad 7+2=2+7, \quad 6+4=4+6$$

This can be generalized as $a+b=b+a$. The use of letters to represent numbers is a big step for children. It is assumed that the readers of this book will not encounter any difficulty in using letters to formulate the generalizations that follow. Children will grasp these ideas more readily if frames are used as placeholders for numerals. Thus children would understand more readily that $\square+\triangle=\triangle+\square$, or that $(\square+\triangle)+\triangledown=\square+(\triangle+\triangledown)$ by writing numerals inside the frames. It is the commutative property for addition. This is why we can add a column of numbers up or down and arrive at the same answer both times.

The Associative Property. If we add three numbers, we group them two at a time, find the sum, and then add the third number.

$$5+3+4=(5+3)+4=5+(3+4)$$

If we add 5 and 3 and get 8 and then add 4 we get the sum 12. We can also add 5 to the sum of 3 and 4, or 5 plus 7 gives 12. Wc can generalize this as

$$(a+b)+c=a+(b+c)$$

This is the associative property for addition.

The Property of Closure. A set is said to be closed under an operation if the element that is the result of the operation is a member of the set. The set of natural numbers is closed under addition because the sum of any two natural numbers is a natural number. Not all sets are closed under operations. The set of natural numbers is not closed under subtraction; for example, $3-8$ is not a natural number. The set of odd numbers is not closed under addition because the sum of two odd numbers is not an odd number. This property will be further developed with other numbers and for other operations.

It should be emphasized that children learn the three properties for addition without necessarily learning the names of the properties. They should not be taught these properties in a formal way. Children should be given the opportunities to discover these properties and once discovered to apply them. The formal analysis of addition will come later, when the child is ready for the study of mathematics as a logical system.

Some authors of textbooks advocate the teaching of the commutative law for addition as some law of compensation that will save work in learning the addition facts. They argue that once the child has learned that 9 plus 2 equals 11, he automatically knows that 2 plus 9 equals 11. In this manner the child needs to learn only one-half of the addition facts. This argument may be logically correct, but it is psychologically and pedagogically unsound. The child who starts with 9 and adds 5 has a different situation from the child who starts with 5 and adds 9. The answers are the same in both cases, but the situations are different and should be treated as different. The child who discovers the addition properties experiences the thrill of discovery and has a better understanding of the nature of mathematics. Of course such a child will not have to learn all of the addition facts. There will be compensation for him because he has discovered the commutative principle. Children should be encouraged to discover such patterns, but not all children can be expected to discover them.

3.7 ADDITION IN OTHER NUMBER BASES

To add in other number bases we must also be able to apply the principle of exchange. Just as in the base ten we exchange 10 units of one kind for a new unit, in the base five we exchange 5 units for a new unit, in the base eight we exchange 8 units for a new unit, in the base twelve we exchange 12 units for a new unit, etc.

EXAMPLE 1. Addition in base five.

324	324	324	324
313	313	313	313
231	231	231	231
144	144	144	144
	2	22	22
	2	22	2122
(*a*)	(*b*)	(*c*)	(*d*)

Fig. 11

In Fig. 11*a* we first add the ones (5°) and find that the sum is 12. In this base we exchange 10 of the ones for 2 fives. We notate the remaining 2 ones in the ones column and the 2 fives in the fives (5^1) column, as in Fig. 11*b*. Now we add the digits in the fives column. Their sum is 12. Again we exchange 10 of the fives for 2 twenty-fives (5^2). We notate the 2 twenty-fives in the twenty-fives column and the 2 fives in the fives column, as in Fig. 11*c*. Now we add the digits in the twenty-fives column and find that their sum is 11. We now exchange 10 of the twenty-fives for 2 one hundred twenty-fives (5^3). We place the remaining 1 twenty-five in the twenty-fives column. The complete work is shown in Fig. 11*d*.

EXAMPLE 2. Addition in base eight.

(*a*)	(*b*)	(*c*)	(*d*)
324	324	324	324
313	313	313	313
231	231	231	231
144	144	144	144
	1	11	11
	4	34	1234

Fig. 12

Example 2 uses the same digits as Example 1, but these numerals represent numbers in the base eight. We now have to remember that it takes 8 units to make a new unit. We first add the ones (8^0). Their sum is 12. We exchange 8 ones for 1 eight (8^1) and record it in the eights column; the four remaining ones are entered in the ones column, as shown in Fig. 12*b*. Now we add the eights. Their sum is 11. We exchange 8 of the eights for 1 sixty-four (8^2) and record it in the sixty-four column; the remaining 3 eights are placed in the eights column, as in Fig. 12*c*. Now we add the sixty-fours and find their sum to be 10. We exchange 8 of the sixty-fours for 1 five hundred twelve. (8^3). The complete work is recorded in Fig. 12*d*.

EXAMPLE 3. Addition in base twelve.

(*a*)	(*b*)	(*c*)	(*d*)
324	324	324	324
313	313	313	313
231	231	231	231
144	144	144	144
	1	1	1
	0	*e*0	9*e*0

Fig. 13

Again we take the numerals of Example 1 but now we let them represent numbers in the base twelve. We can summarize the steps as we did in preceding examples. The sum of the digits in the ones column is 12, just enough to exchange for 1 twelve (Fig. 13*b*). We then add the number of twelves and find the sum to be 11, not enough to exchange for a new unit. We notate the eleven with the symbol *e*. Then we add the one hundred forty-fours (third column) and record the sum 9. The complete record of the work is shown in Fig. 13*d*.

EXAMPLE 4. Addition in base three.

122	122	122	122
112	112	112	112
122	122	122	122
	2	22	22
	0	10	1210
(*a*)	(*b*)	(*c*)	(*d*)

Fig. 14

In the base three we exchange 3 units for 1 new unit. The sum of the digits in the ones column is 6, just enough to exchange for 2 threes. The sum of the threes (second column) is 7. We exchange 6 threes for 2 nines (3^2) with 1 three remaining. Now we add the nines (third column). Their sum is 5. We exchange 3 nines for 1 twenty-seven (3^3). The complete steps are shown in Fig. 14*d*.

EXAMPLE 5. Addition in the base two (binary system).

11101	11101	11101	11101	11101	11101
1011	1011	1011	1011	1011	1011
	1	11	111	1111	1111
	0	00	000	1000	101000
(*a*)	(*b*)	(*c*)	(*d*)	(*e*)	(*f*)

Fig. 15

In this example we have more columns of digits, but the principle of exchange is the same. We now exchange 2 units for one of the next larger size. The steps are detailed in Fig. 15. The analysis for all of the steps is left for the reader.

3.8 TEACHING ADDITION

Children must learn the basic addition combinations. To accomplish this they should be provided with various kinds of manipulative aids so that they can actually count as they combine two groups of objects. They may use actual concrete objects such as blocks, toys, pencils, books, squares cut out of construction paper, counting frame, hundred board, or abacus. Some children will discard the manipulative devices quickly; others will resort to such devices for a long time. It should be understood that the use of concrete devices is a crutch for the child, but it should also be understood that a crutch is an important tool for the children who need it.

The Number Line. One of the most effective devices for teaching number relations is the number line. It is a physical model to represent our abstract concept of numbers. Suppose we have a straight line with points on it that are equally spaced. Let us number the first point 0, the second point 1, the third point 2, and so on, as in Fig. 16.

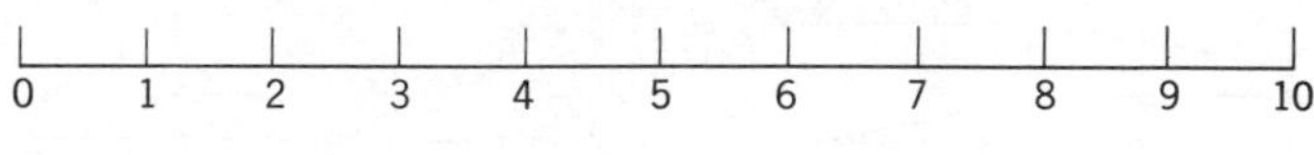

Fig. 16

The point corresponding to 3 is 3 spaces from the zero point, the point corresponding to 7 is 7 spaces from the zero point, the point corresponding to 10 is 10 spaces from the zero point. These points correspond to numbers. If we think of each number point in relation to the number of spaces from the zero point, then we are using the cardinal concept of number. We may, however, think of each point not as a distance from some other point, but as a position. Then we are thinking of the ordinal concept of number. The point corresponding to 6 is a cardinal number if we think of it as 6 spaces from the 0 point. The point corresponding to 6 is an ordinal number if we think of it as a single point that lies between 5 and 7. Thus the number line becomes a concrete device for learning about number and operations with number. Figure 16 represents only a portion of the number line. We may imagine that the line has been continued for a long distance and that we have another portion of it, as in Fig. 17.

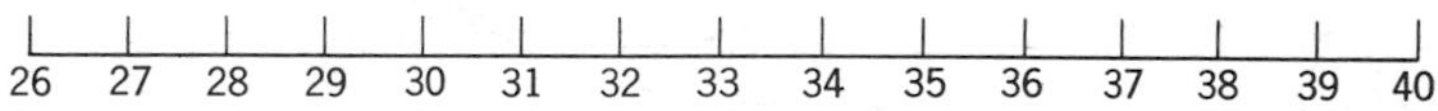

Fig. 17

There is great danger that some teachers will expose children to the number line before they are ready for it. It then becomes mechanical learning. The child should first learn about numbers as associated with sets. When that is thoroughly understood, the number line can be used as a means of representing what the child has already learned about numbers. Seven objects or 7 spaces really represent the same idea. A child may misuse the number line to memorize that 23 comes after 22 without really understanding what 23 or 22 means.

The number line can be used by the child to learn the addition facts. Let us pretend that a cricket jumps a given number of spaces on the number line. What is 4 + 3? The cricket first jumps 4 spaces, beginning with the 0 point and then 3 more spaces. How many spaces has he jumped altogether, or how many spaces would it be if he made it in one jump? This is shown in Fig. 18. A number line may be painted on the floor in front of the classroom or on the concrete in the school yard. Then children may hop or jump a given number of spaces, and thus act out the addition combinations.

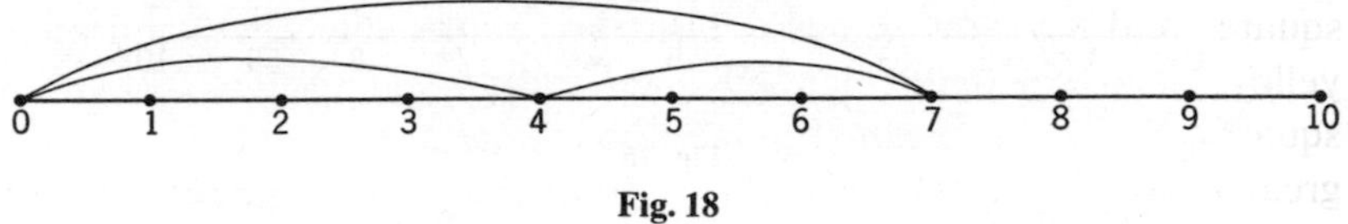

Fig. 18

The number line is also a very effective device to demonstrate the commutative law and the associative law. Figure 19 shows the commutative principle that $4+3=3+4$, and Fig. 20 demonstrates the associative principle that $4+(3+2)=(4+3)+2$. In adding 4 and 3, it is not necessary to begin with the zero point. The cricket may jump 4 spaces and then 3 for a total of 7 spaces no matter where he begins to jump, as is illustrated in Fig. 21

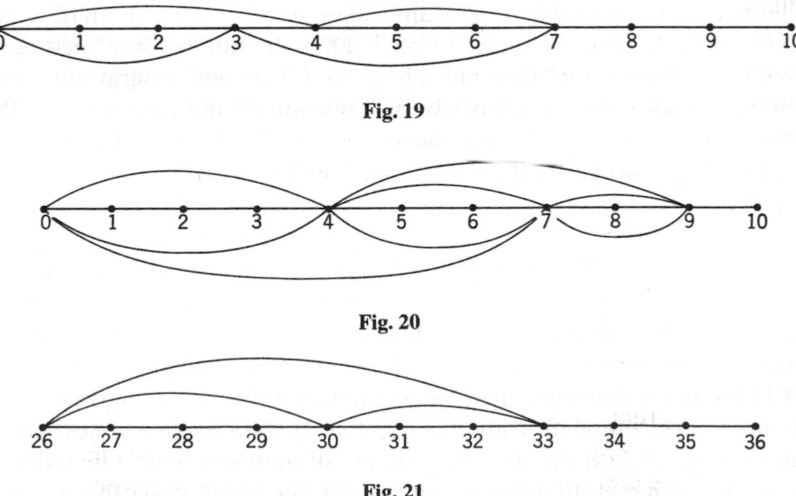

Fig. 19

Fig. 20

Fig. 21

The Process of Exchange. This process can be taught in several ways. One effective device is an open-end abacus which contains rods that can hold only 10 discs on each rod. To add 28 and 36, the child first places 8 discs on the ones rod and 2 discs on the tens rod. Now he places 6 discs on the ones rod and finds that he has more discs than the rod can hold. He exchanges 10 discs for 1 disc and the new disc is placed on the tens rod. The 8 ones plus 6 ones give 14 ones. Ten ones are exchanged for 1 ten. Now he adds 3 discs (the 3 tens of 36) to the tens rod and finds he has 6 discs on the tens rod and 4 discs on the ones rod.

A second technique is to use 2-inch squares cut out of different-colored construction paper. Let the yellow squares represent ones and the red squares represent tens. The numeral 28 is represented by 2 red squares and 8 yellow squares. The 36 is represented by 3 red and 6 yellow squares. Combining the 8 and 6 yellow squares gives 14 yellow squares. Since our decimal numeration system does not allow a digit greater than 9, the child exchanges 10 of the yellow squares for 1 red square. Now there are 2 red squares, 3 red squares, and 1 red square for a total of 6 red squares. This is a concrete way of demonstrating that $28 + 36 = 64$.

Color for demonstrating units of various sizes must be used judiciously. If the same color is always used for the same kind of unit, the child will associate numbers with colors. To overcome this the colors may be changed so that different exercises have different colors for the various units. One time red may represent hundreds, yellow represent tens, and blue represent ones. Another time the yellow may represent hundreds, blue the tens, and red the ones.

Instead of squares of different-colored construction paper the same color but different shapes can be used. Thus squares may represent ones, triangles may represent tens, circles hundreds, hexagons thousands, etc.

The place-value charts may also be used in the same way as colored squares. If the chart is made with pockets the child can place squares, tongue depressers, or ice cream sticks in the pockets. Whenever there are more than 9 sticks or squares it is necessary to make an exchange.

Children will operate at different levels. Some will use the concrete aids, described above, for a long time. Others will use these aids for only a short time and will discard them when they no longer need them. All children will need some practice with various addition exercises in order to develop skill in performing the operation. To challenge each child and not to bore any, the practice exercises should be arranged according to levels of difficulty. Several types are described.

TYPE 1.

7	3	5	8	2	4
+2	+4	+1	+1	+6	+5

These are the addition of two 1-digit addends whose sums are less than 10.

TYPE 2.

8	7	9	4	5	8
+5	+6	+7	+7	+9	+7

These are the addition of two 1-digit addends whose sums are greater than nine and the process of exchange is necessary.

TYPE 3.

23	31	61	53	81
+45	+53	+15	+23	+16

Here we have the addition of two 2-digit addends without exchange.

TYPE 4.

37	49	36	55
+25	+27	+45	+29

Here we have two 2-digit addends that require an exchange of 10 ones for 1 ten.

TYPE 5.

81	72	54	63
+43	+53	+91	+84

In these examples it is necessary to exchange 10 tens for 1 hundred.

TYPE 6.

97	86	74	57
+35	+59	+98	+76

Here we have to apply the process of exchange twice, 10 ones for 1 ten and 10 tens for 1 hundred.

TYPE 7.

324	401	513
+152	+236	+283

TYPE 8.

324	409	513
+158	+237	+269

TYPE 9.

486	574	796
+291	+182	+152

TYPE 10.

823	642	635
+516	+831	+923

TYPE 11.

496	827	896
+258	+419	+756

These five types represent the addition of 3-digit addends with and without exchange. Sometimes the exchange is applied only once, sometimes twice, and some exercises require the process of exchange three times.

These levels of difficulty should be used only if the children need them. The children make this decision, not the teacher. Some children grasp the concept of exchange and have no difficulty applying to 2-digit, 3-digit, or even 4-digit numbers, and it makes no difference to them whether the principle is applied once, twice, or three times in the same exercise. Other children become confused if the numbers are too large, or if they have to apply the concept of exchange more than once in the same exercise. The same assignment should, therefore, not be given to all the children in a class. Each child should work the exercises that will help him learn to add. The child who already knows how does not need any drill.

TYPE 12.

$$\begin{array}{r} 3 \\ 4 \\ +2 \\ \hline \end{array} \qquad \begin{array}{r} 5 \\ 2 \\ +3 \\ \hline \end{array} \qquad \begin{array}{r} 2 \\ 7 \\ +4 \\ \hline \end{array} \qquad \begin{array}{r} 4 \\ 4 \\ +7 \\ \hline \end{array}$$

This type of exercise differs from the others in that it contains three addends. The child adds the first two addends but does not record the sum. He must keep the sum in mind and add the third addend. This requires some skill and effort. Once the child has learned to add three addends, he can practice with 2- and 3-digit addends according to levels of difficulty described previously. Again it should be emphasized that some children will be confused if the process of exchange has to be applied more than once. Others will have no difficulty applying exchange any number of times and will be able to add more than three addends.

Addition in a Problem-Solving Situation. As soon as possible children should learn to represent a problem situation in symbolic terms using an equation. Since addition is a process that is performed with numbers, the equation should reflect this action. Frames may be used as placeholders for numerals. Squares, triangles, rectangles, upside-down triangles are examples of various frames that may be used. Children can be posed the following question, "If James has 3 toys and his father brings him 5 toys, how many toys does James now have?" This is represented in equation form as

$$3+5=\square$$

Or the question may be, "James had 5 toys and his father brought him some toys. Now James has 7 toys. How many toys did his father bring?" This is represented in equation form as

$$5+\square=7$$

The children who know the addition combinations will have no difficulty finding the answer 8 in the square of the first example and 2 in the square of the second example, since $3+5=8$ and $5+2=7$. Another way of representing the above situations is to use an arrow which reads "gives". We write

$$(3,5) \xrightarrow{+} \square$$

The plus sign above the arrow indicates that 3 and 5 are to be added. The child may read the above in this manner. "If we add 3 and 5 we get how many?" Or we may have $(5, \square) \xrightarrow{+} 7$, which is read as "what added to 5 gives 7?"

The problem situation works in two ways. We may have a story and we have to translate the words into mathematical symbols. We may also start with an equation and want to make a story that fits the equation. Children need experience with both types of effort. Let children make up stories to fit the following:

$$9+3 = \square$$
$$7+15 = \square$$
$$7+\square = 15$$
$$(4,7) \longrightarrow \square$$
$$(2,\square) \xrightarrow{+} 9$$
$$\square+9 = 12$$
$$(\square,6) \xrightarrow{+} 11$$
$$\square+\triangle = 13$$
$$(\triangle,\square) \xrightarrow{+} 9$$

3.9 SUMMARY

Addition is related to the union of two or more disjoint sets. A more sophisticated view is that addition is the mapping of a pair of numbers into a third number as in $(1, 2) \xrightarrow{+} 3$. Mathematical addition is an operation performed with numbers: $5+3$ is another name for 8. It is as good a name as "8". A single numeral may be more convenient than a pair of numerals, but it is not always necessary to have the single numeral. The computational process which is traditionally called addition requires the replacement of two or more numerals by a single numeral.

The child learns the basic addition combinations by operating with concrete manipulative devices. He may resort to counting until he learns the addition facts. Once the child learns the basic facts, he applies them in the addition of addends composed of any number of digits. To accomplish this he must learn the concept of exchange.

In the decimal system we exchange 10 units of one kind for a unit of the next larger size. The concept of exchange is used when adding numbers represented in other numeration systems. The base tells us how many units of one kind are needed to exchange for a unit of the next size.

At the earliest opportunity the child learns to describe a situation involving quantity by means of a mathematical equation. Frames may be used as placeholders for numerals. The numerals put into the frame must make the equation a true sentence. A situation that requires a derived answer is a problem-solving situation. Children should learn to use mathematical symbols that fit a problem situation, and they should also learn to compose stories to fit given equations.

EXERCISES

1. Add the following decimal numbers and explain the thought processes involved in deriving the answers.

(*a*)	(*b*)	(*c*)	(*d*)
473	297	802	123
294	586	196	456
165	402	240	789
	134	431	637

2. Add the following numbers in the base five and explain the thought process involved in deriving the answers.

(*a*)	(*b*)	(*c*)	(*d*)
423	334	404	113
204	204	321	433
142	143	103	201
	212	221	440

3. Add the following numbers in the base eight and explain the thought processes.

(*a*)	(*b*)	(*c*)	(*d*)
423	334	404	113
204	206	312	433
142	135	403	201
	221	651	756

4. Add the following numbers in base twelve.

(*a*)	(*b*)	(*c*)	(*d*)
23	49	113	801
45	78	249	19t
96	4t	786	239
78	*e*7	101	143

5. Add the following numbers in base three.

(*a*)	(*b*)	(*c*)	(*d*)
222	1002	2021	1111
112	211	1121	2121
101	102	1012	1212
	111	2001	2002

6. Add these binary numbers and explain the thought processes involved in deriving the answers.

(*a*)	(*b*)	(*c*)	(*d*)
111011	1010101	1101101	10011
10101	101001	1011011	1101
			1011

7. Use squares of colored construction paper to explain the addition in Exercises 1*a*, 2*b*, 3*c*, 4*d*, 5*c*, 6*b*.
8. How would you vary the teaching of addition to children who learn at different rates?
9. Apply the commutative property to the addition of numbers in the other numeration systems.
10. Apply the associative property to the addition of numbers in the other numeration systems.
11. Why is addition a binary operation?
12. What is the difference between addition of numbers and the union of sets?
13. Give examples of a problem situation involving addition that is appropriate for children in the intermediate grades.
14. Give some examples of a problem situation involving addition that is appropriate for children in the primary grades.
15. Show how the knowledge of the commutative property of addition can be helpful to children.
16. Show how the associative property of addition can be used in learning addition combinations whose sums are greater than 9.

SUGGESTED SUPPLEMENTARY READING

1. Bell, Clifford, Clela D. Hammond, and Robert B. Herrera, *Fundamentals of Arithmetic for Teachers.* New York: John Wiley and Sons, 1962. Chap. 3.
2. Brumfield, Charles F., et al, *Principles of Arithmetic.* Reading, Mass.: Addison-Wesley Publishing Company, 1963. Chaps. 3 and 5.
3. Buckingham, Burdette R., *Elementary Arithmetic, Its Meaning and Practice.* Boston: Ginn and Company, 1953. pp. 49–57 and Chap. 5.
4. Dutton, Wilbur H., and L. J. Adams, *Arithmetic for Teachers.* Englewood Cliffs, N.J.: Prentice-Hall, 1961. Chap. 2.
5. Hohn, Franz E., "Automatic Addition," *The Arithmetic Teacher,* March 1963. pp. 127–132.
6. Larsen, Harold D., and H. Glenn Ludlow, *Arithmetic for Colleges.* New York: The Macmillan Company, 1963. Chap. 3.
7. Marks, John L., C. Richard Purdy, and Lucien B. Kinney, *Teaching*

Arithmetic for Understanding. New York: McGraw-Hill Book Company, 1958. Chap. 6.
8. McSwain, E. T., and Ralph J. Cook, *Understanding and Teaching Arithmetic in the Elementary School.* New York: Henry Holt and Company, 1958. Chap. 3.
9. Mueller, Francis J., *Arithmetic, Its Structure and Concepts.* Englewood Cliffs, N. J.: Prentice-Hall, 1956. pp. 48–69.
10. Smith, Rolland R., "The Ten-Tens Counting Frame," *The Arithmetic Teacher,* November 1956. pp. 197–200.
11. Stern, Catherine, "The Concrete Devices of Structural Arithmetic," *The Arithmetic Teacher,* April 1958. pp. 119–131.
12. Swain, Robert L., *Understanding Arithmetic.* New York: Rinehart and Company, 1957. pp. 46–52, 67–72.

Chapter 4 Subtraction

4.1 INTRODUCTION

The large number of articles that have been written about subtraction in the educational journals is ample evidence that this fundamental operation is more complicated and more difficult to teach than addition. We can treat this topic from a purely logical point of view, or we can discuss it from the practical experiences of man in his everyday life. The elementary school teacher needs to understand the mathematical principles involved in subtraction, but the teacher also needs to understand how children learn. It is easy to show children the mechanics of deriving the correct answer, but such mechanical learning will not develop the understanding that will enable the child to apply this knowledge to other areas. Subtraction will be treated in this chapter from two points of view: the child as a learner, and the process as a logical, mathematical operation that adds to one's understanding of mathematics.

4.2 SUBTRACTION AS A TAKE-AWAY PROCESS

When the child operates with concrete objects, he experiences the take-away process in a meaningful way. If the child has 7 marbles and he loses 2 marbles, he wants to know how many marbles he has left. If he has 5 pieces of candy and he eats 2 pieces, he is concerned about how much candy he has left. If he buys a bottle of milk, he may drink only part of it at recess time and save the rest for lunch time. The child experiences the take-away process in a concrete manner.

He may experience the process as a kind of delayed response. He may have saved up some money to buy his mother a gift. First, he wants to know if he has enough money. Second, he wants to know how much money he will have left if he buys the gift.

In the take-away process one starts with a given number of objects, removes some objects, and has a remainder. The number associated with the set of objects he starts with is called the *minuend*, the number he removes is called the *subtrahend*, and the answer is called the *remainder*.

In order to perform the take-away process of subtraction the child has to learn the subtraction facts in the same way that he learned the addition facts. He may learn the addition and subtraction facts at the same time. When he combines 5 objects and 3 objects, he finds that he has a set of 8 objects; this is symbolized by $5 + 3 = 8$. He may start with a set of 8 objects and then remove 5 objects; he finds that he has 3 objects left, which is symbolized by $8 - 5 = 3$. He may be asked to take away 3 objects from 8 objects; now he has a remainder of 5 objects, which is symbolized by $8 - 3 = 5$. The four situations may be summarized in one set of equations:

$$5+3=8, \quad 3+5=8, \quad 8-3=5, \quad 8-5=3$$

In like manner he learns that,

$$3+4=7, \quad 4+3=7, \quad 7-4=3, \quad 7-3=4$$

The child learns 81 or 100 addition facts, and at the same time he learns 81 or 100 subtraction facts. By learning the two processes together the child learns subtraction as the inverse process, or the undoing of addition. In addition we have two addends and we find their sum. In subtraction we have the sum and one of the addends, and we find the second addend.

4.3 SUBTRACTION AS FINDING THE DIFFERENCE

The second interpretation of subtraction is that it is a comparison of two numbers. Suppose Johnny has 8 marbles and Fred has 5 marbles, how many more marbles does Johnny have? Here we do not take away Fred's marbles from Johnny's marbles. We really ask how many marbles must be combined with Fred's marbles in order to equal Johnny's number of marbles. The answer is, of course, 3 marbles. This method is, in contrast to the take-away process, an additive process. The answer is not a remainder since nothing was removed. The answer is the *difference*.

Subtraction, like addition, is an operation performed with numbers. It has nothing to do with things. The child associates the numbers with sets of objects. Just as he combines two sets to form one set, he may separate one set into two sets. A number is associated with the number of elements in a set. Just as addition is an operation with numbers that may be associated with the union of two sets, subtraction is an operation with numbers that may be associated with the separation of a set into two sets.

The additive method of subtraction is the mathematical meaning of subtraction. Here we define $a-b=c$ as another way of saying that $b+c=a$ or $a-b=c$ but if, and only if, $b+c=a$. Whereas the take-away process is an operation on the concrete level, the additive method is an operation on the abstract level. This will become clearer when we discuss the addition and subtraction of integers in a later chapter. In the physical sense we cannot take away a negative number. We can, however, subtract negative numbers because we can add numbers to negative numbers.

In using the take-away method subtraction of zero is rather meaningless. How do we take away 0 objects from a set of 5 objects? But if we compare 5 with 0 we can see very clearly that 5 added to 0 gives 5. On the concrete level we cannot remove 0 objects. On the abstract level, or subtraction as a mathematical operation, $5-0$ is meaningful.

Regardless of whether the take-away or the additive method is used, the minuend must be greater than the subtrahend. When we deal only with positive numbers we cannot have $5-8$. We cannot take away 8 objects from 5 objects. Neither can we add to 8 to get 5 if negative numbers are not available, since 8 is already more than 5.

The additive method has the advantage over the take-away process in that it is not necessary for the child to learn any new facts. The child first learns the addition combinations. In the take-away method he has to learn an equal number of subtraction facts. In the additive method, however, he merely applies the addition facts that he already knows. This is not to imply that the child should not learn the take-away process. On the contrary, he should begin to learn subtraction by the realistic concrete approach of actually and physically removing objects from a group. But the child should progress as soon as possible to the additive method, since it is the mathematical basis for subtraction.

4.4 SUBTRACTION WITH NUMBERS THAT CONTAIN MORE THAN ONE DIGIT

When the minuend and the subtrahend contain more than one digit, we subtract the like-sized units. This means that we subtract ones from ones, tens from tens, hundreds from hundreds, etc. In the following example, $498-236$, we subtract 6 ones from 8 ones, 3 tens from 9 tens, and 2 hundreds from 4 hundreds. Our answer is 262. We may perform the subtraction by the take-away or by the additive method. As long as the minuend has more units of each size than the subtrahend, it does not matter how many digits are needed to write the numbers. Since each size unit is treated separately, we always subtract a 1-digit number from a l-digit number. The size of the numbers is immaterial. Children, however, should work with only the numbers that they understand.

The more difficult subtraction situations arise when the minuend contains fewer units in a given position than the subtrahend, as in $82-37$. It is not possible to take away 7 ones from 2 ones. Neither is it possible to add to 7 ones to get 2 ones. A child who is confronted with this situation may find the answer to the question by either the take-away or the additive methods.

One child may start by taking away 40 from 82 and get the remainder 42. He may then reason that since 40 is 3 more than 37, he took away 3 too many. To compensate for this, he adds 3 to the 42 and derives the correct answer 45. Or, he may take away 32 from 82 and derive the remainder 50. Now he may reason that since 37 is 5 more than 32, he should take away another 5. When he subtracts 5 from 50, he derives the correct answer 45. He may, however, try a different approach. He may first subtract 2, then 30, and then 5 for a total of 37. This will give him the successive remainders 80, 50, and finally 45.

Another child may approach the problem from the additive point of view. The exercise $82-37$ asks the question what must be added to 37 in order to get 82. He adds 3 to 37 and derives the sum 40. Then he adds 42 to 40 in order to derive the sum 82. Thus, he has added 45 to 37 in order to get 82.

As long as we are dealing with relatively small numbers, the child may find the required answer in several ways as described above. Children should be encouraged to find the solutions by themselves. When the numbers are relatively large, as in the example $8264-3976$, the child may find it difficult to follow the reasoning that was applied with small numbers. It becomes necessary to develop an algorithm that will be easy to perform and that is mathematically sound. The decomposition method and the equal additions method will be explained. The complementary method of subtraction is not discussed in this book.

4.5 THE DECOMPOSITION METHOD

EXAMPLE 1. $82-37$, or
$$\begin{array}{r} 82 \\ \underline{-37} \end{array}$$

We analyze as follows:

$$\begin{array}{rl} 82 = & 8 \text{ tens} + 2 \text{ ones} \\ \underline{-37 =} & \underline{3 \text{ tens} + 7 \text{ ones}} \end{array}$$

Our difficulty lies in the fact that the minuend has fewer ones than the subtrahend. To obtain more ones, we exchange one of the 8 tens for 10 ones. We restructure our numbers in the following manner:

$$\begin{array}{r} 82 = 8 \text{ tens} + 2 \text{ ones} = 7 \text{ tens} + 12 \text{ ones} \\ -37 = 3 \text{ tens} + 7 \text{ ones} = 3 \text{ tens} + 7 \text{ ones} \\ \hline 4 \text{ tens} + 5 \text{ ones} \end{array}$$

Since we have a sufficient number of ones in the minuend, there is no longer any difficulty. The answer 45 is easily derived.

EXAMPLE 2. $\begin{array}{r} 842 \\ -275 \\ \hline \end{array}$

We analyze the numbers in the same manner as in Example 1, as follows:

$$\begin{array}{r} 842 = 8 \text{ hundreds} + 4 \text{ tens} + 2 \text{ ones} \\ -275 = 2 \text{ hundreds} + 7 \text{ tens} + 5 \text{ ones} \\ \hline = 8 \text{ hundreds} + 3 \text{ tens} + 12 \text{ ones} \\ 2 \text{ hundreds} + 7 \text{ tens} + 5 \text{ ones} \\ \hline 7 \text{ ones} \end{array}$$

Since we do not have a sufficient number of ones in the minuend, we exchange one of the 4 tens for 10 ones. Now we have 12 ones in the minuend and we are able to subtract 5 ones. But we do not have a sufficient number of tens in our minuend. This time we exchange one of the 8 hundreds for 10 tens. We now have the following:

$$\begin{array}{r} 7 \text{ hundreds} + 13 \text{ tens} + 12 \text{ ones} \\ -2 \text{ hundreds} + 7 \text{ tens} + 5 \text{ ones} \\ \hline 5 \text{ hundreds} + 6 \text{ tens} + 7 \text{ ones} \end{array}$$

It is now possible to subtract the tens as well as the ones. This process of regrouping, or exchanging a larger unit for 10 smaller units, is called decomposition. We exchange 1 ten for 10 ones, 1 hundred for 10 tens, 1 thousand for 10 hundreds, etc.

The decomposition method raises a question of inconsistency. Up to this point the child has learned that he cannot write more than 9 units in a given position or place value. In addition he was told that he must exchange 10 ones for 1 ten, 10 tens for 1 hundred, etc. Now he is told that he can write 12 ones as in Example 1, and 13 tens and 12 ones as in Example 2.

It is true that, according to our numeration system, we cannot record more than 9 units in a given position. If we have 37 chairs, we record the fact by writing 37. But the chairs may be grouped in different ways. Our numeration system expresses the group as 3 tens and 7 ones, but we may group the chairs mentally as 2 tens and 17 ones. We then notate what we are thinking. Although we can represent a number in any numeration system in only one way, we can think about the number in different ways. Thus we can think of 56 as 5 tens and 6 ones, or 4 tens and 16 ones, or 3 tens and 26 ones, or 2 tens and 36 ones, and even as 56 ones. In the two examples above, we wrote in symbols what we were thinking about the numbers.

The numeral 842 represents 8 hundreds 4 tens and 2 ones. We may, however, think of the number represented by 842 in many different ways such as, 8 hundreds 3 tens and 12 ones, 8 hundreds 2 tens and 22 ones, 7 hundreds 14 tens and 2 ones, 6 hundreds 24 tens and 2 ones, 7 hundreds 13 tens and 12 ones. Children should be taught to think of numbers in different ways. The symbols we write are merely a record of what our mind is thinking. In subtraction it is necessary to think of numbers in different ways according to the needs of the situation.

In subtraction we should eliminate the word "borrow" since that does not represent what we are really thinking. The concept of exchange, or regrouping, makes subtraction as well as addition more meaningful.

4.6 THE EQUAL ADDITIONS METHOD

The lack of a sufficient number of units in the minuend may be overcome by adding 10 units to the minuend and 1 unit of the next size to the subtrahend. Since the same amount is added to both minuend and subtrahend, the difference remains the same. In the examples $49-23$, $59-33$, $69-43$, $79-53$ the difference is the same in each case, namely, 26.

In Example 1, $82-37$, we had difficulty in subtracting because there were not enough ones. This deficiency may be overcome by adding 10 ones to the minuend and 1 ten to the subtrahend. This will give the same difference as $82-37$. We reason as follows:

$$\begin{array}{rl} 82 = 8\text{ tens} + 2\text{ ones} & 8\text{ tens} + 12\text{ ones} \\ \underline{-37 = 3\text{ tens} + 7\text{ ones}} & \underline{4\text{ tens} + 7\text{ ones}} \\ & 4\text{ tens} + 5\text{ ones} \end{array}$$

In Example 2, 842 − 275, we add 10 ones to the minuend and 1 ten to the subtrahend, then 10 tens to the minuend, and 1 hundred to the subtrahend, represented as follows:

$$\begin{array}{rl} 842 = & 8 \text{ hundreds} + 4 \text{ tens} + 2 \text{ ones} \\ -275 = & 2 \text{ hundreds} + 7 \text{ tens} + 5 \text{ ones} \\ \hline & 8 \text{ hundreds} + 14 \text{ tens} + 12 \text{ ones} \\ & 3 \text{ hundreds} + 8 \text{ tens} + 5 \text{ ones} \\ \hline & 5 \text{ hundreds} + 6 \text{ tens} + 7 \text{ ones} \end{array}$$

Since we add the same amount to both the minuend and the subtrahend, this method is known as the equal additions method.

There has been considerable controversy in American education regarding the relative merits of these two methods of subtraction. The advocates of a meaningful arithmetic program support the decomposition method as psychologically more effective. The decomposition or regrouping explains, in a way that is meaningful to children, what thought processes are involved. The process of exchange is meaningful to children. The equal additions method may be convincing to adults, but how does one convince children that adding the same amounts to both the minuend and the subtrahend does not affect the difference? Also how does one explain to children that we add the same amounts but not units of the same size?

The advocates of the equal additions method argue that repeated studies have shown that children taught by this method get more correct answers and perform the operation successfully in less time. These results convince them that the equal additions method is superior to the decomposition method.

Brownell and Moser* conducted a study to determine the relative merits of these two methods. Whereas other experiments used the criteria of speed and accuracy to determine the effectiveness of the process, Brownell and Moser considered the ways in which the processes were taught. They divided the children in the study into four groups: those taught the decomposition method mechanically, those taught the decomposition method meaningfully, those taught the equal additions method mechanically, and those taught the equal additions method meaningfully. They found, on the basis of tests administered to all of the groups, that the order of achievement was: (1) decomposition meaningfully, (2) those taught equal additions meaningfully, (3) equal additions mechanically, and (4) decomposition mechanically. If mechanical methods of teaching were used, the equal additions

*William A. Brownell and Harold E. Moser, *Meaningful versus Mechanical Learning: A Study in Grade III Subtraction.* Duke University Research Studies in Education. Number 8. Durham, N.C.: Duke University Press, 1949.

method was superior. If, however, children were taught meaningfully, then the decomposition method was the superior one.

Since the process of exchange is fundamental to the understanding of addition, this knowledge can be carried over easily to the process of subtraction. The decomposition method, based on the concept of exchange, can be applied successfully to subtraction in other number bases. The equal additions method can also be applied successfully to subtraction in other number bases, but it may be more difficult to teach.

4.7 SUBTRACTION IN OTHER NUMBER BASES

If we subtract numbers represented in other number bases, we follow the same principles as with the base ten. To find the difference between two numbers we add enough units of each kind to the subtrahend to equal the number of units in the minuend, as in the following examples:

$$
\begin{array}{cccc}
\textit{Base five} & \textit{Base eight} & \textit{Base twelve} & \textit{Base three} \\
423 & 657 & 89\text{t} & 122 \\
\underline{-211} & \underline{-425} & \underline{-536} & \underline{-21} \\
212 & 232 & 364 & 101
\end{array}
$$

If the number of units in a given position in the minuend is less than the number of units in the same position in the subtrahend, we use the decomposition method. We apply the concept of exchange, but we must remember that the exchange ratio is equal to the base, 5 ones for 1 five, 8 ones for 1 eight, 12 ones for 1 twelve, etc.

Base Five

$$
\begin{array}{rl}
 & 12 \\
432 = & 42\ \not{2} \\
-123 = & 12\ \ 3 \\
\hline
 & 30\ \ 4 \\
(a) & \quad (b)
\end{array}
\qquad\qquad
\begin{array}{rlll}
 & 11 & & 1011 \\
311 = & 30\ \not{1} & = & 2\ \not{0}\ \not{1} \\
-123 - & 12\ \ 3 & = & 1\ 2\ 3 \\
\hline
 & 3 & & 1\ 3\ 3 \\
(c) & \quad (d) & & \quad (e)
\end{array}
$$

Fig. 22

In Fig. 22*a* we notice that there are more ones in the subtrahend than in the minuend. We exchange one of the 3 fives for 5 ones and write the result in Fig. 22*b*. We must understand that the 12 written over the 2 represents 7 in the base five. We find that the answer is 304, read three-o-four. In Fig. 22*c* we note that the minuend has fewer fives and ones than the subtrahend. We first exchange the 1 five for 5 ones, as notated in Fig. 22*d*. The difference between 6 ones and 3 ones is 3 ones. Now we exchange one of the 3 twenty-fives for 5 fives and write the result as in Fig. 22*e*. Now we can perform the subtraction and derive the answer 133.

BASE EIGHT

$$\begin{array}{rr}
 & 12 \\
432 = & 42\ \not{2} \\
-123 = & 12\ \ 3 \\
\hline
 & 30\ \ 7 \\
(a) & (b)
\end{array}
\qquad
\begin{array}{rrr}
 & 11 & 1011 \\
311 = & 30\ \not{1} = & 2\ \not{0}\ \not{1} \\
-123 = & 12\ \ 3 = & 1\ \ 2\ \ 3 \\
\hline
 & 6 = & 1\ \ 6\ \ 6 \\
(c) & (d) & (e)
\end{array}$$

Fig. 23

We use the same digits as in Fig. 22, but they represent numbers in base eight. In Fig. 23*a* we exchange one of the 3 eights for 8 ones as shown in Fig. 23*b*. Remember that 12_{eight} represents 10 ones. The answer is 307_{eight}. In Fig. 23*c* we note that the minuend has an insufficient number of eights and of ones. We first exchange the 1 eight for 8 ones as shown in Fig. 23*d*, and then we exchange one of the 3 sixty-fours for 8 eights. The complete work is shown in Fig. 23*e*. Again it is necessary to remind the reader that the 11 in the ones column represents 9 ones, and that the 10 in the eights column represents 8 eights.

BASE TWELVE

$$\begin{array}{rr}
 & 12 \\
432 = & 42\ \not{2} \\
-123 = & 12\ \ 3 \\
\hline
 & 30\ \ e \\
(a) & (b)
\end{array}
\qquad
\begin{array}{rrr}
 & 11 & 1011 \\
311 = & 30\ \not{1} = & 2\ \not{0}\ \not{1} \\
-123 = & 12\ \ 3 = & 1\ \ 2\ \ 3 \\
\hline
 & t & 1\ \ t\ \ t \\
(c) & (d) & (e)
\end{array}$$

Fig. 24

We now exchange one larger unit for 12 smaller units. The 12 in the ones column in Fig 24*b* represents 14 ones. When we subtract 3 ones, we get 11 ones or *e*. The 11 in the ones column in Fig. 24*e* represents 13 ones, and the 10 in the twelves column represents 12 twelves. The answer represents 1 one hundred forty-fours, 10 twelves, and 10 ones.

BASE THREE

$$\begin{array}{rrrr}
 & 11 & 1011 & 101011 \\
2111 = & 210\ \not{1} = & 20\ \not{0}\ \not{1} = & 1\ \not{0}\ \not{0}\ \not{1} \\
-1212 = & 121\ \ 2 = & 12\ \ 1\ \ 2 = & 1\ \ 2\ \ 1\ \ 2 \\
\hline
 & 2 & 2\ \ 2 & 1\ \ 2\ \ 2 \\
(a) & (b) & (c) & (d)
\end{array}$$

Fig. 25

Here we exchange one larger unit for 3 smaller units. Each successive step is shown in Fig. 25. It is left to the student to explain each step.

Base Two

$$\begin{array}{rcrrrrrrrr} & & & 10 & 10 & & & & 10 & \\ 11001101 & = & \not{1} & \not{0} & \not{0} & 0 & 1 & 0 & \not{0} & 1 \\ -\ 1101011 & = & & 1 & 1 & 0 & 1 & 0 & 1 & 1 \\ \hline & & & 1 & 1 & 0 & 0 & 0 & 1 & 0 \end{array}$$

(*a*) (*b*)

Fig. 26

We first subtract the ones and get the difference 0. Then we attempt to subtract the twos but find that there are not enough twos in the minuend. We exchange the one unit in the third column for two units in the second column, and this is written as 10. We have no difficulty with subtraction in columns 3, 4, and 5. In the sixth column we find that we have no unit in the minuend. We exchange the unit in the seventh column for two units in the sixth column, but this leaves no unit in the seventh column of the minuend. We exchange the one unit in the eighth column for two units in the seventh column. All of the steps are shown in Fig. 26*b*.

4.8 TEACHING SUBTRACTION

Children learning to subtract may need concrete manipulative aids. If they learn the take-away process, they actually remove books from a set of books, toys from a set of toys, and pencils from a set of pencils. If they learn the additive method, they apply their knowledge of the addition facts; however, they may still need concrete objects.

Where the process of exchange has to be applied, the child may use several concrete devices to help him. He may use a placeholder chart containing pockets for the hundreds, tens, and ones places. He may use tongue depressers or ice cream sticks to place in each pocket. When necessary a stick is removed from one pocket and 10 sticks are put in the pocket to the right.

Squares of Colored Construction Paper. The squares of construction paper can be used for subtraction in the same way that they were used for addition. Let us say that the child has the exercise 82 − 37. The minuend can be represented by 8 yellow squares and 2 red squares. It is obvious that he cannot remove 7 red squares when he has only 2. He can exchange 1 of the yellow squares for 10 red squares. Now he has 7 yellow squares and 12 red squares. He removes 3 yellow and 7 red squares, leaving him a remainder of 4 yellow and 5 red squares, or 45. The child uses the colored squares to represent in a concrete way the abstract number operation.

In the exercise $842-275$ the child represents the minuend by 8 yellow, 4 blue, and 2 red squares. Since he does not have enough red squares to remove 5, he exchanges 1 blue square for 10 red ones. He is now able to remove 5 from the 12 red squares. But he does not have enough blue squares in order to remove 7 of them. He exchanges 1 yellow for 10 blue, and now he can remove 7 blue squares from the 13 that he has and 2 yellow squares from the 7. He has a remainder of 5 yellow, 6 blue, and 7 red squares, or 567.

Since there may be some objection to the use of color to identify ones, tens, hundreds, etc., we can use the same color but different shapes. Squares may be used to represent ones, triangles to represent tens, circles hundreds, hexagons thousands, etc.

The Number Line. The number line may be used by the child to perform subtraction in the same manner that he used it for addition. Whereas in the addition of $8+4$ the cricket jumps 8 spaces to the right and then 4 spaces to the right for a total of 12 spaces, in subtraction of $12-4$ the cricket jumps 12 spaces to the right and then 4 spaces to the left, landing on 8. The number line is a graphic concrete representation of subtraction. It can be used to show why the minuend must be greater than the subtrahend. When the child raises questions of what happens if the cricket starts on point 4 and jumps 5 or 6 spaces to the left, he may himself offer suggestions for a solution. This is the beginning of the development of negative numbers. This will be discussed in the chapter on algebra, but each teacher must allow the child to develop such ideas when he is ready for it and not prevent the child from exploring such ideas until the whole class is ready for it.

Subtraction in a Problem-Solving Situation. The children who have learned to use an equation to represent an action that has taken place can also represent a subtraction situation by means of an equation. The class may be asked the following, "If Johnny has 9 toys and he gives 3 toys to his friend, how many toys does he have left?" This is represented in equation form as

$$9-3=\square$$

Or the question may be, "James had 9 toys and his friend took away some toys. Now James has 5 toys. How many did his friend take?" This is represented as

$$9-\square=5$$

Another way of representing the foregoing situations is to use an arrow which reads "gives". We write

$$(9, 3) \xrightarrow{-} \square$$

$$(9, \square) \xrightarrow{-} 5$$

The minus sign above the arrow indicates that 3 is to be subtracted from 9. The child may read it in this manner, "If we take 3 away from 9, how many do we have left?" Or, "What is the difference between 9 and 3?" The second situation is read, "What must be taken away from 9 to get 5?" Or, "The difference between 9 and what number is 5?"

To develop an understanding of problem situations involving subtraction the child should not only learn to translate the words into mathematical symbols but he should also make up stories to fit equations in the same manner that was done for addition. Let children make up stories to fit the following:

$$9 - 4 = \square$$
$$13 - 8 = \square$$
$$12 - \square = 9$$
$$(13, 6) \xrightarrow{-} \square$$
$$(16, \square) \xrightarrow{-} 9$$

$$\square - 8 = 15$$
$$\square - 4 = 7$$
$$\square - \triangle = 3$$
$$(\square, \triangle) \xrightarrow{-} 4$$

4.9 SUMMARY

Subtraction as an operation can be interpreted in two different ways. First, subtraction can be thought of in relation to actually removing concrete objects. This is the take-away process of subtraction. It is a meaningful operation to children because they experience such activities. To apply this method of subtraction children learn the subtraction facts in the same way that they learned the addition facts.

The second interpretation is that subtraction is an inverse operation of addition. In this interpretation we compare two numbers by finding what must be added to the smaller number to get the larger one. In using this additive method of subtraction the child does not have to learn any new facts but uses the addition facts that he already knows.

Although the additive method of subtraction is based on the mathematical meaning of subtraction and is used exclusively in advanced mathematics, both methods should be taught to children because both methods have meaning for children. However, the take-away method should be discarded when children operate on the abstract level.

Concrete manipulative aids should always be available to children who need them, especially when the decomposition method, or the process of exchange, is necessary. The child will discard the manipulative aids when he no longer needs them.

Children should continue to develop problem solving techniques by translating word situations into mathematical symbols. Since subtraction is an operation with numbers, the result of the action can be expressed as a mathematical equation. By solving subtraction exercises as well as addition exercises children will grow in their understanding of the meaning and use of the equation as a mathematical tool.

EXERCISES

1. Subtract the following decimal numbers by the take-away method and explain the thought processes involved in deriving the answers.

(*a*)	(*b*)	(*c*)	(*d*)
876	982	918	634
−235	−264	−254	−187

2. Do Exercise 1 by the additive method and explain the thought processes involved.
3. Perform the following exercises in the base five and explain the thought processes involved.

(*a*)	(*b*)	(*c*)	(*d*)
423	314	412	3012
−114	−123	−134	−234

4. Perform the following exercises in the base eight.

(*a*)	(*b*)	(*c*)	(*d*)
765	765	543	512
−123	−126	−172	−147

5. Perform the following exercises in the base twelve.

(*a*)	(*b*)	(*c*)	(*d*)
579	672	4te	526
−142	−349	−158	−227

6. Perform the following exercises in the base three and explain the thought processes.

(*a*)	(*b*)	(*c*)	(*d*)
121	1211	2011	2101
−12	−122	−222	−1212

7. Explain the thought processes involved in finding the differences of the following binary numbers.

(*a*)	(*b*)	(*c*)	(*d*)
11011	1010	101101	10001
−1001	−111	−11011	−1110

8. Explain the relationship between subtraction and addition.
9. How does working exercises in other number bases help one understand better the subtraction of numbers in the base ten?
10. Explain the difference between subtraction as a mathematical operation and the subtraction process as "applied mathematics."

SUGGESTED SUPPLEMENTARY READING

1. Banks, J. Houston, *Learning and Teaching Arithmetic*. Boston: Allyn and Bacon, 1959. Chap. 7.
2. Bell, Clifford, "Addition, Subtraction, and the Number Base," *The Arithmetic Teacher*, April 1955. pp. 57–59.
3. Bell, Clifford, Clela D. Hammond, and Robert B. Herrera, *Fundamentals of Arithmetic for Teachers*. New York: John Wiley and Sons, 1962. Chap. 5.
4. Brownell, William A., and Harold E. Moser, *Meaningful versus Mechanical Learning: A Study in Grade III Subtraction*. Duke University Research Studies in Education, No. 8. Durham, N.C.: Duke University Press, 1949. pp. 207.
5. Buckingham, Burdette R., *Elementary Arithmetic, Its Meaning and Practice*. Boston: Ginn and Company, 1953. pp. 57–64 and Chap. 6.
6. Dutton, Wilbur H., and L. J. Adams, *Arithmetic for Teachers*. Englewood Cliffs, N.J.: Prentice-Hall, 1961. Chap. 3.
7. Gibb, E. Glenadine, "Children's Thinking in the Process of Subtraction," *Journal of Experimental Education*, September 1956. pp. 71–80.
8. ———, "Take-Away Is Not Enough," *The Arithmetic Teacher*, April 1954. pp. 7–10.
9. Johnson, J. T., *The Relative Merits of Three Methods of Subtraction: An Experimental Comparison of the Decomposition Method of Subtraction with the Equal Additions Method and the Austrian Method*. Teachers College Contributions to Education, No.738. NewYork: Bureau of Publications, Teachers College, Columbia University, 1938.
10. ———, "Whither Research in Compound Subtraction?" *The Arithmetic Teacher*, February 1958. pp. 39–42.
11. Larsen, Harold D., and H. Glenn Ludlow, *Arithmetic for Colleges*. New York: The Macmillan Company, 1963. Chap. 4.
12. Marks, John L., C. Richard Purdy, and Lucien B. Kinney, *Teaching Arithmetic for Understanding*. New York: McGraw-Hill Book Company, 1958. Chap. 6.

13. McSwain, E. T., and Ralph J. Cooke, *Understanding and Teaching Arithmetic in the Elementary School.* New York: Henry Holt and Company, 1958. Chap. 4.
14. Mueller, Francis J., *Arithmetic, Its Structure and Concepts*. Englewood Cliffs, N.J.: Prentice-Hall, 1956. pp. 96–110.
15. Rheins, Gladys B., and Joel J. Rheins, "A Comparison of Two Methods of Compound Subtraction," *The Arithmetic Teacher,* October 1955. pp. 63–69.
16. Weaver, J. Fred, "Whither Research on Compound Subtraction?" *The Arithmetic Teacher,* February 1956. pp. 17–20.
17. Wilburn, D. Banks, "Learning to Use A Ten in Subtraction," *The Elementary School Journal,* April 1947. pp. 461–466.

Chapter 5 *Multiplication*

5.1 COMBINING EQUAL SIZE SETS

Multiplication is closely related to addition because in both operations we ask the question how many in all. In addition we combine two or more sets and consider the resulting set. When we add 5, 3 and 4, we get the sum 12. If we add $4+4+4$, we also get the sum 12. In the first example the three addends are unequal. In the second example the three addends are all equal. Since we have three fours, we write 3×4 and read it as 3 fours. Thus, multiplication is the addition of equal size groups.

If there are 9 apples in each basket, how many apples are there in 3 baskets? We can find the answer by adding 3 nines, $9+9+9$. We may also express the situation as 3×9. Multiplication is sometimes called a shortcut to addition. This is not always true. To find the number of apples in the 3 baskets it does not help to write 3×9 until we know how many 3×9 is. The only thing to do is to add the 3 nines. If we multiply a 1-digit number by a 1-digit number there is no shortcut to finding the answer. It is necessary to learn a set of multiplication facts. Once the multiplication facts are learned we can immediately supply the answer when asked to multiply two 1-digit numbers. Until these facts are learned there is no shortcut, and we must add the equal addends. It is necessary to learn all the products from 1×1 up to 9×9.

The size of the equal groups is called the *multiplicand*. The number of equal size groups is called the *multiplier*. The answer is called the *product*. Another way of interpreting multiplication is that the multiplier is the number of equal addends, the multiplicand is the size of each addend, and the product is the sum of the equal addends.

We are discussing multiplication from the point of view of applied mathematics, namely the combination of sets of objects. A child may learn the multiplication facts by repeated addition of numbers. Many children, however, are not yet ready for this abstract level of thinking. They need concrete examples using concrete objects. They *see* each set of objects. They *see* that all the sets have the same number of objects. "The size of a group" is the applied mathematical equivalent for the cardinal number of a set. The pure mathematician makes no distinction between multiplier and multiplicand. Both are factors of the product. Thus 3×4 is another name for 4×3 because the cardinal number is the same for both sets. The child, however, interprets 3×4 and 4×3 as arrangements of things. Although the total number of objects in both situations is the same, the arrangements of the objects are different.

We can show multiplication as an array of points. For example, 3×4 is represented as an array of 3 rows each containing 4 points as follows:

. . . .
. . . .
. . . .

And 4×3 is represented as 4 rows each containing 3 points as follows:

. . .
. . .
. . .
. . .

The number of points is the same in both arrays.

5.2 MULTIPLICATION IS THE CARTESIAN PRODUCT OF TWO SETS

Multiplication as the addition of equal-sized groups is an operation that children learn easily because they can manipulate concrete devices in order to find the sum. They learn to work with 3 sets of 5 toys, or 4 sets of 3 books, or 3 boxes of 8 crayons.

The mathematician has developed a completely different interpretation of multiplication. Instead of considering sets of equal size, he pairs or matches the elements of one set with the elements of another set. The set of pairs of elements is called the cartesian product of the two sets. Suppose there are 3 boys and 4 girls, how many couples is it possible to arrange? Let the set of boys be made up of (Tom, Frank, Harold) and the set of girls be made up of (Ann, Mary, Susan, Rose). The couples that can be arranged, or the different ways of pairing one boy with one girl, are: Tom-Ann, Tom-Mary, Tom-Susan, Tom-Rose, Frank–Ann, Frank–Mary, Frank–Susan, Frank–Rose, Harold–Ann, Harold–Mary, Harold–Susan, and Harold–Rose. Counting all the pairs we find that there are 12. If we represent the sets of boys by A, the set of girls by B, then the number of pairs or the cartesian product is $A \times B$. We can also represent the cartesian product by means of diagrams, as in Fig. 27. The number of lines connecting a boy with a girl is 12.

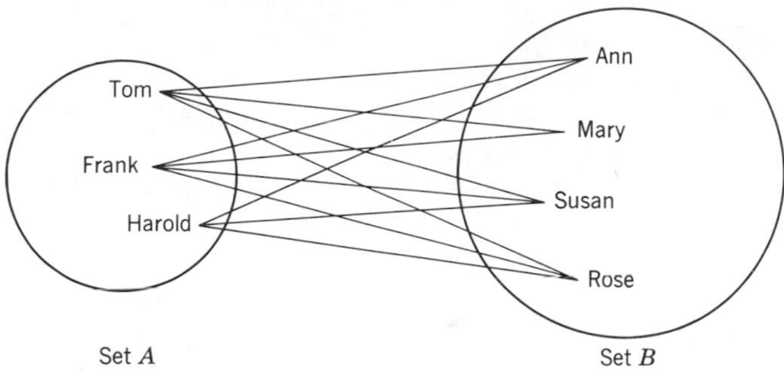

Fig. 27

Another example of a cartesian product of two sets is the matching of a letter with a number as in Fig. 28. Again we find that 12 is the number of possible pairs. Although the cartesian product of two sets

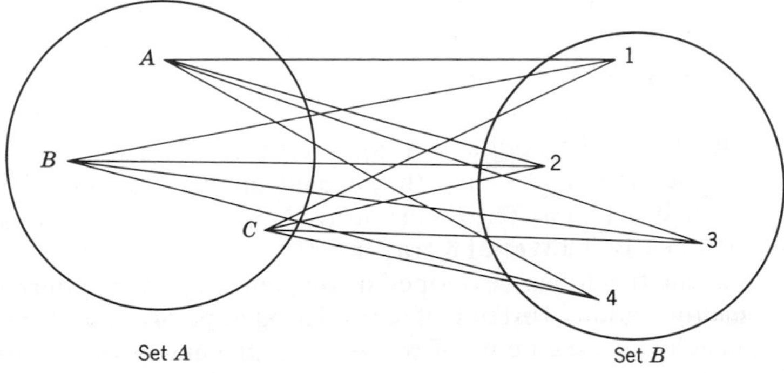

Fig. 28

is a different interpretation of multiplication, it is, nevertheless, related to the addition of equal-sized groups. Let us take the example of pairing 3 boys and 4 girls, as in Fig. 27. If we begin with Tom, we find that he can be paired with each of the 4 girls. Tom is, therefore, a part of 4 pairs. Frank can also be paired with each of the 4 girls and, therefore, he is also a part of 4 pairs. The same can be said for Harold. Each of the 3 boys is a member of 4 pairs. Since there are 3 boys, there are 3 sets of 4 pairs, or 12 pairs.

In Fig. 28 each letter is paired with 4 numbers. The result is that for each letter there are 4 pairs. Since there are 3 letters, there are 3 sets of 4 pairs, or 12 pairs. To find the number associated with the cartesian product of two sets we multiply the number of elements of one set by the number of elements of the second set. The child counts each pair separately, but he will soon discover the shortcut of adding the equal-sized groups. The child learns the multiplication facts not by the cartesian product but by the addition of equal groups. The concept of the cartesian product of two sets follows, rather than precedes, the learning of multiplication as addition of like-sized groups.

One of the difficult situations for a child to deal with is the product of two numbers when one of them is zero. If multiplication is related to combining sets, how does one explain 5×0? To say that we have 5 sets of zero objects is really saying that we have no sets. Yet the child will accept 5×0 as $0+0+0+0+0$, and he will accept the answer 0. But 0×5 is not that easy to explain. In general we resort to the commutative property and conclude that 0×5 is the same as 5×0, and therefore the product is also 0. But this explanation departs from the meaning of multiplication as addition of equal-sized addends. It is apparent that 0×5 states that there are no sets of 5. Why is the answer 0? The child may not be ready to apply the commutative property for multiplication when one of the factors is 0. The concept of multiplication as a cartesian product of two sets offers a reasonable explanation to a child. If one of the sets is empty we have no pairs. If there are no boys but only girls, then we do not have any couples made up of 1 boy and 1 girl. Likewise if there are only boys and no girls there are no couples.

5.3 MULTIPLICATION AS A MAPPING PROCESS

If we have a set made up of elements which are pairs of numbers, we can find a second set made up of elements that are single numbers which are the products of the two numbers in the number pair. Let set $A = \{(3, 4), (2, 1), (4, 2), (5, 3)\}$ and set $B = \{12, 2, 8, 15\}$. We can match, or associate, the elements of *B* with the elements of *A* in the following manner:

$$(3,4) \xrightarrow{\times} 12$$

$$(2,1) \xrightarrow{\times} 2$$

$$(4,2) \xrightarrow{\times} 8$$

$$(5,3) \xrightarrow{\times} 15$$

We can represent this mapping process with diagrams, as in Fig. 29.

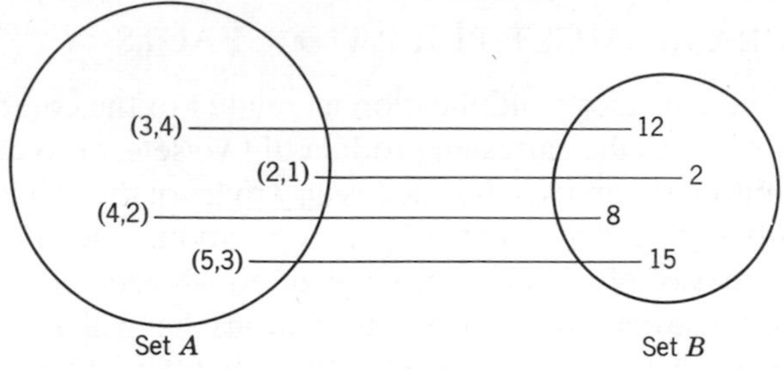

Fig. 29

Multiplication, like addition, is a many-to-one mapping process, as can be seen in Fig. 30.

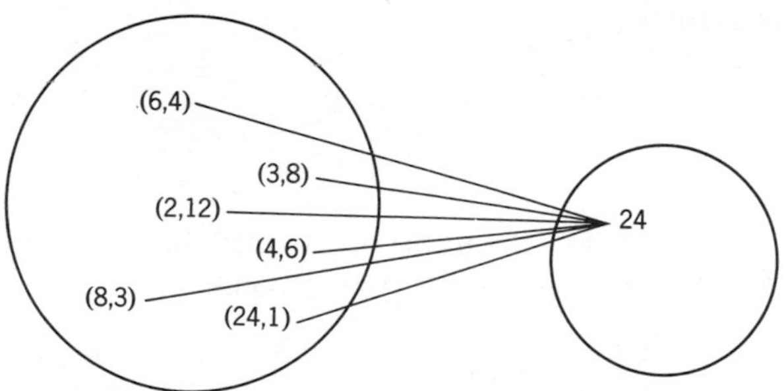

Fig. 30

When one set is mapped onto a second set the image, or the number associated with the number pair, is determined by the operation. Addition and multiplication are both binary operations, since two numbers are associated with a third number. They are, however, different operations and the mappings are different. If we write $(3, 4) \longrightarrow \square$, we do not know what number to put into the box after the arrow unless we know what operation is being performed. If the operation is addition we put 7 into the box, if the operation is multiplication we put 12 into the box. We thus learn to associate one number with a number pair. One association is based on addition, the other on multiplication. Multiplication as a mapping process is a sophistication that comes after a great deal of experience with numbers. It is not a concept to be taught to all children at an early age. The child who is encouraged to study such associations is better prepared to understand the language and ideas of modern mathematics.

5.4 THE BASIC MULTIPLICATION FACTS

Whether we consider multiplication as related to the combination of like-sized sets, or to the cartesian product of two sets, or to the mapping of one set onto a second set, it is necessary to learn the products of two 1-digit numbers in order to perform the operation. The child learns to find the number of objects in a number of equal-sized sets by adding. Once he has learned the basic combinations he will respond automatically when asked questions and will not resort to counting. He has to learn 100 basic multiplication facts from 0×0 to 9×9. (We are assuming that the child has not learned to apply the commutative principle.)

In learning the 100 multiplication facts, the child may discover the distributive property of multiplication over addition. Suppose the child is asked to find 3×6. He may use an array of 3 rows of dots with 6 dots in each row as follows:

· · · · · ·
· · · · · ·
· · · · · ·

He may count the 18 dots in this array. He may, however, see this array as made up of two arrays in the following manner:

· · · ·   · ·
· · · ·   · ·
· · · ·   · ·

These arrays can be represented as 3×4 and 3×2. This is another way of saying that $3 \times 6 = 3 \times (4+2)$, or $3 \times 6 = 3 \times 4 + 3 \times 2$. By separating an array into two arrays the child can learn the multiplication facts faster. Thus $5 \times 7 = 5\ (4+3)$, or $5 \times 7 = 5 \times 4 + 5 \times 3$, or

20 + 15 or 35. Although the distributive property may be useful to the child in learning the basic multiplication facts, this property is of great importance in learning multiplication of large numbers. The importance of the distributive property is shown in later chapters.

5.5 THE MULTIPLICATION ALGORITHM

When the child has learned the 100 basic multiplication facts, he is ready to multiply numbers when the multiplicand, or the multiplier, or both, contain two or more digits.

The Product of a Two, or More, Digit Number by a One-Digit Number. The simplest situation is one where there is no exchange or regrouping. An example of this is 2×34. We can, of course, find the answer by adding 34 and 34. To explain the multiplication aspect of this exercise, we think of it as 2 groups of 34. Since 34 represents 3 tens and 4 ones, we have 2 groups of 3 tens and 2 groups of 4 ones. The complete steps are: $2 \times 34 = 2 \times (30 + 4) = 2 \times (3 \text{ tens} + 4 \text{ ones}) = 6 \text{ tens} + 8 \text{ ones}$, or 68. This is an application of the distributive property. In the same manner, $2 \times 3421 = 2 \times (3000 + 400 + 20 + 1) = 2 \times (3 \text{ thousands} + 4 \text{ hundreds} + 2 \text{ tens} + 1 \text{ one}) = 6 \text{ thousands} + 8 \text{ hundreds} + 4 \text{ tens} + 2 \text{ ones}$, or 6842. We can represent both examples in a vertical array, as in Fig. 31.

$$\begin{array}{r} 34 \\ \times 2 \\ \hline 68 \end{array} \qquad \begin{array}{r} 3421 \\ \times 2 \\ \hline 6842 \end{array}$$

(*a*) (*b*)

Fig. 31

More difficult situations are those in which there is regrouping or exchange.

EXAMPLE 1.

$$\begin{array}{r} 43 \\ \times 7 \\ \hline 21 \\ 280 \\ \hline 301 \end{array}$$

In this exercise we perform the same analysis as with the previous exercises. We have 7 groups of 3 ones and 7 groups of 4 tens. We break up our exercise into the products of two 1-digit numbers and apply our knowledge of the 100 basic multiplication facts. We have 7 groups of 3 ones, or 21 ones. We exchange 20 ones for 2 tens and record the 21.

Then 7 groups of 4 tens are 28 tens. We exchange 20 tens for 2 hundreds and write them in the hundreds place and the remaining 8 tens in the tens place. Now we add the two partial products, 21 and 280, and derive the final product 301. When children are familiar with the steps we ask them if they can remember the 2 tens of the first partial product without writing them down because there will be more tens to add, since we also have 7 groups of 4 tens. The shortened process is as follows:

$$\begin{array}{r} 43 \\ \times 7 \\ \hline 301 \end{array}$$

We begin as before. Seven groups of 3 ones are 21 ones. We exchange 20 ones for 2 tens, and keeping this in mind we write only the 1 one. Then we think, 7 groups of 4 tens are 28 tens and the 2 tens we kept in mind make 30 tens. We exchange the 30 tens for 3 hundreds and write them in the hundreds place and the 0 tens in the tens place.

In the past children have had difficulty with multiplication because they had to keep in mind the number of larger units that resulted from the exchange. Although the same thing had to be done with addition, it was easier for children. The remembered sum was added immediately to the next addend. In multiplication we must find a new product before we add the result of the previous product. Children should be allowed to multiply in the longer form of the above example, and not be forced to use the abbreviated or condensed method until they have learned to keep in mind the larger unit without writing it down.

EXAMPLE 2.

$$\begin{array}{r} 387 \\ \times 9 \\ \hline 63 \\ 720 \\ 2700 \\ \hline 3483 \end{array} \qquad \begin{array}{r} 387 \\ \times 9 \\ \hline 3483 \end{array}$$

(*a*) (*b*)

Fig. 32

Analyzing the steps in Fig. 32*a*, we find 9 groups of 7 ones are 63 ones, which we write as 6 tens and 3 ones, or 63. Nine groups of 8 tens are 72 tens, which we write as 7 hundreds and 2 tens, or 720. Nine groups of 3 hundreds are 27 hundreds, which we write as 2 thousands and 7 hundreds, or 2700. Then we add the partial products to obtain the sum of 3483.

In Fig. 32*b* we have the traditional condensed form which requires different thought processes. Nine groups of 7 ones are 63 ones. We write down the 3 ones but keep in mind the 6 tens. Nine groups of 8 tens are 72 tens, to which we add the 6 tens that we had kept in mind. We write the 8 tens but keep in mind the 7 hundreds. Finally 9 groups of 3 hundreds are 27 hundreds, to which we add the 7 hundreds that we had kept in mind. We write the resulting 3 thousands and 4 hundreds. We obtain, of course, the same answer 3483.

The Product of Two, and More Digit Numbers by a Two-Digit Number

EXAMPLE 1.

```
  74
 ×32
----
 148
2220
----
2368
```

We first multiply the 74 by the 2 ones. This is done in the condensed form of the previous examples. We then multiply the 74 by the 30, or 3 tens. To multiply any number by 10 gives us the next sized unit, according to the decimal place-value system. Ten times 4 ones are 4 tens, ten times 4 tens are 4 hundreds, ten times 4 hundreds are 4 thousands, etc. This is based on the concept of exchange, 10 smaller units for 1 larger unit. Now, when we multiply the 74 by 3 tens we think, since 3 ones times 4 ones are 12 ones, 3 tens times 4 ones are 12 tens. Also since 3 ones times 7 tens are 21 tens, 3 tens times 7 tens are 21 hundreds. The result is that when we multiply any number by some tens, we shift our numerals one place to the left. We do not begin with the rule that when we multiply by tens we indent one place, but rather we first think the problem through and then develop the rule.

EXAMPLE 2.

```
   859
  ×347
------
  6013
 3436
2577
------
298073
```

We are now involved with multiplying the 859 by 3 hundreds as well as by 4 tens and 7 ones. How do we multiply by 100? We again apply the process of exchange to the decimal place-value system. One hundred times 3 ones are 3 hundreds, 1 hundred times 3 tens are 3 thousands. In the decimal system the values of the positions are expressed as powers of 10. These are from right to left, 10^0, 10^1, 10^2, 10^3, 10^4, 10^5, 10^6, etc. If we multiply by 1000 we get the value that is 3 places to the left. $10^3 \times 10^2 = 10^5$, $10^3 \times 10^3 = 10^6$, $10^3 \times 10^4 = 10^7$, etc.

In Example 2 when we multiply by 4 tens, we first multiply by 4 and then by 10. We indent one place to the left. When we multiply by 3 hundreds, we first multiply by 3 and then by 100, or indent two places to the left. Then we add the partial products.

5.6 BASIC POSTULATES FOR MULTIPLICATION

Just as children learned the generalizations that are fundamental to addition, they should discover the generalizations that are fundamental to multiplication. The teacher should help the child to discover these basic generalizations.

The Commutative Property. Children will discover very soon that $5 \times 3 = 3 \times 5$, $2 \times 9 = 9 \times 2$, $6 \times 4 = 4 \times 6$. This can be generalized as $a \times b = b \times a$. It is the commutative property for multiplication. This is why we check a multiplication exercise by reversing the multiplicand and the multiplier. Some teachers stress all multiplication as the product of two factors. They eliminate the words multiplier and multiplicand from the mathematics vocabulary. To them it makes no difference whether we have 3×8 or 8×3. These are equivalent because both result in 24. This is a sophisticated point of view. To the child, however, 3 groups of 8 are not the same as 8 groups of 3. The answers are the same, but the situations are different. Eight people each contributing \$3 is not the same as 3 people each contributing \$8, although the total contribution of \$24 is the same in both cases. Let children discover the commutative property so that they will learn that, as far as the answer is concerned, we can reverse the multiplier and the multiplicand.

The Associative Property. In order to multiply three numbers we multiply two numbers at a time. We can group the first two or the last two.

$$5 \times 3 \times 4 = (5 \times 3) \times 4 = 5 \times (3 \times 4)$$

We can find the product of 5×3 and then the product of 15×4 to get the answer 60. We can also find five times the product of 3×4, or 5×12, and again derive the answer 60. We can generalize this as $a \times (b \times c) = (a \times b) \times c$. This is the associative property for multiplication.

In finding the volume of a rectangular box, we generally use the formula $V = L \times W \times H$. We may think of this as $V = (L \times W) \times H$, or as $V = L \times (W \times H)$. This is an application of the associative property. If we apply the commutative property as well as the associative property, we have other interpretations for the formula such as

$$\begin{aligned} V &= (L \times W) \times H \\ &= (W \times L) \times H \\ &= W \times (L \times H) \\ &= W \times (H \times L), \text{etc.} \end{aligned}$$

The reader should draw a sketch for each of these interpretations.

The Property of Closure. If the product of any two numbers of a given set of numbers is a member of the set, the set is closed under multiplication. The product of any two natural numbers is a natural number. We describe the set of natural numbers as closed under multiplication. If our set is the set of even natural numbers, the product of any two numbers in this set is an even number. We generalize that the set of even numbers is closed under multiplication. If we have a set of only odd numbers, this set is closed under multiplication because the product of two odd numbers is an odd number. This property will be further developed with other numbers. This property is not limited to the product of 1-digit numbers. Children first learn this property when they multiply 1-digit numbers.

The Distributive Property. If we multiply 12 by 3, we may do it by first multiplying 10 by 3 and then 2 by 3. We may also think of 12 as 8 and 4, and then multiply 8 by 3, and 4 by 3 and get the same result. Children may discover different ways of breaking up the multiplicand and then multiply each of the addends by the multiplier. A simple example is $3 \times 9 = 3(4+5) = 3 \times 4 + 3 \times 5$. $3 \times 9 = 27$ and $12 + 15 = 27$. We distribute the multiplication over the addition. This is known as the distributive property and is generalized as

$$a(b+c) = ab + ac$$

We have already applied this property in the previous examples of $7 \times 43 = 7$(4 tens + 3 ones) or 28 tens + 21 ones; $9 \times 387 = 9$(3 hundreds + 8 tens + 7 ones) or 27 hundreds + 72 tens + 63 ones. A more complicated example of the distributive property is the example $32 \times 74 = (30+2) \times (70+4)$, or $30 \times (70+4) + 2 \times (70+4)$, or $30 \times 70 + 30 \times 4 + 2 \times 70 + 2 \times 4$.

The Property of Zero. Zero has a special property. In addition we have learned that any number added to zero gives that number. In multiplication we find that any number times zero, or zero times any number, gives zero. We generalize these properties of zero as

$$a + 0 = a, \text{ and}$$
$$a \times 0 = 0 \times a = 0$$

These properties for multiplication should be discovered by children. Of course time is saved in learning the multiplication facts if the commutative property is applied; however, we should not expect children to know automatically that if $9 \times 3 = 27$ then $3 \times 9 = 27$. If a child discovers the commutative property, he needs to learn only one-half of the multiplication facts. Teachers should use some restraint and not show children the commutative property; allow children to experience the thrill of discovery. Children should be encouraged to look for patterns and generalizations in multiplication. If they discover these by themselves they will have a better understanding of the structure of mathematics, and they will be better able to apply them to other situations.

5.7 MULTIPLICATION IN OTHER NUMBER BASES

To multiply numbers that are written in other number bases it would be necessary to learn the multiplication facts in that base if these facts had not been learned in any other base. In the base five one needs to know the 25 basic facts from 0×0 to 4×4. In the base eight one needs to learn the basic facts from 0×0 to 7×7, in the base twelve from 0×0 to 11×11, in the base three from 0×0 to 2×2, and in the binary system just four facts, namely, 0×0, 1×0, 0×1, and 1×1. In each of the numeration systems we must notate the results in that system and must apply the concept of exchange for that base. Thus $4_{\text{five}} \times 3_{\text{five}} = 22_{\text{five}}$, $3_{\text{eight}} \times 7_{\text{eight}} = 25_{\text{eight}}$, $9_{\text{twelve}} \times 9_{\text{twelve}} = 69_{\text{twelve}}$, $2_{\text{three}} \times 2_{\text{three}} = 11_{\text{three}}$. Having learned the multiplication facts in the base ten, we translate this knowledge to the other numeration systems.

EXAMPLE 1. Multiplication in base five.

(a)	(b)	(c)	(d)
324	143	432	243
×2	×4	×32	×34
1203	1232	1414	2132
		2401	1334
		30424	21022

Fig. 33

In Fig. 33*a* we have to multiply 324_{five} by 2. This means that we have 2 groups of 4 ones, 2 groups of 2 fives, and 2 groups of 3 twenty-fives. Two groups of 4 ones are 8 ones, or 13_{five}. We keep in mind the 1 five and write the 3 ones. Two groups of 2 fives are 4 fives, and the 1 five from the first product makes 5 fives, or 10_{five} fives. We keep in mind the 1 twenty-five and write the 0 fives next to the 3 ones. Then 2 groups of 3 twenty-fives are 6 twenty-fives to which we add the 1-twenty-five from the previous product for a total of 7 twenty-fives. This we write as 12_{five} twenty-fives next to the 03. Thus we obtain the answer 1203_{five}.

In Fig. 33*b* we follow the same procedure. Four groups of 3 ones are 12 ones (22_{five}). We write the first 2 but keep in mind the second 2. Four groups of 4 fives are 16 fives, and the 2 fives are 18 fives (33_{five} fives). We write the first 3 next to the 2 and keep in mind the second 3. Four groups of 1 twenty-five are 4 twenty-fives, and the 3 makes 7 twenty-fives (12_{five} twenty-fives). We write these next to the 32 and obtain the product 1232_{five}.

In Fig. 33*c* we have a 2-digit multiplier. The multiplication by 2 is done in the same manner as in 33*a* and 33*b*. To multiply by the 3 fives we have to recall that multiplying by 5 in the base five has the effect of shifting the numerals one place to the left in the same manner that multiplying by 10 in the base ten has the effect of shifting the numerals one place to the left. In multiplying by 3 fives we first multiply by 3 and then by 5, and shift the numerals one place to the left or indent one place. If we had multiplied the 432_{five} by 3 our answer would have been 2401_{five}. Since we are multiplying by 3 fives, our answer is 24010_{five}. Then, of course, we add the partial products and obtain the product 30424_{five}.

The explanation of the steps in Fig. 33*d* is left to the reader.

EXAMPLE 2. Multiplication in base eight.

(a)	(b)	(c)	(d)
324	143	432	243
×2	×4	×32	×34
650	614	1064	1214
		1516	751
		16244	10724

Fig. 34

In the first example, Fig. 34*a*, we have 2 groups of 4 ones or 8 ones, 10_{eight} ones. We write the 0 but keep in mind the 1 eight. Two groups of 2 eights are 4 eights, and the 1 eight makes 5 eights. We write the 5 in the eights place next to the 0 ones. Then 2 groups of 3 sixty-fours are 6 sixty-fours, which we write in the sixty-fours place next to the 50. Our product is 650_{eight}.

In Fig. 34*b* we apply the process of exchange twice. Four groups of 3 ones are 12 ones, or 14_{eight} ones. We write the 4 but keep in mind the 1 eight. Four groups of 4 eights are 16 eights, and the 1 eight we kept in mind makes 17 eights, or 21_{eight} eights. We write the 1 eight in the eights place next to the 4 ones and keep in mind the 2 sixty-fours. Four groups of 1 sixty-fours are 4 sixty-fours, and the 2 sixty-fours make 6 sixty-fours. We write this in the sixty-fours place and obtain the answer 614_{eight}.

In the third example, Fig. 34*c*, we first multiply by the 2 as in the first example. To multiply by the 3 eights we must remember that multiplying by 8 in the base eight has the effect of shifting the numbers one place to the left. Eight times ones are eights, eight times eights are sixty-fours, etc. If in our example we multiply 432_{eight} by 3, our product is 1516_{eight}. Since we are multiplying by 3 eighths our product is 15160_{eight}. We indent one place to the left in the same manner as with the decimal system. We add the partial products, keeping in mind that we exchange 8 smaller units for 1 unit of the next size. We obtain the answer 16244_{eight}. The explanation of the steps in the fourth example, Fig. 34*d*, is left to the reader.

EXAMPLE 3. Multiplication in base twelve.

(*a*)	(*b*)	(*c*)	(*d*)
324	*e*43	5*t*9	47e
×2	×9	×76	×34
648	8623	2e46	1678
		3533	11e9
		38276	13648

Fig. 35

In the first example, Fig. 35*a*, we multiply by 2, and since there is no exchange, we record the product 648_{twelve}.

In the second example, Fig. 35*b*, we multiply by 9. Nine groups of 3 ones are 27 ones, or 23_{twelve}. We write the 3 ones but keep in mind the 2 twelves. Nine groups of 4 twelves are 36 twelves, and the 2 we kept in mind are 38 twelves, or 32_{twelve} twelves. We write the 2 twelves in the twelves place but keep in mind the 3 one hundred forty-fours. Nine groups of *e* one hundred forty-fours are 99 (one hundred forty-fours), and the 3 we kept in mind make 102 (one hundred forty-fours), or 86_{twelve} one hundred forty-fours. We thus obtain the answer 8623_{twelve}.

In the third example, Fig. 35*c*, we first multiply by the 6 in the same manner as in the first two examples. The successive steps are: (a) 6×9 are 46_{twelve}, (b) $6 \times t$ are 50_{twelve}, and the 4 makes 54_{twelve}, (c) 6×5 are 26_{twelve}, and the 5 makes $2e_{\text{twelve}}$. Our first partial product is $2e46_{\text{twelve}}$. To multiply by the 7 twelves we multiply by 7 and then by 12, remembering that when we multiply by 12 in the base twelve we shift the numbers one place to the left. If we multiply 5*t*9 by 7 the product is 3533_{twelve}. Since we are multiplying 5*t*9 by 7 twelves, the product is 35330_{twelve}. The sum of the partial products is 38276_{twelve}.

The explanation of the steps in the problems of Fig. 35*d* is left to the reader.

EXAMPLE 4. Multiplying in base three.

```
   212         2021          1121
    ×2          ×21          ×121
  ----        ------        -----
  1201         2021          1121
              11112        10012
             ------        1121
             120211       ------
                          221111

   (a)          (b)           (c)
```

Fig. 36

In the first example, Fig. 36*a*, we multiply 2 ones by 2 and derive the product 11_{three} ones. Two times 1 three are 2 threes, and the 1 three from the previous product makes three threes, or 10_{three} threes. Then 2 times 2 nines are 4 nines, and the 1 nine from the previous product makes five nines, or 12_{three} nines. The product is 1201_{three}. In the other two examples we apply the principle that multiplying by 3 in the base three shifts the numerals one place to the left and multiplying by 9 in the base three shifts the numerals two places to the left. The explanation of the steps in Fig. 36*b* and Fig. 36*c* is left to the reader.

EXAMPLE 5. Multiplying binary numbers.

Since multiplication in the base two requires only the knowledge that $1 \times 0 = 0$ and $1 \times 1 = 1$, no explanation is given for the three examples in Fig. 37. The reader will supply the explanations.

In all of the number bases the numeral 10 represents the base. Thus it is 10 in the base ten, 8 in the base eight, 5 in the base five, 12 in the base twelve, etc. That is why when we multiply by the base or 10 we shift the numbers one place to the left. The numeral 100 represents 10^2 regardless of the base. It stands for 1 hundred in the base ten, 25 in the base five, 64 in the base eight, 9 in the base three, etc. That is why when we multiply by 100 we shift the numerals two places regardless of the base.

(a)	(b)	(c)
1011	11011	1011101
×1	×101	×111
1011	11011	1011101
	11011	1011101
	10000111	1011101
		1010000011

Fig. 37

To Change from One Base to Another Base. In Chapter 2 we changed the numeral in one base to the equivalent expression in the base ten, and then we changed from base ten to the second base. A number expressed in the decimal system was rewritten in the base five. The decimal system was an intermediary step in changing from one base to another. With a knowledge of multiplication in the various bases we can change from one base directly to a second base without first changing to the decimal system. Suppose we want to change 765_{eight} to the base five, the procedure is as follows:

Base eight *Base five*

$$765_{\text{eight}} = 7 \times (10)^2 + 6 \times (10)^1 + 5 \times (10)^0 = 12 \times (13)^2 + 11 \times (13)^1 + 10 \times (10)^0$$

$$= 12 \times 224 + 11 \times 13 + 10 \times 1$$
$$= 3243 + 143 + 10$$
$$= 4001$$

$$765_{\text{eight}} = 4001_{\text{five}}$$

The numeral 765_{eight} represents 7 units of 8 squared plus 6 units of eights plus 5 units of ones. Eight in the base eight is written as 10. We now write all the base eight numbers in the base five: $10_{\text{eight}} = 13_{\text{five}}$, $7_{\text{eight}} = 12_{\text{five}}$, $6_{\text{eight}} = 11_{\text{five}}$, and $5_{\text{eight}} = 10_{\text{five}}$. All of the calculations in the base five column were made in the base five. The reader should verify that $(13_{\text{five}})^2$ is equal to 224_{five}, and that 12×224 does give 3243.

$$\begin{array}{rl} \textit{Base eight} & \textit{Base twelve} \\ 765_{\text{eight}} = 7 \times (10)^2 + 6 \times (10)^1 + 5 \times (10)^0 & = 7 \times (8)^2 + 6 \times (8)^1 + 5 \times (8)^0 \\ & = 7 \times 54 + 40 + 5 \\ & = 314 + 40 + 5 \\ & = 359 \\ 765_{\text{eight}} & = 359_{\text{twelve}} \end{array}$$

The reader should verify the multiplication in the base twelve.

$$\begin{array}{rl} \textit{Base eight} & \textit{Base three} \\ 765_{\text{eight}} = 7 \times (10)^2 + 6 \times (10)^1 + 5 \times (10)^0 & = 21 \times (22)^2 + 20 \times (22)^1 \\ & \qquad + 12 \times (22)^0 \\ & = 21 \times 2101 + 1210 + 12 \\ & = 121121 + 1210 + 12 \\ & = 200120 \\ 765_{\text{eight}} & = 200120_{\text{three}} \end{array}$$

We must verify that the numerals in the base eight column represent the same numbers as the numerals in the base three column. It is left to the reader to verify the multiplications in the base three.

5.8 TEACHING MULTIPLICATION

Children must learn the basic multiplication facts. They should learn them as answers to questions posed by the teacher, such as "If each child at a party receives 3 pieces of candy, how many pieces of candy will 4 children get? If 1 postage stamp costs 5 cents, what will 6 stamps cost? If 7 children sit in 1 row, how many children are there in 3 rows? In 4 rows? In 8 rows?"

Children will find the answers in their own way. Most children will add enough addends to find the result. Children should not be asked to memorize multiplication tables or to write down the various products on flash cards. They should derive the products by themselves. If they answer many questions requiring multiplication, they will learn the multiplication facts. Some will need concrete devices to help them find the answers, and those children should have such aids. Most children, however, will discard these aids and perform the addition mentally or on paper until they have learned the basic multiplication combinations.

The Counting Frame. This device is very helpful to children who are learning the multiplication facts. Since there are 10 beads on each of 10 rods, the child can move a number of beads to one side on each rod and count the number of beads. If he wants to know how much are 3 twos, or 3×2, he moves 2 beads to one side on each of 3 rods. Then he can count the 3 twos and derive the answer 6. In like manner he learns to find 4×2, 5×2, 6×2, etc. He can also learn 3×3, 4×3, 5×3, 6×3, etc. The counting frame is effective because it is a concrete, visual, manipulative device. The peg board and one hundred board are similar to the counting frame and are used in the same manner. The peg board contains holes where a child can put pegs or golf tees, and he can count the total pegs in a given number of rows or columns, each row containing the same number of pegs. One hundred hooks can be arranged in a square matrix, and children can hang keys on them. The child counts beads, pegs, keys, or any other objects.

The Number Line. The number line can also be used for teaching multiplication in the same way that it was used in teaching addition. The cricket jumps a number of spaces on the number line. In addition the cricket could jump a different number of spaces each time, but in multiplication he must jump the same number of spaces each time. The statement 4×3 means that the cricket jumps 4 times and he jumps 3 spaces each time.

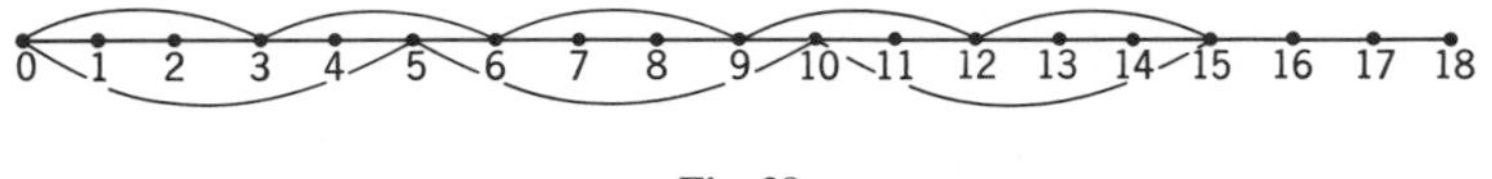

Fig. 38

In Fig. 38 the lines above the number line show 5 jumps of 3 spaces each. The lines below the number line show 3 jumps of 5 spaces each. The child uses the number line to determine the result of a certain number of equal-sized jumps. He can also use the number line to discover some generalizations, such as the commutative property of multiplication. He sees that 5×3 and 3×5 give the same result. He also learns that a given number may have different pairs of factors, as in the example $12 = 4 \times 3$, $12 = 3 \times 4$, $12 - 6 \times 2$, $12 - 2 \times 6$, $12 = 1 \times 12$, and $12 = 12 \times 1$. All of these can be diagramed on the number line.

Since our model of the number line has a limited length, it may be difficult to show some of the larger products. We may draw a series of number lines, as in Fig. 39, and have the children pretend that they are connected. The beginning of the second line is a continuation of the first line, the third line is a continuation of the second, etc.

Squares of Colored Construction Paper. These two-inch squares made up of different colors can be used to aid children when the multiplicand contains more than one digit and, especially, when exchange or regrouping has to be done. Suppose the child has to find 2×34. He can represent the 34 by 3 yellow squares and 4 blue squares. Since he needs 2 groups of these squares, he lays down 2 groups of 4 blue and 2 groups of 3 yellow squares. He now has 6 yellow and 8 blue squares. If his problem is to find 2×234, he can use brown squares for the hundreds. He lays down 2 groups of 2 brown squares in addition to the others.

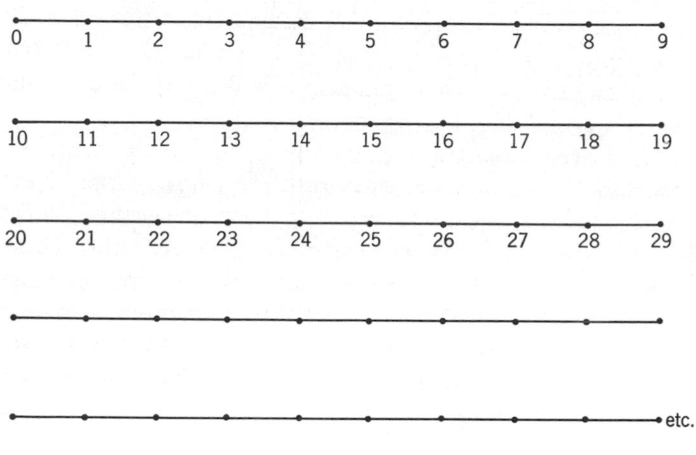

Fig. 39

If his problem is to find 3×34, he needs to exchange smaller units for a larger unit. The 3 groups of 4 blue squares are 12. He exchanges 10 blue for 1 yellow square. Then 3 groups of 3 yellow squares are 9 and with the 1 yellow from the exchange he has 10 yellow squares. He exchanges them for 1 brown. In the problem 3×542, he has 3 groups of 2 blue squares, or 6. Then he has 3 groups of 4 yellow squares, or 12. He exchanges 10 of the yellow for 1 brown. Then 3 groups of 5 brown are 15 and the 1 brown from the previous exchange make 16 brown squares. He exchanges 10 brown for 1 red. He now has 1 red, 6 brown, 2 yellow, and 6 blue squares, or 1626. Again we must keep in mind that the same colors should not always be used for the same kind of unit so that certain colors will not be associated with certain numbers.

The colored squares can be used to help children multiply in other number bases. The exchange ratio is different for each base, but the concept of exchange is the same for all bases. In the example $3 \times 543_{\text{eight}}$, the numeral can be represented by 5 brown, 4 yellow, and 3 blue squares. First we have 3 groups of 3 blue squares, or 9. We exchange 8 blue squares for 1 yellow. Then 3 groups of 4 yellow squares make 12, to which we add the 1 from the previous exchange. We now exchange 8 of the 13 yellow squares for 1 brown square.

Then 3 groups of 5 brown make 15 squares, and the 1 from the exchange makes 16. We exchange the 16 brown squares for 2 red squares. We now have 2 red, no brown, 5 yellow, and 1 blue square, or 2051_{eight}.

If the exercise were to find $3 \times 543_{\text{twelve}}$, we would exchange 12 squares of one color for 1 of the next color. The process of exchange becomes clearer when used with other number bases.

As was indicated with addition and subtraction we can use the same color but different shapes. The explanation given above still applies.

Multiplication in a Problem-Solving Situation. We have many problem situations that require the use of multiplication. Again frames can be used in an equation to describe the action taking place. If each child gets 3 pieces of candy and there are 5 children, how many pieces of candy are there all together. We represent this situation as

$$5 \times 3 = \square$$

or we may ask, five times how many pieces of candy will give 20 pieces of candy? This is represented by

$$5 \times \square = 20$$

The child answers this question by applying his knowledge of the 100 basic multiplication facts.

Instead of using equations we can represent the above situations by a pair of numbers and an arrow. We represent them by the following:

$$(5,3) \xrightarrow{\times} \square$$

$$(5,\square) \xrightarrow{\times} 20$$

The arrow tells us that we get a result, but it does not tell what operation is used. The statement $(5, 3) \longrightarrow \square$ has no answer. If the operation is addition, the box requires the numeral 8. If the operation is subtraction, we write 2 in the box. If the operation is multiplication, we write 15 in the box.

Just as we want children to write mathematical equations to represent given situations, we also want them to make up stories that fit a given equation. Children should learn to write stories to fit such situations as:

$$4 \times 3 = \square$$

$$4 \times \square = 20$$

$$(5, 2) \xrightarrow{\times} \square$$

$$(7, \square) \xrightarrow{\times} 28$$

$$(\square, \triangle) \xrightarrow{\times} 24$$

Now that the child has learned three different operations, he may be given exercises in which he has to figure out what operations were used. Examine the following and tell what operations were used:

$$\begin{aligned}
(7,6) &\longrightarrow 13\\
(3,8) &\longrightarrow 24\\
(9,2) &\longrightarrow 18\\
(9,2) &\longrightarrow 7\\
(8,4) &\longrightarrow 32\\
(8,2) &\longrightarrow 16\\
(9,2) &\longrightarrow 11
\end{aligned}$$

More difficult examples are those that have more than one operation. Examine the following sets of three numbers and determine what operations were used to derive the answers:

(*a*) $(4, 2, 3) \longrightarrow 24$
(*b*) $(4, 2, 3) \longrightarrow 18$
(*c*) $(4, 2, 3) \longrightarrow 6$
(*d*) $(4, 2, 3) \longrightarrow 5$
(*e*) $(4, 2, 3) \longrightarrow 5$
(*f*) $(4, 2, 3) \longrightarrow 9$
(*g*) $(4, 2, 3) \longrightarrow 11$

The answers are not obvious. In (*d*) and (*e*) we arrive at the same answer in two different ways, namely, $4 \times 2 - 3$ or $(4-2)+3$ gives the result 5. This type of challenge will help children to learn how to solve problems or at least challenge them to look for different ways of finding a solution.

5.9 SUMMARY

Multiplication can be defined in several ways. The simplest meaning is that multiplication is related to the addition of equal-sized groups. The cartesian product of two sets is the set of pairs it is possible to form by pairing, or matching, each element of one set with each element of the second set. Although the second interpretation is different from the first one, the number of pairs in the cartesian cross product is derived by considering the union of sets of equal size. The third interpretation of multiplication, that of a mapping process, is a highly sophisticated one that is based on the association of a pair of numbers in one set with a single number in a second set. This association is different from the addition mapping process. The multiplication facts have to be thoroughly understood before the mapping process can be understood.

The child has to learn the basic multiplication facts. He can learn them by counting, by adding, or by discovering patterns. Children should be provided with various kinds of manipulative devices to help them learn the facts, if they need such aids.

Children should be challenged to solve different problem situations. They continue to use the equation as a mathematical statement for a given action that is taking place. They should continue to make up stories that fit given equations. They should not always be told the process to be used. On the contrary, they should learn to determine the process or processes needed to solve mathematical exercises.

EXERCISES

1. Discuss the three meanings of multiplication from the point of view of mathematical, psychological, and pedagogical principles.
2. Multiply the following decimal numbers and explain the thought processes involved in deriving the answers.

(*a*)	(*b*)	(*c*)
349	284	567
×7	×39	×256

3. Complete the following base-eight multiplication table:

×	1	2	3	4	5	6	7
1	1	2	3	4	5	6	7
2	2	4	6	10	12	14	16
3	3	6	11	14	17	22	
4	4	10	14	20	24		
5	5	12	17	24			
6	6	14	22				
7	7	16					

4. Complete the following base-twelve multiplication table:

×	1	2	3	4	5	6	7	8	9	*t*	*e*
1	1	2	3	4	5	6	7	8	9	*t*	*e*
2	2	4	6	8	*t*	10	12	14	16	18	1*t*
3	3	6	9	10	13	16	19	20	23	26	
4	4	8	10	14	18	20	24	28	30		
5	5	*t*	13	18	21	26	2*e*	34			
6	6	10	16	20	26	30	36				
7	7	12	19	24	2*e*						
8	8	14	20	28							
9	9	16	23								
t	*t*	18	26								
e	*e*	1*t*									

5. Multiply the following numbers in the base-five:

(*a*)	(*b*)	(*c*)
34	243	1032
×4	×42	×243

6. Multiply the following numbers in the base-eight:

(*a*)	(*b*)	(*c*)
73	625	517
×6	×47	×254

7. Multiply the following numbers in the base-twelve:

(*a*)	(*b*)	(*c*)
97	4*t*8	8*e*9
×7	×*e*5	×17*e*

8. Perform the following exercises in the base-three:

(*a*)	(*b*)	(*c*)
122	2012	10121
×21	×122	×212

9. Perform the following exercises in the base-two:

(*a*)	(*b*)
1101	111011
×111	×1101

10. Use squares of colored paper to demonstrate and explain the multiplication in Exercises 2*a*, 5*a*, 6*a*, and 7*a*.
11. Change directly from one base to the indicated base:
    (*a*) 376_{eight} to base-twelve
    (*b*) 593_{twelve} to base-five
    (*c*) 21121_{three} to base-two
    (*d*) 4432_{five} to base-eight
    (*e*) 11000111_{two} to base-twelve
12. Examine the multiplication tables that were completed in Exercises 3 and 4 for any patterns that they may reveal.
13. Give some examples in which the commutative property of multiplication is applied.
14. Give some examples in which the associative property of multiplication is applied.
15. Give some examples in which the distributive property is applied.
16. Give several examples that would help children learn and understand the cartesian product of two sets.

17. Make up some word problems involving multiplication that are appropriate for children in the primary grades.
18. Show how multiplication as a mapping process could be taught to children.

SUGGESTED SUPPLEMENTARY READING

1. Bell, Clifford, Clela D. Hammond, and Robert B. Herrera, *Fundamentals of Arithmetic for Teachers*. New York: John Wiley and Sons, 1962. Chap. 4.
2. Brumfiel, Charles F. et al, *Principles of Arithmetic*. Reading, Mass.: Addison-Wesley Publishing Company, 1963. Chaps. 4 and 6.
3. Buckingham, Burdette R., *Elementary Arithmetic, Its Meaning and Practice*. Boston: Ginn and Company, 1953. pp. 64–73 and Chap. 7.
4. Dutton, Wilbur H., and L. J. Adams, *Arithmetic for Teachers*. Englewood Cliffs, N.J.: Prentice-Hall, 1961. Chap. 4.
5. Grossnickle, Foster E., "Discovering the Multiplication Facts," *The Arithmetic Teacher,* October 1959. pp. 195–198.
6. Grossnickle, Foster E., and Leo J. Brueckner, *Discovering Meanings in Arithmetic*. New York: Holt, Rinehart, and Winston, 1959. Chap. 8.
7. Haines, Margaret, "Concepts to Enhance the Study of Multiplication," *The Arithmetic Teacher,* February 1963. pp. 95–97.
8. Hannon, Herbert, "A New Look at the Basic Principles of Multiplication with Whole Numbers," *The Arithmetic Teacher,* November 1960. pp. 357–361.
9. Hickerson, J. Allen, "Why 'Indent' in Multiplication?" *The Arithmetic Teacher,* December 1956. pp. 236–241.
10. Marks, John L., C. Richard Purdy, and Lucien B. Kinney, *Teaching Arithmetic for Understanding*. New York: McGraw-Hill Book Company, 1958. Chap. 7.
11. Mueller, Francis J., *Arithmetic, Its Structure and Concepts*. Englewood Cliffs, N.J.: Prentice-Hall, 1956. pp. 69–95.
12. Swain, Robert L., *Understanding Arithmetic*. New York: Rinehart and Company, 1957. Chap. 5.
13. Van Engen, Henry, "The Reform Movement in Arithmetic and the Verbal Problem," *The Arithmetic Teacher,* January 1963. pp. 3–6.

Chapter 6 *Division*

6.1 INTRODUCTION

Division, the fourth of the fundamental operations, is the most difficult. This is evidenced by the difficulty that adults as well as children have with division. Although there is general agreement that arithmetic should be meaningful to children and that teachers should teach it meaningfully to children, there is less certainty about division. Some writers have even concluded that some aspects of division cannot be meaningful to children. Division by a 2-digit divisor is very difficult to explain. Some educators have concluded that such division should be taught mechanically so that children can find the answers when the division process is necessary. They believe that this is one case where children will learn the meaning, or understand the process, of division by a 2-digit divisor when they are older and more mature. Learning the skill, according to them, should come first and understanding will come later. Although division may be difficult for many children, it is not true that all children will have difficulty with division by a 2- or 3-place divisor. Some children are capable of learning all division meaningfully. Others may have to learn division in slower and simpler stages. Every teacher should endeavor to look for ways of making the process meaningful to every child. Though the process is difficult, children should understand it just as they should understand the other processes. Teachers should not compromise by teaching the process mechanically with the hope that children will learn the explanations at some later time. Process refers to the algorithm, which is not the same as the mathematical operation.*

*We distinguish between the abstract operation of division and process as the rules for obtaining answers to problems of division.

6.2 DIVISION AS THE INVERSE OF MULTIPLICATION

Division is directly related to multiplication. In multiplication we combine a number of equal-sized sets to find the total. The expression 8×2 relates to 8 sets each containing two elements. The result is 16. Division relates to the separation of a set into sets of equal size. The expression $16 \div 2$ asks the question how many twos are in 16. The answer is 8 because we know that 8 twos are 16. To answer a division question one needs to know the multiplication facts. We know that 36 divided by 9 is 4 because $4 \times 9 = 36$, and that $36 \div 4 = 9$ because $9 \times 4 = 36$. Division is the inverse of multiplication. We generalize the two processes thus:

$$a \div b = c \qquad \text{is equivalent to} \qquad c \times b = a$$

Just as multiplication can be interpreted as a continued process of addition, so division can be interpreted as a continued process of subtraction. To find what 9×4 is we can add 9 fours. To find how many fours in 36 we can subtract fours until we have no remainder, or a remainder that is less than 4. This is illustrated in Fig. 40.

9×4	$36 \div 4$
4	36
+4	−4
8	32
+4	−4
12	28
+4	−4
16	24
+4	−4
20	20
+4	−4
24	16
+4	−4
28	12
+4	−4
32	8
+4	−4
36	4
	−4
	0

Fig. 40

When we add 9 fours we derive the sum 36. When we begin with 36 and subtract fours continually, we find that we can subtract 9 fours. Although subtraction is a method for finding out how many equal groups we have in a given number, it is a lengthy process. Since the multiplication facts are already known, they can be used to find the answers to division questions.

6.3 DIVISION FACTS

Although the division facts are directly related to multiplication facts (inverses), division does pose a problem that does not exist in multiplication. There are no remainders in multiplication whereas there may be remainders in division. When we multiply one natural number by another natural number, we get an answer that is a natural number. But when we divide one natural number by another, we do not always get an answer that is a natural number. It is true that when we divide 36 by 4 we get the answer 9; however, when we divide 41 by 4 we do not get a natural number. We see that the set of natural numbers is not closed under division. This means that we have to apply the knowledge of the multiplication facts to the nearest multiple of the divisor. If one is asked how many groups of 3 can be formed out of 13, it is necessary to recall the multiples of 3 that are nearest to 13. Recall of the multiplication facts supplies the numbers 12 and 15. We know that 4 groups of 3 are 12; therefore we can get 4 groups of 3 in 13. We also know that we cannot get 5 groups of 3 because that would be 15. Thus we get 4 groups with a remainder of 1.

Children should be given the opportunity to experience exact divisions by doing multiplication in reverse. In multiplication we have two factors and we seek their product. Thus we write $5 \times 3 = \square$. The question is what numeral should be placed in the frame. Multiplication in reverse is really division. Here we have the product and one of the factors and we seek the second factor. Thus we write $5 \times \square = 15$ or $\square \times 5 = 15$. The question is what numeral should be placed in the frame.

Children should then experience division with remainders. Division facts must be learned. It is also clear that division is directly related to multiplication, but it is also true that division facts are somewhat different from multiplication facts.

6.4 TWO MEANINGS OF DIVISION

Since division is related to separation into sets of equal size, there are two questions that may be asked. Suppose we have 28 apples. We may know the size of each group of the separation, or we know how many equal groups we want. Each question has a different answer.

Measurement Division. We may want to separate the 28 apples into groups of equal size, each one containing 4 apples. The question is how many groups do we have? We know from the multiplication facts that the answer is 7. We can find the answer, however, in a concrete way. We put 4 apples in one pile, then another group of 4 apples in a pile, and continue until all of the 28 apples have been separated into groups of 4. We count the number of piles, or groups, of 4 apples and find that we have 7 groups.

Since each group is a definite measure (4 apples in the example just cited), this process of separation is known as measurement division. In measurement division we know the size of the group. The question that is asked is, "How many groups do we have?"

Partitive Division. Suppose we start again with 28 apples. This time we want to separate the apples into 4 equal groups. Our question now is, "How many apples are there in each group?" We cannot find the answer by measuring out a group because we do not know how big the group is. We create 4 groups by first placing an apple in each group, then another apple in each group, and we continue to place an apple in each pile until all 28 apples have been distributed. When we have finished we count the apples in each group. The answer, of course, is 7. We call this method of separation partitive, or partition, division because we partition the total into groups of the same size.

Measurement and partitive division ask two different questions and, therefore, result in two different answers. If we know the size of the groups, the answer tells the number of groups. If we know the number of groups, the answer indicates the size of each group. The answer is determined by the question. Thus the division $28 \div 4 = 7$ may be interpreted on the one hand as the answer to the question of how many sets of 4 apples each may be formed from a set of 28 apples or, alternatively, as the answer to the question of how many apples each of 4 children gets when 28 apples are divided equally among them.

It must be emphasized that we do not divide 28 apples by 4 apples. We are separating a set of 28 apples into sets of 4 apples. We find that there are 7 sets each containing 4 apples. We are also separating a set of 28 apples into 4 equal sets. We find that each set contains 7 apples. We thus have two physical interpretations for $28 \div 4 = 7$.

Mathematicians are concerned only with abstract relationships. To them multiplication is the product of two factors. If the factors are known, the product is sought. In division the product and one of the factors is known, and the problem is to find the other factor. On the abstract level it is immaterial which number is the multiplier and which number is the multiplicand. In the same manner, on the abstract level of division it is immaterial whether we have measurement or partitive division.

Children, however, do not begin with the abstract level. They learn concepts by associating them with concrete illustrations. Concrete situations that require the measurement or the partitive concepts of division are, to children, realistically two different kinds of situations. They should experience both types and they should learn to label their answers. As far as the mathematical process of division is concerned it is the same for both ideas. In a practical situation we should understand the question in order to understand the answer. We perform the division algorithm the same way for both questions.

6.5 THE DIVISION ALGORITHM

Division has always been a difficult operation because children learned the process mechanically without understanding the basic meanings involved. It should be taught in simple progressive stages. The first stage is mastering the division facts, which includes the multiplication facts and the division remainders that result when the dividend is not a multiple of the divisor. It is necessary to know not only that $18 \div 3$ is 6 but also that $19 \div 3$ is 6 with a remainder of 1 and that $20 \div 3$ is 6 with a remainder of 2. Children should learn to express these relationships as $19 = 6 \times 3 + 1$ and $20 = 6 \times 3 + 2$.

There is one caution that must be emphasized. Division by zero is not possible. We can divide 0 by 6 because 6 groups of 0 equals 0; however, we cannot divide 6 by 0 because no matter how many zeros we have their sum can never be 6. Since we have defined $a \div b = c$ as another way of stating that $c \times b = a$, we apply this to all division situations. Thus $0 \div 6 = 0$ because $0 \times 6 = 0$. But $6 \div 0$ has no answer because no number times 0 equals 6.

Division by a One-Digit Number without Exchange. The simplest division exercise, excluding the basic division facts, is by a l-digit divisor.

EXAMPLE 1. Suppose we want to divide 648 by 2.

We may attempt to find the answer by continued subtraction, but this would be a long drawn out process. The number 648 represents 6 units of hundreds, 4 units of tens, and 8 units of ones. We can separate each of these denominations into 2 equal groups. The 6 hundreds can be divided into 2 groups, each containing 3 hundreds. The 4 tens can be divided into 2 groups, each containing 2 tens. The 8 ones can be divided into 2 groups, each containing 4 ones. Thus we find that each of the 2 equal groups contains 3 hundreds, 2 tens, and 4 ones, or 324. The process can be summarized in the following manner:

$$\begin{array}{r} 324 \\ 2\overline{)648} \end{array} = \begin{array}{l} \text{3 hundreds} + \text{2 tens} + \text{4 ones} \\ 2\overline{)\text{6 hundreds} + \text{4 tens} + \text{8 ones}} \end{array}$$
$$= \text{324 (groups of 2) or 324 in each of two equal groups}$$

EXAMPLE 2. $3\overline{)9639}$

The number 9639 represents 9 units of thousands, 6 units of hundreds, 3 units of tens and 9 units of ones. We divide the units of each denomination by 3, using our knowledge of the multiplication facts. We derive the answer 3 thousands, 2 hundreds, 1 ten, and 3 ones, or 3213. The answer to a practical situation represents the number of groups or the size of the groups, according to the question in the exercise. The division process can be illustrated in the same manner as in the first example.

$$\begin{array}{r} 3213 \\ 3\overline{)9639} \end{array} = \begin{array}{l} \text{3 thousands} + \text{2 hundreds} + \text{1 ten} + \text{3 ones} \\ 3\overline{)\text{9 thousands} + \text{6 hundreds} + \text{3 tens} + \text{9 ones}} \end{array}$$

Division by a One-Digit Number with Exchange. As in the other processes, it is sometimes necessary to exchange 1 larger unit for 10 smaller units.

EXAMPLE 1.

$$\begin{array}{r} 17 \\ 2\overline{)34} \\ \underline{2} \\ 14 \\ \underline{14} \end{array} = \begin{array}{l} \text{1 ten} + \text{7 ones} \\ 2\overline{)\text{3 tens} + \text{4 ones}} \\ \underline{\text{2 tens}} \\ \text{1 ten} + \text{4 ones} \\ \underline{\text{1 ten} + \text{4 ones}} \end{array}$$

We separate 34 into 2 equal groups. The 34 represents 3 tens and 4 ones. When we separate the 3 tens into 2 equal groups, we have 1 ten in each group and we have a remainder of 1 ten. Since the 1 ten is not enough to separate into 2 groups, we exchange the 1 ten for 10 ones. Together with the 4 ones of the 34 there are now 14 ones. When these are separated into 2 equal groups, there are 7 ones in each group. Thus we derive the answer 17, the size of each group.

If we use the measurement concept of division we get the same result. We first separate the 3 tens into groups of 2. We have 1 group of 2 and 1 ten remaining. We exchange the 1 ten for 10 ones, and then we separate the 14 ones into groups of 2. We find that there are 7 groups. Thus we derive the answer 1 ten and 7 ones, but this time the 17 represents the number of groups of 2.

We will no longer make a distinction between measurement and partitive division. We use the same algorithm but label the answer according to the question.

EXAMPLE 2.

```
    458
 4) 1832
    16
     23
     20
      32
      32
```

We perform the division in the same manner as in Example 1. The 1 thousand is not enough to make a group of 4. We exchange the 1 thousand for 10 hundreds and now we have 18 hundreds. These are enough to make 4 groups of 4. Since the denomination is hundreds, we place the 4 in the hundreds place of the quotient. We have a remainder of 2 hundreds, not enough to make a group of 4. We exchange the 2 hundreds for 20 tens, and this makes a total of 23 tens. These are enough to form 5 groups of 4, whose denomination is tens. The remainder of 3 tens is exchanged for 30 ones, and the 32 ones are separated into 8 groups of 4. We have 458 groups of 4, or we have 458 in each of 4 equal groups. We label the answer according to the question.

EXAMPLE 3.

```
    8479
 9) 76315
    72
     43
     36
      71
      63
       85
       81
        4
```

The 7 ten thousands are not enough to form a group of 9. We exchange them for 70 thousands. The 76 thousands are enough to form 8 groups of 9. The remainder 4 thousands is exchanged for 40 hundreds and the 43 hundreds are separated into 4 groups of 9. The remainder of 7 hundreds is exchanged for 70 tens and the 71 tens are separated into 7 groups of 9. The remainder 8 tens is exchanged for 80 ones, and the 85 ones are separated into 9 groups of 9. Each of the number of groups is placed in the same denomination of the quotient as the dividend. We have 8479 groups of 9 and a remainder of 4. The remainder is an indication that we do not have enough units to form another group of 9. In each successive step we exchange larger units for smaller units.

Division by a Two-Digit Divisor. If the divisor is a 2-place divisor, we consider the higher size unit as thc trial divisor. If the number in the ones place is less than 5, we use the digit in the tens place as the trial divisor. If the number in the ones place is 5 or more, we increase the number in the tens place by 1.

EXAMPLE 1.

```
     25
32)816
   64
   176
   160
    16
```

The 8 hundreds are not enough to make a group of 32. We exchange the 8 hundreds for 80 tens, and the 81 tens are enough to make groups of 32. But we have not learned the multiplication facts of 32. We consider the 3 tens as the trial divisor and ignore the 2 ones temporarily. The 81 tens has the number 81, which has 8 tens and 1 one. We compare the 3 tens of the divisor with the 8 tens of the 81. We can form 2 groups of 3 tens in 8 tens. The 2 is the trial quotient. We place thc 2 in the tens place of the quotient because we were dividing 81 tens into groups of 32. We multiply the 32 by 2. The product is 64 (tens). We place the 64 under the 81, since they represent the same kind of units. The remainder of 17 tens is exchanged for 170 ones. We now have 176 ones. We now compare the 3 tens of the 32 with the 17 tens of the 176. There are enough to form 5 groups of 3 tens. We place the 5 in the ones place of the quotient because we are dividing 176 ones into groups of 32. When we multiply the 32 by 5 we have 160. The remainder of 16 is an indication that we do not have an exact number of groups of 32 in 816.

EXAMPLE 2.

```
     34
68)2365
   204
    325
    272
     53
```

In this example we proceed as before. The 2 thousands are not enough to form a group of 68; neither are the 23 hundreds. We exchange the 23 hundreds for 230 tens, and now we have 236 tens. The divisor contains 6 tens and 8 ones. Since the 8 ones are more than 5, we make the trial divisor 7 tens. We compare the 7 tens with the 23 tens of the number 236. We can form 3 groups of 7 tens. The 3 is placed in the tens place of the quotient because we are dividing 236 tens into groups of 68. We multiply the 68 by the 3 tens and subtract the 204 tens from the 236 tens. The remainder of 32 tens is exchanged for 320 ones. Now there are 325 ones. We compare the 7 tens of the trial divisor with the 32 tens of the 325 and find that we can form 4 groups. The 4 is placed in the ones place of the quotient, since we divided 325 ones into groups of 68. We multiply the 68 by 4, and the product 272 leaves a remainder of 53.

Division by a Three-Digit Divisor. In a three-place divisor the highest size of unit is the hundreds. If the tens digit is less than 5, we drop that part of the divisor from the trial divisor. If the tens digit is 5 or more, we increase the hundreds digit by 1.

EXAMPLE 1.

```
        146
431)62978
    431
    1987
    1724
     2638
     2586
       52
```

In Example 1 there are not enough ten thousands nor thousands to form a group of 431, but the 629 hundreds are enough. We compare the 4 hundreds of the 431 with the 6 hundreds of the 629. We can form 1 group. The remainder of 198 hundreds is exchanged for 1980 tens. Now we have 1987 tens. We compare the 4 hundreds of the 431 with the 19 hundreds of the 1987. We can form 4 groups. We multiply the 431 by the 4 tens and subtract the 1724 tens from the 1987 tens. We exchange the remainder of 263 tens for 2630 ones. Now we have 2638 ones. We compare the 4 hundreds of the divisor with the 26 hundreds of the 2638 and obtain the quotient 6. We thus obtain the quotient 146 with the remainder of 52.

EXAMPLE 2.

```
        206
783 ) 161369
      1566
       476
       000
      4769
      4698
        71
```

In Example 2 we consider the trial divisor to be 8 hundreds. The first denomination of units of the dividend is hundreds. We compare the 8 hundreds of the divisor with the 16 hundreds of the 1613. We can form 2 groups. The explanation for the remaining steps are left to the reader.

The division examples presented show how we can perform division regardless of the number of places in the divisor, using only the knowledge of the basic multiplication facts. We compare the largest units of the divisor with the same kind of units of the partial dividend. This requires an ability to think of numbers in many different ways. For example, the number 23489 represents 2 units of ten thousands, 3 units of thousands, 4 units of hundreds, 8 units of tens, and 9 units of ones. We may think of this number as composed of 23 units of thousands, or 234 units of hundreds, or 2348 units of tens, or even 23489 units of ones. The way we think of the number is determined by the divisor. If the divisor is 2, we think of the number as made up of 2 ten thousands, etc. If the divisor is 4, we think of the number as made up of 23 thousands, etc. If the divisor, however, is 47, we think of the number as made up of 234 hundreds, etc. If the divisor is 719, we think of 23489 as being made up of 2348 tens. If the divisor is 3259, then we think of the number as 23489 ones.

6.6 DIVISION BY CONTINUED SUBTRACTION

We can find the number of groups of a given size that can be formed out of a given number by subtracting multiples of the divisor until the remainder is less than the divisor.

Since we are trying to find out how many groups of 2 there are in 648, we can find the answer by subtracting groups of 2 from 648 and keeping a record of the number. In Fig. 41*a*, one can think of 100 groups of 2 and then subtract the 200 from 648. We keep a record of this to the right of the original number. The remainder 448 allows us to remove another 100 groups of 2. We continue the process as shown until there is no remainder, or a remainder that is less than 2. The record of the subtractions shows that we have removed 324 groups of 2.

EXAMPLE 1.

(a)

2)648	
200	100
448	
200	100
248	
200	100
48	
20	10
28	
20	10
8	
8	4
	324

(b)

2)648	
200	100
448	
400	200
48	
40	20
8	
8	4
	324

(c)

2)648	
600	300
48	
40	20
8	
8	4
	324

Fig. 41

We can remove different multiples of 2, as shown in Fig. 41*b*. Here we begin as in the first example and remove 100 groups of 2. We then think that 200 groups are twice as many as 100 groups, namely, 400. Then we remove 200 groups of 2, then 20 groups of 2, and finally, 4 groups of 2. We have removed 324 groups of 2, as before.

In Fig. 41*c* we remove 300 groups of 2 at the very beginning and, thus, hurry the process. The result is the same as before. By this method it is possible for many children to find the answer by doing it in different ways. As the children do a number of exercises by this method, they learn to subtract larger numbers of groups. The slower child may have to perform more subtractions, but he understands what he is doing.

EXAMPLE 2.

(a)

68)2365	
680	10
1683	
1360	20
325	
136	2
189	
136	2
53	34

(b)

68)2365	
1360	20
1005	
680	10
325	
272	4
53	34

(c)

68)2365	
2040	30
325	
272	4
53	34

Fig. 42

In Fig. 42 we have three different ways of subtracting groups of 68. There are other ways of obtaining the same answer. Again each child arrives at the answer in his own way.

EXAMPLE 3.

783) 161369	
7830	10
153539	
15660	20
137879	
31320	40
106559	
62640	80
43919	
31320	40
12599	
7830	10
4769	
3915	5
854	
783	1
71	206

(*a*)

783) 161369	
78300	100
83069	
78300	100
4769	
3915	5
854	
783	1
71	206

(*b*)

Fig. 43

In Fig. 43 we have two different ways of arriving at the answer. One child may subtract 10 groups of 783, then 20 groups, 40 groups, and continue to subtract any number of groups of 783 that he thinks of. He may require many steps. Another child begins by subtracting 100 groups of 783 because that is the way he sees it. Each child performs his own subtractions, but all children derive the correct answers. After a child has had sufficient experience with the subtraction method of division, he will learn to subtract larger groups of the divisor and, thus, shorten the number of steps.

The subtraction method is an effective method for obtaining the quotient. It has the advantage over the method described in Section 6.3 in that children may work the exercises, each in his own way, and obtain the correct answer. It allows each child to think out his own way of deriving the answer. This method has the disadvantage that the child does not develop the idea of division as an inverse operation of multiplication. It should be taught to children, however, especially to those who have difficulty learning the division algorithm.

6.7 DIVISION IN OTHER NUMBER BASES

We apply the same principles, or thought processes, to other number bases as was applied to division in the decimal system. The only difference is in the exchange of larger units for smaller units, the exchange ratio.

EXAMPLE 1. Division in base five.

```
  122          224
3)423        4)2013
  3            13
  --           --
  12           21
  11           13
  --           --
   13           33
   11           31
   --           --
    2            2
  (a)          (b)
```

Fig. 44

In Fig. 44*a* we have 4 units of a certain kind. This is enough to make 1 group of 3. We have 1 unit remaining after the subtraction. We exchange this unit for 5 of the next smaller size. We now have 12_{five} units of that size or 7. This is enough to form 2 groups of 3, or 11_{five}. Again we have a remainder of 1 unit which we exchange for 5 of the next size. We now have 13_{five} units or 8. This is enough to form 2 groups of 3. Thus we obtain the quotient 122_{five} with a remainder of 2.

In Fig. 44*b* we find that the 2 units of the greatest size are not enough to form a group of 4. We exchange the 2 units for 20_{five} units of the next size. These are enough to form 2 groups of 4, or 13_{five}. The remainder 2 is exchanged for 10 units (20_{five}), and now there are 21_{five} units or 11. These are enough to form 2 groups of 4. The remainder 3 is exchanged for 30_{five} smaller units making a total of 33_{five} units or 18. We can form 4 groups of 4 or 31_{five}. The quotient is 224_{five} with a remainder of 2.

EXAMPLE 2. Division in base eight.

```
   45          256
 5)273       7)2306
   24          16
   --          --
    33          50
    31          43
    --          --
     2           56
                 52
                 --
                  4
  (a)          (b)
```

Fig. 45

In Fig. 45*a* the 2 units are not enough to form a group of 5. We exchange each of the 2 units for 8 of the next size. We then have 27_{eight} units or 23 units. These are enough to form 4 groups of 5 or 24_{eight} units. The remainder 3 is exchanged for 24 units of the next size, and then the 33_{eight} units are enough to form 5 groups of 5 or 31_{eight}. The quotient is 45_{eight} with a remainder of 2.

In Fig. 45*b* we have the following successive steps:

The 23_{eight} units are enough to form 2 groups of 7 or 16_{eight}.
The 50_{eight} units are enough to form 5 groups of 7 or 43_{eight}.
The 56_{eight} units are enough to form 6 groups of 7 or 52_{eight}.
The quotient is 256_{eight}, remainder 4.

EXAMPLE 3. Division in base twelve.

```
      47           396
   8)312         9)2t1e
     28            23
      52            71
      48            69
       6             4e
                     46
                      5
     (a)            (b)
```

Fig. 46

In Example 3 we have to remember that we exchange 1 larger unit for 12 smaller units. In Fig. 46*a* the 31_{twelve} represents 37 or enough to make 4 groups of 8. The thirty-two is notated as 28_{twelve}. The remainder of 5 with the 2 smaller units represents 62 units or 7 groups of 8 (48_{twelve}). The quotient is 47_{twelve} with a remainder of 6.

The successive steps in Fig. 46*b* are: $2t_{\text{twelve}}$ (34) will form 3 groups of 9 or 23_{twelve}. Then 71_{twelve} (85) will form 9 groups of 9 or 69_{twelve}. Then $4e_{\text{twelve}}$ (59) will form 6 groups of 9 or 46_{twelve}. The quotient is 396_{twelve}, remainder 5.

EXAMPLE 4. Division in base three.

```
     112
  2)1002
    2
    10
     2
     12
     11
      1
```

The explanation for the successive steps in the above exercise is left to the reader.

EXAMPLE 5. Division in other bases with 2-digit divisors.

```
          110                      14                      111100
31five ) 4031five      67eight ) 1246eight      11two ) 10110110two
         31                      67                     11
         --                     ---                     ---
          43                    356                     101
          31                    334                      11
          --                    ---                     ---
           21                    22                      100
                                                          11
                                                         ---
                                                           11
                                                           11
                                                          ---
                                                             1
                                                             0
                                                            --
                                                            10
                                                            00
                                                            --
                                                            10

          (a)                   (b)                     (c)
```

```
                 309                         112
72twelve ) 19e8t twelve         21three ) 10211three
           196                             21
           ---                            ---
            58                            111
            00                             21
            --                            ---
            58t                           201
            546                           112
            ---                           ---
             44                            12

            (d)                           (e)
```

Fig. 47

In Fig. 47*a* we see that the first set of units that will enable us to form a group of 31 is 40. We compare the 3 of the 31 with the 4 of the 40, since they both represent the same kind of unit in the numerals. The 1 group gives a remainder of 4. The 43 will again form 1 group. The remainder 2 is now exchanged for 20 units, but these are not enough to form a group of 31. The quotient is 110_{five}, remainder 21_{five}.

In Fig. 47*b* we think of the divisor 67_{eight} as 70_{eight}. The first set of units that will be sufficient to form a group is 124. We compare the 7 of the divisor with the 12 of the 124. We have enough to form 1 group.

There is a remainder of 35. Now we compare the 7 of the 70 with the 35 of the 356, and we find that we can form 4 groups or 334_{eight}. Thus we get the quotient 14_{eight}, with a remainder of 22_{eight}.

In Fig. 47*c* we have the interesting situation that by inspection we can tell whether or not we have enough for a group. If we have enough we can form only 1 group. The analysis of all the steps is left to the reader.

In Fig. 47*d* we compare the 7 of the divisor with the 19 of the 19*e*. We can form 3 groups. In the second step we see that 58 is less than 72, so we have 0 groups of that denomination. Now we compare the 7 of the 72 with the 58 of the 58*t*. We can form 9 groups. We must read all of the numerals in the base twelve. The quotient is 309_{twelve}, remainder 44_{twelve}. The explanation for the steps in Fig. 47*e* is left to the reader.

6.8 TEACHING DIVISION TO CHILDREN

Since division is so closely related to multiplication, children may use the same concrete manipulative devices. Some children will not need any concrete aids at all. They will apply their knowledge of the multiplication facts to the solution of questions involving division. The children who need the aids should be provided with as many different kinds of aids as possible.

The Counting Frame. Children can use the counting frame to separate a number of beads into equal-sized groups. They may start out, for example, with 36 beads and separate them into groups of 4. They find that there are 9 groups. If they start with 39 beads, they find that there are 9 groups of 4 and that there is a remainder of 3, which is not enough to make another group. In this manner children learn the basic division facts, the exact divisions, and those with remainders.

The Number Line. The number line can be used effectively by children not only to learn the division facts but to learn division as the inverse of multiplication. In previous examples we have pretended that a cricket makes a number of equal-sized jumps. We were asked to find where the cricket would land. Now the question is reversed. If the cricket wants to land on 12, how many jumps of 4 spaces each must he make? If he jumps 2 spaces each time? 3 spaces? 6 spaces? 1 space?

Figure 48 illustrates how the child will find the answers to the questions. The number line is a limited device because the representation of its length is limited, but it is a concrete aid that children enjoy using.

Squares of Colored Paper. Squares of colored paper can be used to help children learn the division algorithm, especially where large numbers in the dividend are involved and where the concept of exchange or regrouping is necessary. If the child is asked to divide 648 by 2, he can represent the number by 6 red squares, 4 blue squares, and 8 yellow squares. He can then separate each group of colored squares into 2 equal groups. He will have 3 red, 2 blue, and 4 yellow squares in each group or 324.

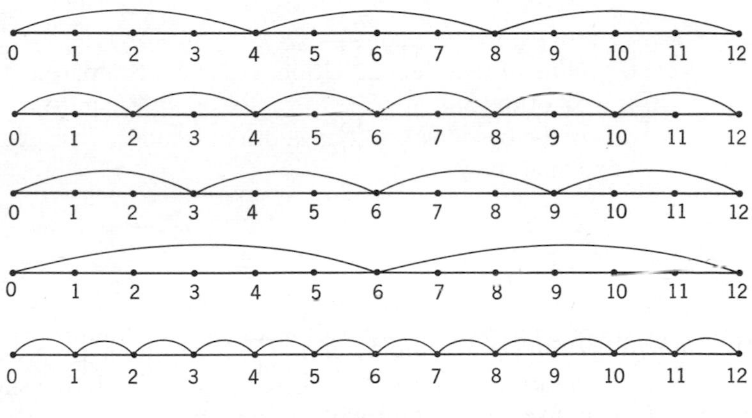

Fig. 48

If he is asked to divide 746 by 3, he can represent the number by 7 red, 4 blue, and 6 yellow squares. Then he separates the 7 red squares into 3 equal groups. He will have 2 red squares in each group, but he will have 1 red square left over. He exchanges the red square for 10 blue squares, and now he has 14 blue squares, he separates into 3 equal groups. There will be 4 blue squares in each group, but he will have 2 squares left. He exchanges them for 20 yellow squares and now he has 26 yellow squares. Now when he divides them into 3 equal groups, he will have 8 yellow squares in each group with 2 squares remaining. The child actually sees the 2 red, 4 blue, and 8 yellow squares in each group, and he also sees the 2 yellow squares that represent the remainder in this uneven division. The squares of paper help the child see the exchange of a larger unit for 10 smaller units in the operation of division.

The squares of colored paper are very effective in learning division in other number bases. One example will suffice. Suppose the child is asked to divide 2331_{eight} by 3. He can represent the number by 2 brown, 3 yellow, 3 blue, and 1 red squares. He cannot separate the 2 brown squares into 3 equal groups. He exchanges the 2 brown for 16 yellow squares. Now he has 19 yellow squares. These are divided into 3 equal groups, 6 squares in each group with 1 left over. He exchanges the 1 yellow for 8 blue squares, and now he has 11 blue. These are divided into 3 equal groups, 3 squares in each group with 2 remaining. He exchanges the 2 blue for 16 red, and now he has 17 red squares. He divided them into 3 equal groups, 5 squares in each group with 2 remaining. The child sees the 6 yellow, 3 blue, and 5 red squares in each group with 2 red squares left. His answer is 635_{eight}, remainder 2. The symbolic division is shown in Fig. 49.

$$\begin{array}{r} 635 \\ 3\overline{)2331} \\ \underline{22} \\ 13 \\ \underline{11} \\ 21 \\ \underline{17} \\ 2 \end{array}$$

Fig. 49

Division in a Problem Solving Situation. There are many problem situations that require division for their solution. A child is asked a question. He may use an equation with frames to describe the action. How many 5-cent stamps can he buy for 35 cents? This can be represented as.

$$35 \div 5 = \square$$

If 9 erasers cost 36 cents, how much does 1 eraser cost? This is represented as,

$$36 \div \square = 9$$

The child answers both questions by applying his knowledge of the multiplication facts. For example, $35 \div 5 = \square$ is another way of saying $\square \times 5 = 35$, and $36 \div \square = 9$ is another way of saying $9 \times \square = 36$.

Instead of using frames in an equation, we may represent the above situation by using frames and an arrow with a pair of numbers in the following manner:

$$(35, 5) \xrightarrow{\div} \square$$

$$(36, \square) \xrightarrow{\div} 9$$

The arrow tells us that we get a result, but it does not tell what process has been used. We indicate the process by a symbol above the arrow. The following $(8, 2) \longrightarrow \square$ has no answer. If the operation is addition we place a 10 in the frame. If the operation is subtraction we need a 6 in the frame. We write 16 or 4 in the frame for multiplication or division.

Children can make up stories to fit a division equation in the same way that they write stories for other operations. They should learn to make up stories to fit situations like the following:

$$27 \div 9 = \square$$
$$32 \div \square = 4$$
$$(45, 5) \xrightarrow{\div} \square$$
$$(21, \square) \xrightarrow{\div} 7$$
$$(\square, \triangle) \xrightarrow{\div} 4$$

Children should also be challenged to figure out the operations used in given situations as, for example, the following:

$$(8, 3) \longrightarrow 24$$
$$(32, 4) \longrightarrow 8$$
$$(32, 8) \longrightarrow 40$$
$$(8, 3) \longrightarrow 5$$
$$(32, 4) \longrightarrow 36$$
$$(12, 3) \longrightarrow 9$$
$$(12, 3) \longrightarrow 4$$
$$(12, 3) \longrightarrow 36$$
$$(12, 3) \longrightarrow 15$$

More difficult challenges are the situations involving more than one operation. Examine the following sets of three numbers and determine the operations that were used and the order in which they were used.

(*a*) $(8, 2, 3) \longrightarrow 7$
(*b*) $(8, 2, 3) \longrightarrow 13$
(*c*) $(8, 2, 3) \longrightarrow 18$
(*d*) $(8, 2, 3) \longrightarrow 3$
(*e*) $(8, 2, 3) \longrightarrow 2$
(*f*) $(8, 2, 3) \longrightarrow 9$
(*g*) $(8, 2, 3) \longrightarrow 19$
(*h*) $(8, 2, 3) \longrightarrow 1$
(*i*) $(8, 2, 3) \longrightarrow 12$

It is apparent that the answers are not obvious. Several of the answers can be derived by a different sequence of operations. A child exposed to such challenging situations may be better prepared for verbal problem solving.

6.9 SUMMARY

Division is admittedly the most difficult of the four operations. One should not conclude that because of its difficulty it need not be taught in a meaningful way. Teachers should accept the challenge of finding ways of explaining the operation to children. They should not compromise by saying that children may learn the process mechanically and the explanation some years later when they are more mature.

Division is interpreted as the inverse of multiplication. If multiplication is related to the combination of equal-sized sets, then division is related to the separation into equal-sized sets. We are concerned sometimes with the number of sets and at other times with the size of the sets. We call the first measurement division and the second partitive division. The pure mathematician is concerned with neither one. He looks for the second factor when the product and one of the factors are known.

In division by a 1-digit divisor we think of the dividend as made up of units of different denominations. We then divide the units of each denomination into equal groups. Sometimes it is necessary to exchange larger units for smaller units. Concrete aids, such as squares of colored paper, can help children understand the process of division. In dividing by a 2-digit divisor we first determine the largest denomination of units that will form a group of the divisor. Then we compare the largest size unit of the divisor with the same size unit in the dividend.

The answer to a division question can be derived by continued subtraction. This method enables each child to devise his own way of deriving the answer.

Children should be motivated to solve problems that require division. They should be encouraged to set up mathematical equations that describe the problem situation. With more operations learned and understood, children can be challenged to answer more difficult questions. Situations that involve several operations are more challenging than those that require only one operation.

EXERCISES

1. Discuss the two meanings of division and give illustrations explaining them.

2. Perform the following division exercises and explain the thought processes involved in deriving the answers.

(a)	*(b)*	*(c)*
$7\overline{)1389}$	$8\overline{)4962}$	$9\overline{)19037}$

3. Perform the following exercises and explain the thought processes involved.

(a)	*(b)*	*(c)*
$23\overline{)8196}$	$38\overline{)7169}$	$613\overline{)11782}$

4. Perform Exercise 3 by using the subtraction method.
5. Check the answers of Exercise 2 and Exercise 3 by multiplying the divisor by the quotient.
6. Explain the meaning of the remainder in a division exercise.
7. Divide the following numbers in base five.

(a)	*(b)*	*(c)*
$2\overline{)301}$	$3\overline{)1024}$	$4\overline{)3243}$

8. Divide the following numbers in base eight.

(a)	*(b)*	*(c)*
$4\overline{)7301}$	$6\overline{)1524}$	$7\overline{)16324}$

9. Divide the following numbers in base twelve.

(a)	*(b)*	*(c)*
$4\overline{)7301}$	$7\overline{)2t19}$	$e\overline{)345t1}$

10. Divide the following numbers in base three.

(a)	*(b)*
$2\overline{)10112}$	$21\overline{)10211}$

11. Divide the following numbers in base two.

(a)	*(b)*
$11\overline{)1110111}$	$1101\overline{)10111011}$

12. Use squares of colored paper to explain the steps in Exercises 2*a*, 7*b*, 8*a*, and 9*b*.

13. Check the answers in Exercises 2*c*, 7*c*, 8*c*, 9*c*, 10*b*, and 11*b* by multiplying the divisor and the quotient.
14. Is there a commutative property for division? Use concrete examples to explain your answer.
15. Is there an associative property for division? Use concrete examples to explain your answer.
16. Is there a distributive property for division?
    (a) Is $a \div (b+c) = (a \div b) + (a \div c)$?
    (b) Is $(b+c) \div a = (b \div a) + (c \div a)$?

SUGGESTED SUPPLEMENTARY READING

1. Adams, Belle W., "A Method in Division of Whole Numbers," *The Arithmetic Teacher,* April 1958. pp. 145–148.
2. Banks, J. Houston, *Learning and Teaching Arithmetic*. Boston: Allyn and Bacon, 1959. pp. 205–232.
3. Bell, Clifford, Clela D. Hammond, and Robert B. Herrera, *Fundamentals of Arithmetic for Teachers*. New York: John Wiley and Sons, 1962. Chap. 6.
4. Benz, Harry E., "Two-Digit Divisors Ending in 4, 5, or 6," *The Arithmetic Teacher,* November 1956. pp. 187–191.
5. Buckingham, Burdette R., *Elementary Arithmetic, Its Meaning and Practice*. Boston: Ginn and Company, 1953. pp. 73–82 and Chap. 8.
6. Capps, Lelon R., "Making Divison Meaningful and Logical," *The Arithmetic Teacher,* April 1962. pp. 198–202.
7. Dutton, Wilbur H., and L. J. Adams, *Arithmetic for Teachers*. Englewood Cliffs, N. J.: Prentice-Hall, 1961. Chap. 5
8. Flournoy, Frances, "Children's Success with Two Methods of Estimating the Quotient Figure," *The Arithmetic Teacher,* March 1959. pp. 100–104.
9. Crossnickle, Foster E., and Leo J. Brueckner, *Discovering Meanings in Arithmetic*. New York: Holt, Rinehart, and Winston, 1959. Chap. 9.
10. Gunderson, Agnes, "Thought-Patterns of Young Children in Learning Multiplication and Division," *Elementary School Journal,* April 1955, pp. 453–461.
11. Hartung, Maurice L., "Estimating the Quotient in Division," *The Arithmetic Teacher,* April, 1957. pp. 100–111.
12. Hilaire, Paul A., "Let's Take A Look at Division," *The Arithmetic Teacher,* May 1961. pp. 220–225.
13. Hill, Edwin H., "Teachers! Two Kinds of Division," *Journal of Education,* May 1955. pp. 16–18.
14. Izzo, Ruth K., "Division is Understandable," *The Arithmetic Teacher,* January 1960. pp. 32–34.
15. McSwain, E. T., and Ralph J. Cooke, *Understanding and Teaching Arithmetic in the Elementary School.* New York: Henry Holt and Company, 1958. Chap. 6.
16. Mueller, Francis, J., *Arithmetic, Its Structure and Concepts*. Englewood Cliffs, N. J.: Prentice-Hall, 1956. pp. 111–134.
17. Ruddell, Arden K., "Levels of Difficulty in Division," *The Arithmetic Teacher,* March 1959. pp. 97–98.

Chapter 7 *Fractions*

7.1 INTRODUCTION

For many centuries man found the counting numbers that he had developed sufficient for his needs. When he began to measure, however, he found that his counting numbers were not enough. In order to measure he had to create a unit, something that he repeated again and again in his measurement. Counting does not require a unit. Each object is counted as a one. Thus man counted the number of sheep or the number of people. He did not make any distinction between the sheep with regard to color, size, or weight. Every sheep was counted as one.

When man measured he counted units. To find the length of something he counted the number of linear units. All units were the samc length. To find the surface he counted area units. To find the volume, he counted capacity units. The linear units may have been ells, cubits, spans, paces, feet, yards, rods, meters, or whatever unit he decided to use. The number of units was the measure of the length. In the same manner, he developed area units such as hectares, acres, square inches, square yards, square meters, etc. Different tribes, nations and clans developed different units of volume, weight, and time as well as of length and area. Units of measurement were developed by man before he began to record his history.

The need to measure forced man to invent a new kind of number. As long as he counted objects, he needed to know only whole numbers or counting numbers. Later when he developed a place-value numeration system, he created the symbol 0 (zero) to indicate an absence of a particular group, such as an absence of tens or of ones. The set of counting numbers constitute the set of natural numbers. But when man measured he often found that the number of units in the thing he measured was not exact. Either the distance had some left over or it was too short to include another unit, so he generally gave the approximate number of units. When he sought greater precision, he had to think about a part of a unit or a fractional unit.

In dealing with fractions we always have to consider both explicitly and implicitly that there are two kinds of units. The unit we start with is the base unit. The foot, meter, mile, and light-year are base units. The base unit can be divided into equal parts. Each of the equal parts is a fractional unit. It is a unit because, like the base unit, it can be repeated in measurement. The architect may use one-fourth inch to represent one foot. The fractional unit is related to the base unit. One-fourth means one-fourth of a base unit. If a base unit is divided into four equal parts, then each of these equal parts is one-fourth of a base unit. In much of the work with fractions we forget the base unit.

Although the concept of fraction arose when man found a need to measure, the mathematician looks upon fractions as a new kind of number, a rational number that has its own properties. This raises some questions of educational psychology and pedagogy as well as mathematical logic. In this chapter we shall discuss both aspects of fractions, namely, fractions as measurements or applied mathematics, and fractions as rational numbers.

7.2 THE FRACTION SYMBOL

In creating a new kind of unit, fractional unit, man had to devise a symbol or language to communicate this new idea. We shall use the traditional symbol for a fraction. We write two numerals, one above the other, with a horizontal line between them as $\frac{2}{3}$. The fraction symbol represents a number, an abstract concept, but in using this symbol man has given several meanings to it. The difficulty that children and adults have had with fractions in the past has often resulted from the fact that they were not aware that there are several meanings to the symbol.

The Fraction as a Symbol of Operation. The fraction symbol may be looked upon as an operational symbol. From this point of view it tells us to do something. The symbol $\frac{5}{8}$ instructs us to divide a base unit into 8 equal parts and to keep 5 of them. The symbol $\frac{7}{8}$ tells us to divide the base unit into 8 equal parts and to keep 7 of them. In like manner, the symbol $\frac{5}{6}$ tells us to divide the base unit into 6 equal parts and to keep 5 of them. The fraction symbol can be compared to the symbols that a motorist is confronted with when he is driving his car. One symbol tells him to stop, another symbol tells him to slow down, another that he is approaching railroad tracks, whereas still another warns him that the road ahead curves in a certain way. In the fraction symbol the lower numeral tells us into how many equal parts we are to divide the base unit. We call it the denominator because it indicates the denomination of the fractional unit. The upper numeral tells how many of the fractional units we are to keep. We call this the numerator because we enumerate, or count, the fractional units. Thus the symbol $\frac{7}{12}$ tells us to divide a base unit into 12 equal parts and to keep 7 of them.

The Fraction Symbol as a Statement of Quantity. The fraction symbol can also be looked on as a statement of quantity. As such, the symbol $\frac{5}{8}$ tells us that we have 5 fractional units, each of which is $\frac{1}{8}$. The symbol $\frac{7}{8}$ tells us that we have 7 fractional units, each of which is $\frac{1}{8}$, and the symbol $\frac{5}{6}$ tells us that we have 5 fractional units, each of which is $\frac{1}{6}$. We do not have to perform any operation at all. It has already been done for us. The numerator tells us how many units we have, and the denominator describes the kind of unit.

As a statement of quantity the fraction symbol represents a whole number. We can write $\frac{7}{8}$ as $7(\frac{1}{8})$ or as 7 eighths. The number of units is a whole number. To measure $\frac{7}{8}$ inches we count 7 one-eighths in the same way as when we measure 7 inches we count 7 one-inch units. We think of 7 inches as a whole number but $\frac{7}{12}$ feet as a fraction. If a foot is the base unit, then 7 inches represents 7 fractional units. If the inch is the base unit, then 7 inches represents 7 base units. A foot is a fractional unit of a yard, a yard is a fractional unit of a rod, a rod is a fractional unit of a mile, etc. It is important to see the relationship of the fractional unit to the base unit.

As a statement of quantity the numerator of a fraction is a coefficient. Just as $5y$ tells us how many y's we have, $\frac{5}{8}$ tells us how many eighths we have. One should learn to write fractions in three different ways. Thus $\frac{5}{16}$ can be written also as $5(\frac{1}{16})$ and as 5 sixteenths.

The Fractional Symbol as an Indicated Division. If we were asked to divide 3 base units into 4 equal parts, our first reaction would be that we do not have enough units either to form groups of 4 or to form 4 equal groups. If we divide the 3 base units into fractional units, then we could perform the division. Let us divide each of the base units into 4 fourths. We now have 12 fourths. We certainly can divide the 12 fourths into 4 equal groups. We find that we have 3 fourths, or $\frac{3}{4}$, in each group. It is understood, of course, that $\frac{3}{4}$ means $\frac{3}{4}$ of a base unit. We can conclude that the symbol $\frac{3}{4}$ may indicate that 3 is to be divided by 4, or $3 \div 4$.

In the same manner, $\frac{7}{8}$ indicates that we are to divide 7 by 8, or $7 \div 8$, and $\frac{5}{6}$ indicates $5 \div 6$. We can write $5 \div 8$ as $\frac{5}{8}$, and $7 \div 16$ as $\frac{7}{16}$.

The Fraction Symbol as a Ratio. If we want to compare two numbers, we have two ways of making the comparison. To compare 8 with 2 we may ask the question 8 is now much more than 2? To find the answer we subtract. Thus 8 is 6 more than 2. We could have asked a different question such as 8 is how many times as great as 2? In that case we divide 8 by 2 and say that 8 is 4 times as great as 2. In comparing two numbers we must indicate whether we mean a subtraction comparison or a division comparison.

The division comparison is called a ratio. The ratio of 12 to 4 is 3 because 12 is 3 times as great as 4. We also say that 12 is to 4 as 3 is to 1. Ratio comparisons are not always whole numbers. It is true that the following ratios yield whole numbers: 8 to 4, 12 to 6, 28 to 4, 28 to 14, 28 to 2, etc. But what if we compare 3 with 4? Our question is, "3 is how many times as great as 4?" Our first inclination is to say that 3 is not as great as 4. This is true and our question cannot be answered if we limit ourselves to integers. With the use of fractions we can answer the question because 3 is $\frac{3}{4}$ as great as 4, just as 7 is $\frac{7}{8}$ as great as 8, and 5 is $\frac{5}{12}$ as great as 12.

The fraction symbol can now be examined from four different points of view. The symbol $\frac{7}{12}$ can mean any one of the following: (1) it is an operation symbol that tells us to divide a base unit into 12 equal parts and to keep 7 of them, (2) as a statement of quantity it tells us that we have 7 fractional units each of which is $\frac{1}{12}$ of a base unit, (3) it is an indicated division or another way of writing $7 \div 12$, or (4) it is a ratio comparison in which we compare 7 base units with 12 base units.

Again it must be emphasized that a fraction is a number and, as such, that it has certain properties. The four interpretations of the symbol given above are for pedagogical purposes in order to explain some of the operations with fractions.

7.3 PROPERTIES OF FRACTIONS

If we arrange the fractional units in order of size, we find the following: $\frac{1}{2}, \frac{1}{3}, \frac{1}{4}, \frac{1}{5}, \frac{1}{6}, \frac{1}{7}, \frac{1}{8}, \frac{1}{9}, \frac{1}{10}, \frac{1}{12}, \frac{1}{16}$, etc. It is understood, of course, that these are fractional units of the same base unit. It is clear that $\frac{1}{2}$ of a base unit is greater than $\frac{1}{6}$ of the same base unit, but that $\frac{1}{2}$ of a foot is not greater than $\frac{1}{6}$ of a mile.

It is evident that if we compare unit fractions (one fractional unit), the greater the denominator the smaller the fraction. This can be explained by the fact that if we divide a base unit into equal parts, the greater the number parts the smaller the parts. We generalize this by representing the unit fraction by $\frac{1}{n}$ and declaring that as $\frac{1}{n}$ increases n decreases.

If we compare one-half with sixths we find that $\frac{1}{2}=\frac{3}{6}$. In like manner by comparing different fractions, we find that many are equivalent. Here are a few: $\frac{1}{2}=\frac{2}{4}$, $\frac{1}{2}=\frac{4}{8}$, $\frac{1}{2}=\frac{6}{12}$, $\frac{1}{3}=\frac{2}{6}$, $\frac{1}{3}=\frac{4}{12}$, $\frac{1}{4}=\frac{3}{12}$, $\frac{1}{6}=\frac{2}{12}$, $\frac{2}{3}=\frac{4}{6}$, $\frac{2}{3}=\frac{8}{12}$, $\frac{3}{4}=\frac{6}{8}$, $\frac{3}{4}=\frac{9}{12}$, $\frac{5}{6}=\frac{10}{12}$. We can rationalize these relationships by demonstrating that if the units are smaller, it takes more of them to equal the same amount. We can generalize these relationships with the statement that if we multiply the numerator and the denominator of a fraction by the same number, we do not change the value of the fraction, or we get a second fraction that is equivalent to the first one. In modern terminology a fraction has many names. Thus $\frac{6}{8}$, $\frac{9}{12}$, $\frac{12}{16}$, $\frac{18}{24}$ are different names for $\frac{3}{4}$.

7.4 ADDITION OF FRACTIONS

In Chapter 2 we discussed addition as combining two or more sets and expressed the result as if it were one set. It is easy to explain how to add fractions whose denominators are the same, for then the units are the same. We can add $\frac{3}{8}$ and $\frac{1}{8}$; $\frac{3}{8}$ and $\frac{2}{8}$; $\frac{5}{12}$ and $\frac{5}{12}$, etc. The respective sums are $\frac{4}{8}$, $\frac{5}{8}$, and $\frac{10}{12}$. We add the numerators because they tell us how many fractional units we have.

To add fractions with different denominators we apply the principle that we can multiply the numerator and denominator of a fraction by the same number. To add $\frac{1}{4}$ and $\frac{3}{8}$ we multiply the numerator and denominator of $\frac{1}{4}$ by 2. Instead of $\frac{1}{4}+\frac{3}{8}$ we write $\frac{2}{8}+\frac{3}{8}$ and derive the sum $\frac{5}{8}$. If we want to add $\frac{2}{3}$ and $\frac{1}{6}$, we must express the $\frac{2}{3}$ as $\frac{4}{6}$ and then add $\frac{1}{6}$.

If two fractions do not have the same denominators, we rewrite the fractions as equivalent fractions having the same denominators. If one denominator is a multiple of the other, it is relatively easy to change the second fraction symbol to another with the same denominator as the first fraction symbol. If one denominator is not a multiple of the other, then we have to change both fraction symbols. In the example $\frac{1}{2}+\frac{1}{3}$ we change both $\frac{1}{2}$ and $\frac{1}{3}$ to sixths so that we rewrite the symbols as $\frac{3}{6}+\frac{2}{6}$ and obtain the sum $\frac{5}{6}$.

In adding $\frac{5}{6}$ and $\frac{2}{3}$ we replace the $\frac{2}{3}$ by $\frac{4}{6}$ and thus add $\frac{5}{6}$ and $\frac{4}{6}$. The sum $\frac{9}{6}$ indicates that we have enough fractional units to form a base unit. The $\frac{9}{6}$ can be rewritten as $\frac{6}{6}+\frac{3}{6}$, or as $1+\frac{3}{6}$. We generally do not write the plus sign but write $1\frac{3}{6}$ and read it 1 and $\frac{3}{6}$. Just as multiplying numerator and denominator by the same number does not change the value of the fraction, dividing numerator and denominator by the same number (other than zero) does not change the value of the fraction. We may write the $\frac{3}{6}$ as $\frac{1}{2}$.

To add mixed numbers such as $5\frac{1}{4}$ and $3\frac{3}{8}$ we may add the integers and the fractions separately. We write the $5\frac{1}{4}$ as $5\frac{2}{8}$. Then we add the $\frac{2}{8}$ and $\frac{3}{8}$, and the 5 and 3. We obtain the sum $8\frac{5}{8}$.

If we add more than two fractions, we express all fraction symbols with the same denominator. The more fractions we have the more difficult the process of finding the common denominator. We may find the common denominator by trial and error, but when the denominators are large numbers this is not convenient. Although any common denominator will do, we generally desire the least common denominator. Suppose we want to add $\frac{1}{2}$, $\frac{2}{3}$, and $\frac{5}{6}$. We can write them as $\frac{3}{6}$, $\frac{4}{6}$, and $\frac{5}{6}$, or as $\frac{6}{12}$, $\frac{8}{12}$, and $\frac{10}{12}$, or as $\frac{12}{24}$, $\frac{16}{24}$, and $\frac{20}{24}$. As long as the denominators are the same the fractions represent the same fractional units. We then add the numerators. In the above example we prefer to add sixths rather than twenty-fourths, but it is perfectly correct to utilize the fractions written as twenty-fourths.

If we want to add $\frac{7}{15}$ and $\frac{19}{40}$, we can multiply 15 by 40 in order to find a common denominator. This will not be the least common denominator. To find the least common denominator we use the method of prime factors. A number other than one is prime if its only factors are the number itself and one. The first eight prime numbers are 2, 3, 5, 7, 11, 13, 17, 19. We find the prime factors of the denominators 15 and 40. We can express 15 as 3×5, and 40 as $2 \times 2 \times 2 \times 5$. The common denominator must contain the factors of each denominator, but no unnecessary factor should be repeated. The least common denominator for 15 and 40 is $3 \times 5 \times 2 \times 2 \times 2$ or 120. If we were to add $\frac{9}{35}$, $\frac{17}{40}$, and $\frac{13}{56}$, we would try to find the smallest multiple of 35, 40, and 56. We first express each of these numbers as the product of prime numbers. We can express 35 as 5×7, 40 as $2 \times 2 \times 2 \times 5$, and 56 as $2 \times 2 \times 2 \times 7$. The smallest number that is a multiple of 35, 40, and 56 is $5 \times 7 \times 2 \times 2 \times 2$ or 280. To add $\frac{9}{35}$, $\frac{17}{40}$, and $\frac{13}{56}$ we write the equivalent of each of these fractions with the denominator 280 by multiplying the numerator and denominator of each fraction by the same number. Since we have to multiply 35 by 8 to get 280, we also multiply the 9 by 8. Since we multiply 40 by 7 to get 280, we multiply the 17 by 7. Since we multiply 56 by 5 to get 280, we multiply the 13 by 5. Thus $\frac{9}{35} + \frac{17}{40} + \frac{13}{56} = \frac{72}{280} + \frac{119}{280} + \frac{65}{280}$. The sum is $\frac{256}{280}$.

7.5 SUBTRACTION OF FRACTIONS

Subtraction of fractions is the inverse of addition of fractions. It is easy to explain how to subtract fractions whose denominators are the same. Since the fractional units are the same, we subtract the numerators. To subtract fractions with different denominators, we can apply the principle that we can multiply the numerator and denominator of a fraction by the same number. The following are examples of what is done in subtraction:

$$\frac{5}{6}-\frac{3}{6}=\frac{2}{6}$$

$$\frac{7}{8}-\frac{1}{4}=\frac{7}{8}-\frac{2}{8}=\frac{5}{8}$$

$$\frac{5}{6}-\frac{3}{4}=\frac{10}{12}-\frac{9}{12}=\frac{1}{12}$$

In subtracting mixed numbers we can subtract the fractions and the integers separately. A problem arises when the fractional part of the minuend is less than the fractional part of the subtrahend, as in $7\frac{1}{4}-2\frac{3}{4}$. Since we cannot subtract $\frac{3}{4}$ from $\frac{1}{4}$, we apply the decomposition method in the same manner as with integers. We exchange onc of the 7 ones for $\frac{4}{4}$. We exprcss $7\frac{1}{4}$ as $6\frac{5}{4}$. Now it is possible to subtract $2\frac{3}{4}$ from $6\frac{5}{4}$ using this procedure.

7.6 MULTIPLICATION OF FRACTIONS

In dealing with whole numbers multiplication was defined as the addition of equal-sized sets. This meaning of multiplication cannot always be applied to fractions. We shall consider several possibilities involving the multiplication of fractions. Among these are (1) the multiplier is an integer and the multiplicand is a fraction, (2) the multiplier is a fraction and the multiplicand is an integer, (3) the multiplier and multiplicand are both fracions, and (4) the multiplier and multiplicand are both mixed numbers.

The Multiplier is an Integer. If the multiplier is an integer, we apply the concept of multiplication as the sum of equal-sized sets.

EXAMPLE 1. $6\times\frac{2}{3}$

Just as we can interpret 6×4 as $4+4+4+4+4+4$, we can interpret $6\times\frac{2}{3}$ as $\frac{2}{3}+\frac{2}{3}+\frac{2}{3}+\frac{2}{3}+\frac{2}{3}+\frac{2}{3}$ and derive the sum $\frac{12}{3}$, or 4. We can also think of $6\times\frac{2}{3}$ as $6\times 2(\frac{1}{3})$, or $12(\frac{1}{3})$. To multiply a fraction by an integer we multiply the numerator by the integer. This tells us how many fractional units we have altogether. The denominator tells us what kind of fractional units we have. This interpretation leads to the general rule that, for m, a, and b whole numbers with $b\neq 0$,

$$m\times\frac{a}{b}=\frac{ma}{b}$$

EXAMPLE 2. $8 \times \frac{5}{6}$

Again we consider the 8 addends, each of which is 5 one-sixths. Just as 8 sets of 5 apples are 40 apples, 8 sets of 5 sixths are 40 sixths. The numerator of the fraction tells us how many fractional units we have, and the multiplier tells us how many sets of fractional units we have. It is evident that this multiplication exercise is similar to multiplication of integers.

The Multiplier is a Fraction. When the multiplier is a fraction, we may look upon the fraction symbol not as a statement of quantity but as a symbol of operation. We must remember that as a symbol of operation the denominator tells us to divide a base unit into equal parts. If the multiplier is a unit fraction we divide. If the fraction is not a unit fraction, the numerator tells how many groups of the equal divisions we should keep. It is in this case that we have a multiplication situation.

EXAMPLE 1. $\frac{3}{4} \times 8$

The $\frac{3}{4}$ as a symbol of operation tells us to divide the 8 into 4 equal parts and to take 3 of them. If we divide the 8 into 4 equal parts, we have 2 in each part. If we take 3 of them we have 6.

We can think of this example as $3[\frac{1}{4} \times 8]$. The multiplier $\frac{1}{4}$ is viewed as a symbol of division, since $\frac{1}{4}$ means that a base unit is divided into 4 equal parts. The 3 is a multiplier, since it tells us how many groups we have. If we perform the operation that is indicated in the brackets we get 2. The 3 is a multiplier so we have 3×2, or 6.

The $\frac{3}{4} \times 8$ can also be interpreted as $\frac{3}{4}$ of each of the 8 base units. We can illustrate both meanings by the following drawings:

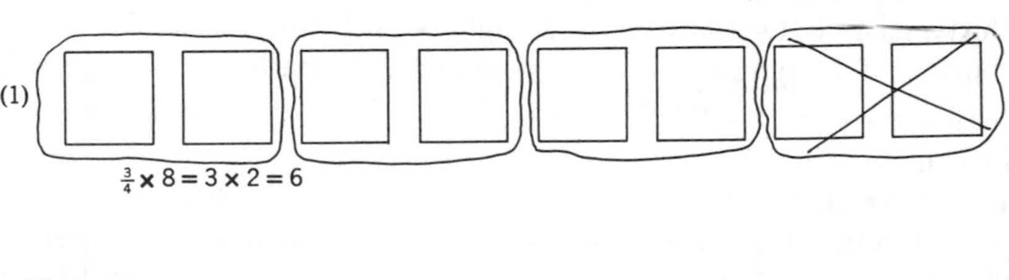

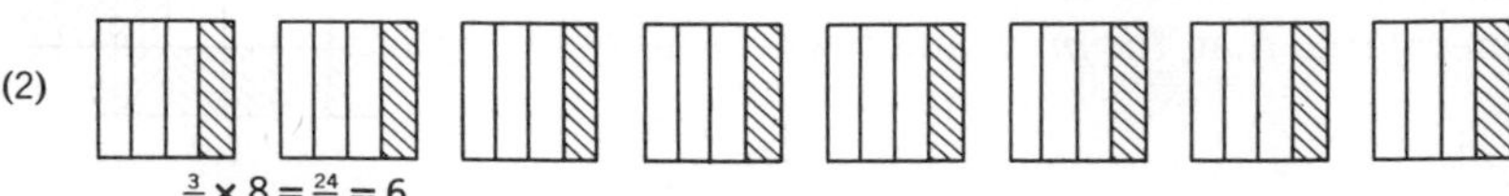

EXAMPLE 2. $\frac{3}{4} \times 5$

We divide each of the 5 ones into 4 equal parts and take 3 of them. We can illustrate this concretely:

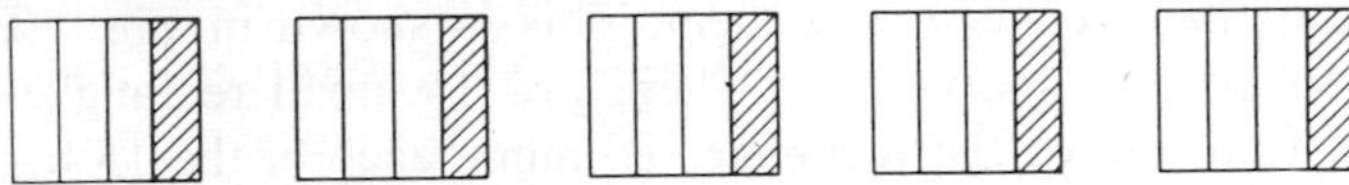

If we confine the unshaded fractional units, we conclude that $\frac{3}{4} \times 5 = \frac{15}{4}$. Again we derive the numerator of the answer by multiplying the numerator of the fraction by the integer.

In $5 \times \frac{3}{4}$ we also get $\frac{15}{4}$. Let us examine the two examples $\frac{3}{4} \times 5$ and $5 \times \frac{3}{4}$. The two fraction symbols represent two different meanings. In the second example the fraction is a statement of quantity. Yet, in both examples the answer is the same. We conclude that the commutative principle for multiplication works when one factor is a fraction and the other factor is an integer. We also conclude that, as far as the answer is concerned, it does not make any difference whether the fraction symbol is considered as a statement of quantity or as a symbol of operation. It does, however, make a difference in our understanding of how the answer is derived.

The Multiplier and the Multiplicand Are Both Fractions. In multiplying one fraction by another, we consider the first fraction symbol as a symbol of operation, and the second fraction symbol as a statement of quantity.

EXAMPLE 1. $\frac{3}{4} \times \frac{5}{8}$

This expression tells us that we have 5 eighths and that we are to take 3 fourths of them. As a symbol of operation, $\frac{3}{4}$ tells us to divide something into 4 equal parts and to take 3 of them. If we divide the 1 eighth into 4 equal parts, we get thirty-seconds. One-fourth of 1 eighth is 1 thirty-second. One-fourth of 5 eighths is 5 thirty-seconds. Three-fourths of 5 eighths is 15 thirty-seconds. In mathematical symbols, $\frac{1}{4} \times \frac{1}{8} = \frac{1}{32}$, $\frac{1}{4} \times \frac{5}{8} = \frac{5}{32}$, and $\frac{3}{4} \times \frac{5}{8} = \frac{15}{32}$. We can illustrate this operation by using a rectangle as a base unit.

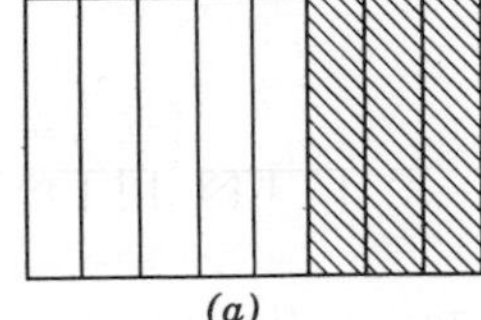

(*a*)

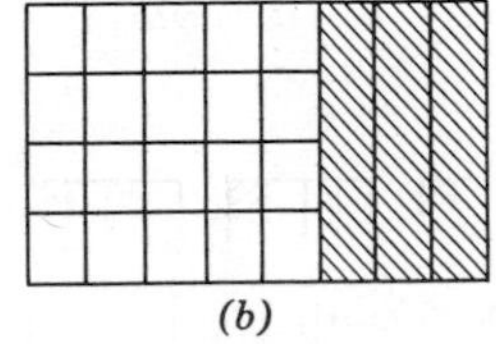

(*b*)

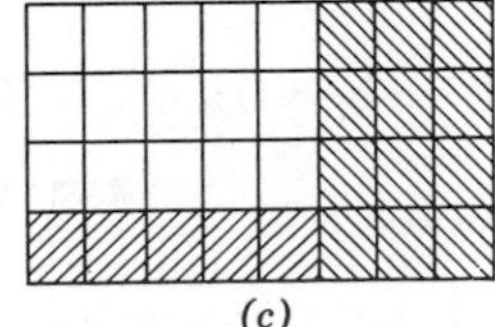

(*c*)

Fig. 50

The unshaded portion of the rectangle in Fig. 50*a* represents $\frac{5}{8}$ of the rectangle, the base unit. We have 5 unshaded rectangles each of which is $\frac{1}{8}$. Now we divide each of these 5 rectangles into 4 equal parts as shown in Fig. 50*b*. Next we shade 1 of these equal parts as an indication that we keep 3 of them. This is shown in Fig. 50*c*. The unshaded portion shows $\frac{3}{4}\times\frac{5}{8}$. There are 15 small rectangles in the unshaded portion of the rectangle. To name each of the 15 fractional units we must determine how many such small rectangles are contained in the large rectangle, the base unit. If we extend the horizontal lines over the shaded portion of the rectangle, we find that the base rectangle contains 32 small rectangles. Therefore each small rectangle is $\frac{1}{32}$ of the large rectangle. The 15 small rectangles represent $\frac{15}{32}$ of the base unit.

EXAMPLE 2. $\frac{2}{3}\times\frac{7}{8}$

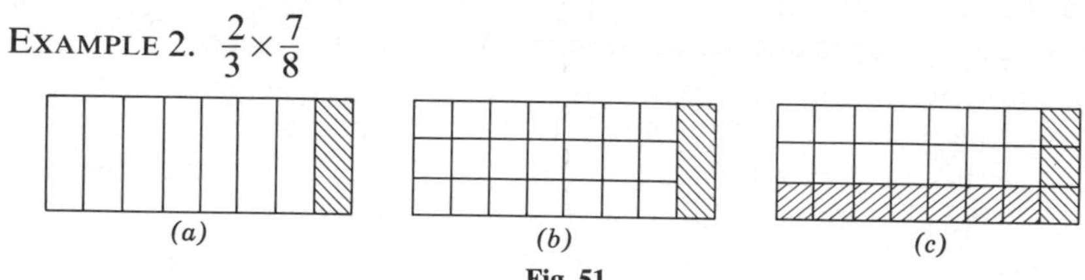

Fig. 51

The unshaded portion of the rectangle in Fig. 51*a* represents $\frac{7}{8}$ of the rectangle. To take $\frac{2}{3}$ of it means that we have to divide $\frac{7}{8}$ into 3 equal parts, as in Fig. 51*b*. Now we shade 1 part since we want to keep 2 parts. The unshaded portion in Fig. 51*c* shows the result of the operation. We have 14 small rectangles. Again we must determine what kind of fractional units they are. If we extend the horizontal lines over the shaded portion up to the end of the rectangle, we find that there are 24 small rectangles in the large one. The 14 small rectangles represent $\frac{14}{24}$ of the base rectangle.

The two examples demonstrate, although they do not prove, the generalization about finding the product of two fractions. We multiply the numerators to obtain the numerator of the product, and we multiply the denominators to obtain the denominator of the product. We may generalize that

$$\frac{a}{b}\times\frac{c}{d}=\frac{ac}{bd}$$

where $b \neq 0$ and $d \neq 0$.

EXAMPLE 3. $\frac{5}{8}\times\frac{3}{4}$

If we compare Example 3 with Example 1 we notice that the same fractions are used, but the multiplier and the multiplicand are reversed.

The $\frac{3}{4}$ now represents a quantity (3 fourths) and the $\frac{5}{8}$ is looked on as a symbol of operation. The result of this operation is shown in Fig. 52.

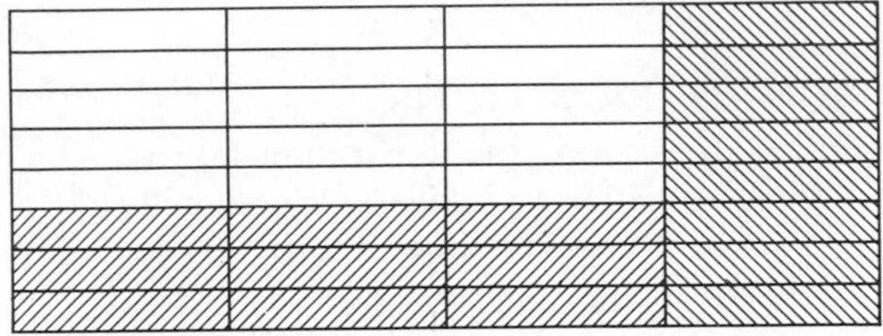

Fig. 52

Again we find that the result of the operation is $\frac{15}{24}$. This shows that $\frac{5}{8}\times\frac{3}{4}=\frac{3}{4}\times\frac{5}{8}$, and indicates that the commutative principle for multiplication also holds for fractions.

Multiplying Two Mixed Numbers. We apply the same principles as in multiplication of integers. Suppose we have $2\frac{1}{2}\times 3\frac{1}{4}$. This is a statement that we have $2\frac{1}{2}$ groups, each containing $3\frac{1}{4}$. We can actually take a group of $3\frac{1}{4}$ rectangles and repeat it so that we have 2 such groups, and then we take a third group but divide it into 2 equal parts. See Fig. 53.

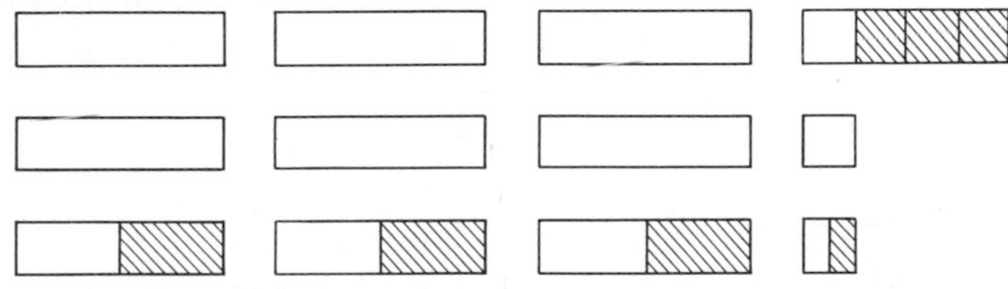

Fig. 53

The unshaded rectangles show $2\frac{1}{2}$ groups of $3\frac{1}{4}$. To find the total we notice that there are 2×3 rectangles, $2 \times \frac{1}{4}$ rectangles, $\frac{1}{2} \times 3$ rectangles, and $\frac{1}{2}\times\frac{1}{4}$ rectangles. All of these add up to $8\frac{1}{8}$ base rectangles. We could express $2\frac{1}{2} \times 3\frac{1}{4}$ as $\frac{5}{2}\times\frac{13}{4}$ and thus find the product $\frac{65}{8}$, or $8\frac{1}{8}$. The first method, however, is a demonstration of the distributive principle. We can show it as follows:

$$
\begin{aligned}
2\tfrac{1}{2}\times 3\tfrac{1}{4} &= (2+\frac{1}{2})\times(3+\frac{1}{4})\\
&= 2\times(3+\frac{1}{4})+\frac{1}{2}\times(3+\frac{1}{4})\\
&= 2\times 3+2\times\frac{1}{4}+\frac{1}{2}\times 3+\frac{1}{2}\times\frac{}{4}\\
&= 6+\frac{1}{2}+1\frac{1}{2}+\frac{1}{8}\\
&= 8\tfrac{1}{8}
\end{aligned}
$$

The second method in which mixed numbers are changed to fractions is the preferred method of multiplication. Thus, for example $2\frac{1}{2} \times 3\frac{1}{4} = \frac{5}{2} \times \frac{13}{4} = \frac{65}{8} = 8\frac{1}{8}$.

7.7 DIVISION OF FRACTIONS

The concept of division as the separation into equal-sized groups applies to fractions as well as to integers. We may illustrate $28 \div 4 = 7$ by separating a set of 28 baskets into sets of 4 baskets. Our answer is 7 (sets of 4 baskets). In the same manner, if we divide $\frac{28}{5}$ by $\frac{4}{5}$, we are separating 28 (fifths) into groups of 4 (fifths). Our answer, once more, is 7 (groups of $\frac{4}{5}$). We are dealing here with division as applied mathematics rather than as pure mathematics.

The Common Denominator Method of Division.

EXAMPLE 1. $\dfrac{7}{8} \div \dfrac{3}{8}$

We separate $7(\frac{1}{8})$ into groups of $3(\frac{1}{8})$. Our answer is $7 \div 3$, or $\frac{7}{3}$, or $2\frac{1}{3}$. It is necessary to label the answer. The quotient tells us how many groups of the divisor there are in the dividend. In this example we have $\frac{7}{3}$ groups of $\frac{3}{8}$ in $\frac{7}{8}$, or $2\frac{1}{3}$ groups of $\frac{3}{8}$ in $\frac{7}{8}$. We check the answer by multiplying the divisor by the quotient. In this case $2\frac{1}{3} \times \frac{3}{8} = \frac{7}{3} \times \frac{3}{8} = \frac{7}{8}$.

EXAMPLE 2. $\dfrac{7}{8} \div \dfrac{3}{4}$

How can one separate $7(\frac{1}{8})$ into groups of $3(\frac{1}{4})$? This would be the same as attempting to separate 7 cows into groups of 3 pencils. We can separate whatever objects we have into groups of the same objects. Since fourths and eighths are different fractional units, we cannot separate eighths into groups of fourths. We express the $\frac{3}{4}$ as $\frac{6}{8}$. Now we divide $\frac{7}{8}$ by $\frac{6}{8}$ and we derive the answer $\frac{7}{6}$ (groups of $\frac{6}{8}$ or $\frac{3}{4}$). We check the results: $\frac{7}{6} \times \frac{3}{4} = \frac{21}{24} = \frac{7}{8}$.

EXAMPLE 3. $\dfrac{3}{4} \div \dfrac{1}{3}$

In this example it is necessary to change both fraction symbols to new fractions containing the same denominator. We express both fractions as twelfths. We now have $\frac{9}{12} \div \frac{4}{12}$ and the answer is $\frac{9}{4}$ or $2\frac{1}{4}$ (groups of $\frac{1}{3}$).

EXAMPLE 4. $3\frac{1}{4} \div 1\frac{2}{3}$

We first express the mixed numbers as fractions. The exercise then becomes $\frac{13}{4} \div \frac{5}{3}$. Since they represent different units, we change them to the same units, twelfths. The exercise now is $\frac{39}{12} \div \frac{20}{12} = \frac{39}{20} = 1\frac{19}{20}$ (groups of $1\frac{2}{3}$). We check the answer:

$$1\frac{19}{20} \times 1\frac{2}{3} = \frac{39}{20} \times \frac{5}{3} = \frac{195}{60} = 3\frac{15}{60} = 3\frac{1}{4}$$

In Examples 1, 2, and 3 the dividend and the divisor must be expressed in the same units. To change a fraction to a new fraction we multiply the numerator and the denominator of each fraction by the same number. The two new fractions must have the same denominator. Then the division becomes the separation of a certain number of fractional units into groups of the same unit. It is for this reason that this method of division is called the common denominator method. All three examples can be illustrated in a like manner.

EXAMPLE 5. $\frac{7}{8} \div \frac{3}{8}$

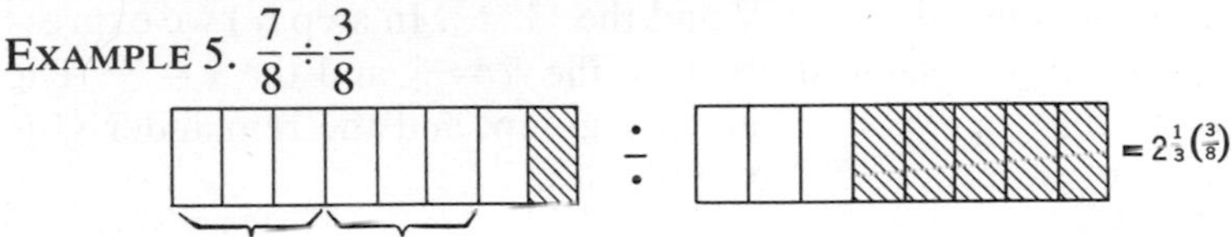

We have 2 groups of $\frac{3}{8}$ in $\frac{7}{8}$. The remainder $\frac{1}{8}$ is $\frac{1}{3}$ of $\frac{3}{8}$. Hence, our answer is $2\frac{1}{3}$.

EXAMPLE 6. $\frac{7}{8} \div \frac{3}{4}$

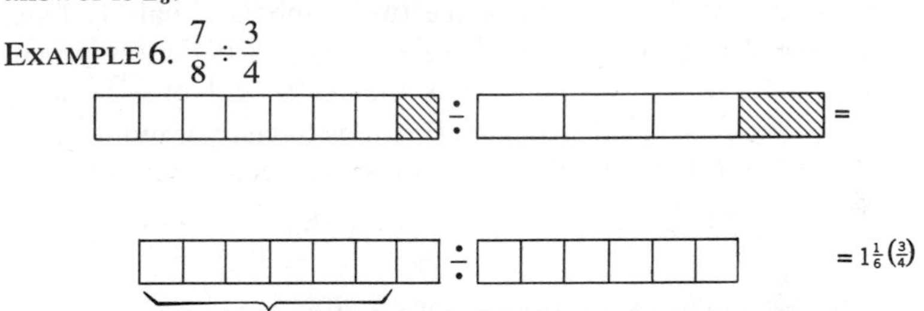

In Example 6 we change the $\frac{3}{4}$ to $\frac{6}{8}$ so that dividend and divisor are made up of the same kind of unit, namely, $\frac{1}{8}$. The $\frac{7}{8}$ contains 1 group of $\frac{6}{8}$, and the remainder $\frac{1}{8}$ is $\frac{1}{6}$ of 1 group of $\frac{6}{8}$. Hence, the answer is $1\frac{1}{6}$.

EXAMPLE 7. $\frac{3}{4} \div \frac{1}{3}$

$= 2\frac{1}{4}\left(\frac{1}{3}\right)$

In Example 7 we change the $\frac{3}{4}$ to $\frac{9}{12}$ and the $\frac{1}{3}$ to $\frac{4}{12}$. We count off groups of $\frac{4}{12}$ in the $\frac{9}{12}$. We have 2 groups of $\frac{4}{12}$ and the remainder $\frac{1}{12}$ is $\frac{1}{4}$ of a group of $\frac{4}{12}$.

EXAMPLE 8. $3\frac{1}{4} \div 1\frac{2}{3}$

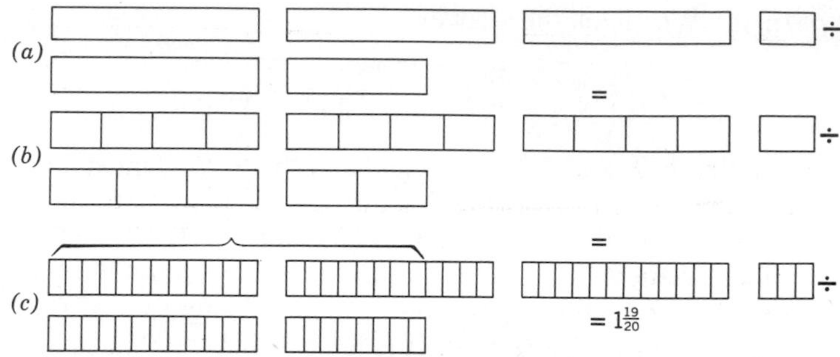

In step (*a*) of Example 8 we show the $3\frac{1}{4}$ base units in the dividend and the $1\frac{2}{3}$ base units in the divisor. In step (*b*) we express the mixed numbers as fractions, the $3\frac{1}{4} = \frac{13}{4}$ and the $1\frac{2}{3} = \frac{5}{3}$. In step (*c*) we express both fractions in the same units, $(\frac{1}{12})$, the $\frac{13}{4} = \frac{39}{12}$ and the $\frac{5}{3} = \frac{20}{12}$. The $\frac{39}{12}$ separated into groups of $\frac{20}{12}$ gives 1 group, and the remainder $\frac{19}{12}$ is $\frac{19}{20}$ of 1 group of $\frac{20}{12}$. Hence, the answer is $1\frac{19}{20}$.

The Reciprocal Method of Division of Fractions. The concept of reciprocal is important in mathematics. One number is the reciprocal of another number if the product of the two numbers equals 1. Thus $\frac{2}{3}$ is the reciprocal of $\frac{3}{2}$ because $\frac{2}{3} \times \frac{3}{2} = \frac{6}{6} = 1$. Also, $\frac{7}{8}$ is the reciprocal of $\frac{8}{7}$ because $\frac{7}{8} \times \frac{8}{7} = \frac{56}{56} = 1$, and 3 is the reciprocal of $\frac{1}{3}$ because $3 \times \frac{1}{3} = 1$. It is quite evident that if two fractions have their numerators and denominators reversed, these fractions are reciprocals of each other. We generalize this statement by saying that $\frac{b}{a}$ is the reciprocal of $\frac{a}{b}$.

Since a fraction may represent an indicated division, we can write the division of fractions as complex fractions in which the dividend is the numerator and the divisor is the denominator. We may write $\frac{3}{5} \div \frac{2}{7}$ as the complex fraction $\frac{\frac{3}{5}}{\frac{2}{7}}$. We shall now show four division-of-fraction examples as complex fractions.

EXAMPLE 1. $\frac{7}{8} \div \frac{3}{8}$ or $\frac{\frac{7}{8}}{\frac{3}{8}}$

The complex fractions would be much simpler if the denominator were 1 instead of $\frac{3}{8}$. We can make the denominator 1 if we multiply the $\frac{3}{8}$ by its reciprocal $\frac{8}{3}$. If we multiply the denominator by $\frac{8}{3}$ we must also multiply the numerator by $\frac{8}{3}$. We have the following:

$$\frac{7}{8} \div \frac{3}{8} = \frac{\frac{7}{8}}{\frac{3}{8}} = \frac{\frac{7}{8} \times \frac{8}{3}}{\frac{3}{8} \times \frac{8}{3}} = \frac{\frac{7}{8} \times \frac{8}{3}}{1} = \frac{7}{8} \times \frac{8}{3} = \frac{7}{3}$$

(*a*) (*b*) (*c*) (*d*) (*e*) (*f*)

In (*a*) we have the division exercise. In (*b*) we write the indicated division as a fraction. It is a complex fraction because the numerator and the denominator are themselves fractions. In step (*c*) we multiply the numerator and the denominator by $\frac{8}{3}$, which is the reciprocal of the denominator $\frac{3}{8}$. In step (*d*) we get the resulting denominator 1. Since dividing by 1 gives the number we start with, step (*e*) shows the numerator by itself. At this point we compare step (*a*) with step (*e*). We notice that the division sign has been replaced by the multiplication sign, and that the divisor has been inverted. This has resulted in a rule that in order to divide one fraction by another invert the divisor and multiply. This rule has been applied by many people who have never really understood why this is done. The intermediate steps (*b*), (*c*), and (*d*) explain why the rule works, but these steps have rarely been taught.

EXAMPLE 2. $\frac{7}{8} \div \frac{3}{4}$

$$\frac{7}{8} \div \frac{3}{4} = \frac{\frac{7}{8}}{\frac{3}{4}} = \frac{\frac{7}{8} \times \frac{4}{3}}{\frac{3}{4} \times \frac{4}{3}} = \frac{\frac{7}{8} \times \frac{4}{3}}{1} = \frac{7}{8} \times \frac{4}{3} = \frac{7}{6}$$

EXAMPLE 3. $\frac{3}{4} \div \frac{1}{3}$

$$\frac{3}{4} \div \frac{1}{3} = \frac{\frac{3}{4} \times \frac{3}{1}}{\frac{1}{3} \times \frac{3}{1}} = \frac{\frac{3}{4} \times \frac{3}{1}}{1} = \frac{3}{4} \times \frac{3}{1} = \frac{9}{4}$$

EXAMPLE 4. $3\frac{1}{4} \div 1\frac{2}{3} = \frac{13}{4} \div \frac{5}{3}$

$$= \frac{\frac{13}{4}}{\frac{5}{3}}$$

$$= \frac{\frac{13}{4} \times \frac{3}{5}}{\frac{5}{3} \times \frac{3}{5}}$$

$$= \frac{\frac{13}{4} \times \frac{3}{5}}{1}$$

$$= \frac{13}{4} \times \frac{3}{5}$$

$$= \frac{39}{20}$$

Of the two methods for division of fractions, the common denominator method is the meaningful method of separation into equal-sized groups, and it is a continuation of the concept of division that was developed with integers. The invert-the-divisor and multiply method is a method of convenience. Both methods are mathematically sound and should be taught to children. The method of reciprocals should be taught after the other, and only when children understand the meaning of reciprocal. It can be taught meaningfully and it helps develop the concept that

$$a \div b = a \times \frac{1}{b}$$

This is an important mathematical concept independent of division of fractions. Since division is the inverse of multiplication, $a \div b = c$ if, and only if, $c \times b = a$. To show that $a \div b = a \times \frac{1}{b}$ we have to demonstrate that $a \times \frac{1}{b} \times b = a$. By applying the associative property of multiplication and the definition of reciprocal we derive the following: $a \times \left(\frac{1}{b} \times b\right) = a \times 1 = a$. To divide by a number we can multiply by its reciprocal, that is $5 \div 8 = 5 \times \frac{1}{8}$, or $\frac{1}{8} \times 5$. Of course, this is consistent with the statement that the fraction symbol can be considered as a symbol of operation.

7.8 THE FRACTION AS A RATIONAL NUMBER

Man first developed counting numbers, and when he found it necessary to measure he created units of measurement. Measurement consisted of counting these units or calculating them, sometimes indirectly. His concern for parts of units resulted in the development of fractions. Rules for operation with fractions were developed as a result of man's experience with fractions.

The mathematician takes a second look at fractions and considers them as a new kind of number. He examines them in the light of a logical system based on undefined terms, definitions, and postulates. His need for fractions is based on his interest in performing a mathematical operation that could not be accomplished with counting numbers.

We shall now re-examine our concept of number from the point of view of logical analysis. We start with a set of counting numbers which we do not define. We merely assume that we know what we are talking about when we mention the term *counting numbers*. As children we learned to count and to give names to different collections of objects. With the development of the decimal notation system, or of any place-value numeration system, it was necessary to invent a symbol to show an absence of units. We have given the name zero and the symbol 0 for this concept. It functions as a placeholder as well as an indication of an absence of units. This new number has characteristics of its own which will be discussed in a later section.

The set {1, 2, 3, . . . } is called the set of *natural numbers*. Since zero is so important, we generally speak of the set of natural numbers and zero, or the set of *counting numbers* {0, 1, 2, 3, . . . }.

A number of postulates were established in order to make possible some operations with natural numbers. These are the postulates of closure for addition and for multiplication, the associative and commutative postulates for addition and for multiplication, and the distributive postulate for multiplication over addition. Addition was not defined, although it was understood as the result of counting. Multiplication was defined as the addition of equal addends. New definitions had to be made. Thus subtraction was defined as the inverse of addition, and division as the inverse of multiplication. With these definitions, undefined terms, and postulates, various generalizations were obtained.

It was evident from the very beginning that there is no property of closure for subtraction or for division of natural numbers. If the minuend is greater than the subtrahend, as in $8-3$, then subtraction is possible. If the minuend is less than the subtrahend, as in $5-8$, then subtraction is not possible within the set of natural numbers. If the dividend is a multiple of the divisor, as in $28 \div 4$, then division is possible. If the dividend is not a multiple of the divisor, as in $5 \div 3$, then division is not possible within the set of natural numbers.

The inability to perform certain operations was a frustrating experience to some people. They then attempted to assume that division was possible even when 5 was divided by 3. The result of such an operation was a new kind of number called a rational number. It is now assumed that for any pair of numbers, such as (5, 3) there is a number which is their quotient. This number is generally written as $\frac{5}{3}$. We now have a set of ordered pairs of natural numbers which represent their quotients. It is understood that the order in which the pairs are written is significant. Thus (5, 3) is not the same as (3, 5). The first pair is represented by $\frac{5}{3}$ whereas the second pair is represented by $\frac{3}{5}$. It is also understood that the second number in the number pair cannot be 0 because division by zero is not possible. We can now define the *rational numbers* as the set of ordered pairs of numbers (a, b) in which a and b are natural numbers, (except that b cannot be 0), then $a \div b$ is an alternate symbol for (a, b).

Definitions and Operations. Now that we have this new kind of number, what can we do with it? Can we perform the fundamental operations with rational numbers? We need some new definitions and postulates.

1. *Equal rational numbers.* Two rational numbers are equal if the product of the extremes equals the product of the means, that is

$(3, 4) = (9, 12)$ because $3 \times 12 = 4 \times 9$, or $\frac{3}{4} = \frac{9}{12}$ because $3 \times 12 = 4 \times 9$. Also $(7, 8) = (14, 16)$ because $7 \times 16 = 8 \times 14$, or $\frac{7}{8} = \frac{14}{16}$. However, $(5, 3) \neq (8, 6)$ because $5 \times 6 \neq 3 \times 8$. The symbol $\neq$ is read "not equal." We can generalize that $(a, b) = (c, d)$ if $ad = bc$. In the above example a and d are called the extremes and b and c are called the means.

2. If the two numbers that form the rational number are multiplied by the same number, the result is a rational number that is equal to the first one, that is, $(3, 5) = (9, 15)$, or $\frac{3}{5} = \frac{9}{15}$, because $3 \times 15 = 5 \times 9$. We generalize $(a, b) = (ma, mb)$, provided $m \neq 0$.

The set of rational numbers contains subsets of equal rational numbers. The fraction $\frac{3}{4}$ can be considered as the standard name for the set of rational numbers $\{(3, 4), (6, 8), (9, 12) \ldots (3m, 4m)\}$ where $m \neq 0$. The fraction $\frac{5}{6}$ can be considered as the standard name for $\{(5, 6), (10, 12), (15, 18), (20, 24) \ldots (5m, 6m)\}$ where $m \neq 0$.

3. If the two numbers that form the rational number are divided by the same number, the rational number formed is equal to the first one, that is, $(28, 16) = (7, 4)$ or $\frac{28}{16} = \frac{7}{4}$. Again it must be remembered that we cannot divide by zero.

4. *Multiplication.* In $(a, b) \times (c, d) = (ac, bd)$ or $\frac{a}{b} \times \frac{c}{d} = \frac{ac}{bd}$, the product of two rational numbers is found by multiplying the two first numbers of the number pair and the two second numbers.

5. *Addition.* Addition is simply defined as follows:

$$\frac{a}{b} + \frac{c}{d} = \frac{ad + bc}{bd}$$

As an example,

$$\frac{3}{4} + \frac{2}{5} = \frac{3 \times 5 + 4 \times 2}{4 \times 5} = \frac{23}{20}$$

$$\frac{3}{4} + \frac{5}{8} = \frac{3 \times 8 + 4 \times 5}{4 \times 8} = \frac{44}{32}$$

which can be reduced to $\frac{11}{8}$. Here we do not look for a least common denominator.

6. *Subtraction.* Subtraction is defined as the inverse of addition. $\frac{7}{8} - \frac{2}{3}$ asks what should be added to $\frac{2}{3}$ in order to equal $\frac{7}{8}$. We find the answer to be $\frac{5}{24}$. It can be shown that

$$\frac{a}{b} - \frac{c}{d} = \frac{ad - bc}{bd}$$

By applying this generalization to the numerical example we derive $\frac{5}{24}$.

7. *Division.* Division is defined as the inverse of multiplication. In the example $\frac{7}{8} \div \frac{2}{3}$, we are really asked to find the rational number that multiplies $\frac{2}{3}$ and gives $\frac{7}{8}$. We replace $\frac{7}{8}$ by its equal, $\frac{14}{16}$, or $\frac{21}{24}$ or $\frac{42}{48}$. We find that $\frac{21}{16} \times \frac{2}{3} = \frac{42}{48}$, or $\frac{7}{8}$. Therefore we say that $\frac{7}{8} \div \frac{2}{3} = \frac{21}{16}$. However, we find that $\frac{7}{8} \times \frac{3}{2} = \frac{21}{16}$.

We have indicated that to divide one fraction by änother we can find the answer by multiplying the dividend by the reciprocal of the divisor. We can define $a \div b$ as $a \times 1/b$.

8. *The relation between natural and rational numbers.* Since rational numbers are made up of natural numbers, we can consider a relationship between the set of natural numbers and the set of rational numbers. We can divide any number by 1 and get the same number as a result. Therefore we can express 2 as $\frac{2}{1}$, 3 as $\frac{3}{1}$, 7 as $\frac{7}{1}$, etc. We thus see that the set of rational numbers has a subset whose elements can be associated with the set of natural numbers. We must be careful not to confuse natural numbers with their equivalent rational numbers. A natural number is a single number whereas a rational number is a pair of numbers. All natural numbers can be associated with rational numbers, but not all rational numbers can be associated with natural numbers. With the introduction of rational numbers we can divide any number by any non-zero number.

7.9 TEACHING FRACTIONS TO CHILDREN

Children have a fair knowledge of counting numbers before they enter the elementary school but their knowledge of fractions is very limited. They can count beyond ten and associate sets with number names, but their knowledge of fractions is probably limited to one-half, one-fourth, and perhaps one-third. It is the school that has to provide children with many experiences with fractions. Such experiences should be activities, actually cutting base units into equal parts. One of the best concrete devices for learning about fractions is a set of circles of the same size made out of construction paper of different colors. Let the children fold a red circle into 2 equal parts and then cut the circle along the crease. They now have 2 equal parts of the circle. They are given the name one-half but not the symbol $\frac{1}{2}$. They learn the names for fractional units. The symbols are taught after the children have had experience and have become familiar with fractional units. Next the children take a yellow circle and fold it twice. Then they cut along the creases and find that they have four equal parts of a circle. Next they take a circle of a different color, fold it three times, and cut along the creases. They now have halves, fourths, and eighths. The colors help the children identify the different fractional units.

Thirds are not easy for children to fold. The teacher should have lines drawn on the circles that will divide them into thirds. The children cut these circles along the lines already drawn. They are asked to compare the pieces to see if they are all equal. Now the children again cut a circle of a different color into thirds and fold each piece into two parts. The cut parts are sixths. The next time the sixths are cut into two equal parts, forming twelfths.

Children first learn to count the number of equal parts in a circle and to associate a name for each part. In this manner they learn about fractional units. They learn, by actually placing one unit on another, that one-half is greater than one-third, that one-fourth is greater than one-sixth, etc. When they have the concrete fractional units, they can arrange them in order of size.

The experience with fractions can be enlarged by using different colors for the different fractional units so that children will not associate size with color. Now they repeat the construction of fractional units by using circles of different sizes. If five-inch circles were used the first time, six- and seven-inch circles are used this time. In this way children learn the concept of a base unit. One-fourth of a circle is not the same size as one-fourth of a larger or smaller circle. It will become clear to children that one-third is greater than one-fourth only if the same base unit is used.

After children have experienced fractional units with circles, they can repeat the same activities with rectangles as base units. Circles have an advantage over rectangles because the child who has a part of a circle knows that he does not have the whole circle, but merely a part of a circle. The child who has a part of a rectangle is never quite sure what the base unit is, since any rectangle can be a base unit. The advantage of using rectangles, however, is that it is easier to fold a rectangle into equal parts than to fold a circle. Whether the child uses circles or rectangles as base units, he should always have the base units as well as fractional units so that he can make comparisons when necessary. When the child has had sufficient experience with fractional units, he is ready for the study of fractional relationships and operations with fractions.

The child's first learning experience with fractions is on the operational level. He actually compares fractional units of different size and of the same base unit. He learns, by comparing actual fractional units, that one-half equals two-fourths, three-sixths, four-eighths, or six-twelfths. He learns that one-fourth equals two-eighths, or three-twelfths. He learns to express one-third, two-thirds, three-fourths, and five-sixths in other fractional units. He learns the symbols for fractions. As a result of his experience on the operational level, he may discover the generalization that one may multiply the numerator and the denominator of a fraction by the same number to get equivalent fractions.

The teacher should allow children to make their own discoveries. The skillful teacher knows how to ask the kind of questions that lead children to discover generalizations. Some children need more time with the operational level than others. Children should be challenged and encouraged to rationalize the discovery, that is, give the explanation of why the generalization is true. It must be understood that not all children are capable of rationalization. The teacher who knows and understands the children in the class allows each child to work at his own rate. In the same classroom there will be children at all levels of learning. The principle of individual differences is a sound one. Children who are on the operational level of learning should not be expected to rationalize their discoveries.

The children can be taught to add, subtract, multiply, and divide fractions according to the explanations of these operations that were given in the preceding sections of this chapter. They add like-fractional units, subtract like-fractional units, and compare groups of like-fractional units. They actually perform the operation of taking three-fourths of five-sixths. Where the fractions are made up of different units, children learn to replace one fraction by an equivalent fraction so that the units are the same.

Again we have three levels of learning. Children perform the four operations by actually using concrete objects. They discover the generalizations, such as, to multiply two fractions one multiplies the numerators and the denominators, to add fractions one adds the numerators if the denominators are the same, etc. Once the generalizations are learned, the children apply them and no longer need to operate with concrete aids.

EXERCISES

1. Explain what happens to a fraction when the following is done:
   (*a*) The numerator is doubled and the denominator remains the same;
   (*b*) The denominator is doubled and the numerator remains the same;
   (*c*) Both numerator and denominator are doubled.
2. Generalize the results of Exercise 1 by multiplying by 3, 4, 5 or any integer.
3. Select any three fractions and test for:
   (*a*) The associative principle for addition;
   (*b*) The associative principle for multiplication;
   (*c*) The distributive principle.
4. Use the method of prime factors to determine the least common denominator.

(a) $\frac{3}{14}+\frac{5}{21}+\frac{7}{30}$

(b) $\frac{3}{55}+\frac{7}{30}+\frac{2}{32}+\frac{5}{6}$

5. Show how the number line can be used to teach fractions.
6. When we multiply a number by a fraction, the answer is sometimes greater than and sometimes smaller than the original number. Explain why this is so.
7. When we divide a number by a fraction, the answer is sometimes greater than and sometimes smaller than the original number. Explain why this is true.
8. List the meanings of the fundamental operations with integers. Show where the meanings of the operations with fractions are the same as with integers and where they are different.
9. Write the following fractions in the base two:

   (a) $\frac{7}{8}$ (b) $\frac{3}{4}$ (c) $\frac{19}{32}$ (d) $\frac{1}{2}$ (e) $\frac{9}{16}$

10. Write the following fractions in base five.

    (a) $\frac{7}{8}$ (b) $\frac{9}{10}$ (c) $\frac{73}{100}$ (d) $\frac{5}{18}$ (e) $\frac{37}{48}$

11. Show that the commutative property for addition is valid for rational numbers.
12. Show that the commutative property for multiplication is valid for rational numbers.
13. In dividing $a \times b$ by 2, we can divide either a by 2 or b by 2 but not both. Explain why this is true.
14. How would you teach the concept of reciprocal to children?

SUGGESTED SUPPLEMENTARY READING

1. Bell, Clifford, Clela D. Hammond, and Robert B. Herrera, *Fundamentals of Arithmetic for Teachers*. New York: John Wiley and Sons, 1962. Chaps. 9 and 10.
2. Brumfiel, Charles F., et al, *Principles of Arithmetic*. Reading, Mass.: Addison-Wesley Publishing Company, 1963. Chaps. 10 and 11.
3. Carnahan, Walter H., "The Unit Fraction of Ancient Egypt," *School Science and Mathematics*, January 1960. pp. 5–9.
4. Crumley, Richard D., "Teaching Rate and Ratio in the Middle Grades," *School Science and Mathematics*, February 1960. pp. 143–150.
5. Duker, Sam, "Rationalizing Division of Fractions," *The Arithmetic Teacher*, December 1954. pp. 20–23.
6. Dutton, Wilbur H., and L. J. Adams, *Arithmetic for Teachers*, Englewood Cliffs, N.J.: Prentice-Hall, 1961. Chaps. 8 and 9.
7. Eagle, Edwin, "Don't Let that Inverted Divisor Become Mysterious," *The Arithmetic Teacher*, October 1954. pp. 15–17.
8. Gunderson, Agnes G., and Ethel Gunderson, "Fraction Concepts Held by Young Children," *The Arithmetic Teacher*, October 1957. pp. 168–173.
9. Gunderson, Ethel, "Fractions – Seven-Year-Olds Use Them," *The Arithmetic Teacher*, November 1958. pp. 233–238.

10. Hartung, Maurice L., "Fractions and Related Symbolism in Elementary-School Instruction," *Elementary School Journal,* April 1958. pp. 377–384.
11. Keedy, Mervin L., *A Modern Introduction to Basic Mathematics.* Reading, Mass.: Addison-Wesley Publishing Company, 1963. Chap. 9.
12. Latino, Joseph J., "Take the Folly Out of Fractions," *The Arithmetic Teacher,* November 1955. pp. 113–118.
13. McSwain, E. T., and Ralph J. Cooke, *Understanding and Teaching Arithmetic in the Elementary School.* New York: Henry Holt and Company, 1958. Chap. 7.
14. Mueller, Francis J., "On the Fraction as a Numeral," *The Arithmetic Teacher,* May 1961. pp. 234–238.
15. ———, *Arithmetic Its Structure and Concepts.* Englewood Cliffs, N.J.: Prentice-Hall, 1956. pp. 150–188, 214–215.
16. Mulholland, Vernie, "Fifth Grade Children Discover Fractions," *School Science and Mathematics,* January 1954. pp. 13–30.
17. Peterson, John, and Joseph Hashisaki, *Theory of Arithmetic.* New York: John Wiley and Sons, 1963. Chap. 7.
18. Rappaport, David, "The Meanings of Fractions," *School Science and Mathematics,* April 1962. pp. 241–244.
19. Riess, Anita P., "A New Approach to the Teaching of Fractions in the Intermediate Grades," *School Science and Mathematics,* February 1964. pp. 111–119.
20. Sanders, Walter J., "The Use of Models in Mathematics Instruction," *The Arithmetic Teacher,* March 1964. pp. 157–165.
21. Van Engen, Henry, "Rate Pairs, Fractions, and Rational Numbers," *The Arithmetic Teacher,* December 1960. pp. 389–399.

Chapter 8 *Decimal Fractions*

8.1 INTRODUCTION

The term decimal fraction is considered by many people to be a contradiction of terms. In their opinion $\frac{3}{10}$ is a fraction, but 0.3 is a decimal, not a fraction. They believe that it is a mistake to combine the two words, since each represents a different notation. Their misconception lies in confusing the idea with the notation of the idea. If we have a base unit and we divide it into equal parts, we have a fractional unit, or a fraction. How we notate, or communicate, our idea of the fraction is another matter. We may use a vertical arrangement of a pair of numerals with a horizontal line between them as in $\frac{3}{10}$, or we may use a decimal point and the place-value system, as in 0.3. But we could use other symbols such as an apostrophe, as in 3′, or a horizontal bar over the numeral, as in 3, to indicate the same fraction. What is important is the concept of fraction rather than its notation.

Historically there were two expressions for the same concept: common fractions (originally called vulgar fractions) and decimal fractions. The common fractions were widely used, hence their name whereas decimal fractions were rarely used. In language usage the word *common* was dropped from common fraction, and the word *fraction* was dropped from decimal fraction. Thus we have the words fractions and decimals, but they both refer to the fraction concept.

Another group of "mathematics educators" recommend that we eliminate common fractions from the curriculum, since these are now very rarely used. They proposed to teach only decimals. Common fractions would be introduced later, when the need for them actually arose. The concept of decimal fractions is considered to be merely an extension of the place-value idea. In proceeding from right to left, the units are progressively ten times as great. Thus we have units of ones, tens, hundreds, thousands, etc. But in proceeding from left to right, the units are progressively one-tenth as great. Thus we have units of tens, ones, tenths, hundredths, thousandths, etc. This may be correct, but it is not psychologically or pedagogically sound.

The child developed his concept of number and place value by first counting ones. Then he grouped objects into groups of 10 ones, 10 tens, 10 hundreds etc. He learned about the decimal place value notation. He learned to exchange ten smaller units for one larger unit, and he also learned to exchange one larger unit for ten smaller units. He undid the grouping when he reversed the order of this process. But how is a child expected to undo the process when he reaches ones? He has never grouped smaller units to get *one*. A *one* is the base unit. He must learn to divide the base unit into equal parts in order to form fractional units. That is why he must have experience with fractions before he can extend the decimal place-value system. Having experienced different kinds of fractions, he can understand the fractions with a denominator of 10, or 100, or any power of 10. The concept of fractions must precede the decimal notation for fraction.

8.2 THE DECIMAL POINT

Most people, when asked to explain the purpose of the decimal point, will say that the decimal point separates the whole numbers from the fractions. It is just as proper to say that every digit separates one kind of unit from another. Thus in the numeral 384.79 the 8 separates the hundreds from the ones, and the 4 separates the tens from the tenths. The idea of the decimal point as a point of separation may be correct and valid, but it poses some difficult questions. A child may ask why it is that, in the numeral 342.76, the hundreds place is three places to the left of the decimal point whereas the hundredths place is only two places to the right of the decimal point. Likewise, why is the tens place two places to the left and the tenths place only one place to the right of the decimal point.

It is more appropriate to think of the decimal point as an indicator of the ones place. We could write 342.76 as 34276, or 34276, or 34|2|76, or even as 34.276 (if it is understood that the decimal point is placed to the left instead of the right of the ones place). If we think of the ones place as the center of the notation system, then the system is symmetrical. The hundreds place is two places to the left of the ones place and the hundredths place is two places to the right of the ones place. The tens place is one place to the left of the ones place and the tenths place is one place to the right of the ones place. In like manner, the thousands place is three places to the left of the ones place and the thousandths place is three places to the right of the ones place.

The concept of the ones place as the center of the notation system helps one to understand and use the scientific notation of numbers more effectively than the concept of the decimal point as the center. Thus in $34200000 = 3.42 \times 10^7$ the exponent is 7 because the 3 is seven places to the left of the ones place. In $0.0000000732 = 7.32 \times 10^{-8}$ the exponent is a negative 8 because the 7 is eight places to the right of the ones place.*

8.3 EXTENDING THE PLACE VALUE SYSTEM

When the concept of fraction is fully understood, it is possible to extend the decimal place-value system to include fractional units. Since we are dealing with a decimal system, the fractional units must be decimal units (tenths, hundredths, thousandths, etc.) in which the denominator is a power of 10. We use the same concept of exchange as with integers. It takes 10 tenths to make 1 one, 10 hundredths to make 1 tenth, 10 thousandths to make 1 hundredth, etc.

We can express any number by combining the units. The numeral 345.63 represents 3 units of hundreds, 4 units of tens, 5 units of ones, 6 units of tenths, and 3 units of hundredths. The digit to the right of the ones place is the numerator of the fraction indicating the number of units, and the position of the digit is the denominator indicating the kind of unit. We can also express the above number as:

$$3 \times 100 + 4 \times 10 + 5 \times 1 + 6 \times \tfrac{1}{10} + 3 \times \tfrac{1}{100}$$

We can also express it in terms of powers as follows:

$$3 \times 10^2 + 4 \times 10^1 + 5 \times 10^0 + 6 \times 10^{-1} + 3 \times 10^{-2}$$

The negative exponents indicate the power of 10 that is the denominator of the fractional unit. The 0 exponent is the center of the system and indicates the ones place.

*Although the study of logarithms is beyond the scope of this book, the use of the ones place as the center of our notation system makes it possible to use only one rule instead of two for determining the characteristic of the logarithm. If the first significant digit, as in 3489.6, is three places to the left of the ones place, the characteristic is a positive three. If the first significant digit, as in 0.00349, is three places to the right of the ones place, the characteristic is a negative three.

8.4 ADDING DECIMALS

We recall that in addition we combine two or more sets and express the result as if it were one set. We also recall that we add only like units, ones to ones, tens to tens, etc. The same is true for fractional units. We add tenths to tenths, hundredths to hundredths, thousandths to thousandths. We write the numerals in a vertical arrangement in which the decimal points are aligned so that the numerals in the same column represent the same units.

EXAMPLE 1.

(a)	(b)	(c)
3.4	4.17	5.412
+2.3	+2.32	+3.146

Fig. 54

We perform the addition in the same manner as with integers. In Fig. 54*a* we add 4 tenths and 3 tenths, and then 3 ones and 2 ones. The sum is 5.7. In Fig. 54*b* we add the 7 hundredths and the 2 hundredths, the 1 tenth and the 3 tenths, and the 4 ones and the 2 ones. The sum is 6.49. In Fig. 54*c* we add the thousandths, the hundredths, the tenths, and the ones to derive the sum 8.558.

EXAMPLE 2.

(a)	(b)	(c)
4.8	5.93	3.627
+3.6	+4.48	+5.845

Fig. 55

Example 2 differs from Example 1 because it is necessary to apply the concept of exchange. In Fig. 55*a* we add 8 tenths and 6 tenths for a sum of 14 tenths. We exchange 10 tenths for 1 one and add it to the sum of the 4 ones and 3 ones. The sum is 8.4. In Fig. 55*b* we first add the 3 hundredths and 8 hundredths and derive the sum 11 hundredths. We exchange 10 hundredths for 1 tenth, leaving 1 hundredth. Now we add 9 tenths, 4 tenths, and the 1 tenth, and derive the sum 14 tenths. We exchange 10 tenths for 1 one, leaving 4 tenths. Now we add the 5 ones, 4 ones, and 1 one for a sum of 10 ones, or 1 ten. The sum is 10.41. In Fig. 55*c* we add the thousandths, then the hundredths, the tenths, and the ones. Whenever we have more than 9 units of one kind, we exchange 10 units for 1 of the next larger size. We derive the sum 9.472.

These two examples illustrate the process of adding decimals as well as integers. There may, of course, be more than two addends, and the sum of the units may be enough to exchange for more than 1 unit of the next size.

8.5 SUBTRACTING DECIMALS

In subtraction we can subtract only like units. We line up the minuend and the subtrahend so that the decimal points are in a column. This will assure that the same units are in the same column. We use the additive method of subtraction. Where the particular place has less units in the minuend than in the subtrahend, we use the decomposition method. We regroup by exchanging 1 larger unit for 10 smaller units.

EXAMPLE 1.

$$\begin{array}{r} 8.976 \\ -2.342 \\ \hline \end{array}$$

We add enough thousandths to the 2 thousandths to equal 6 thousandths, then enough hundredths to the 4 hundredths to equal 7 hundredths, then tenths to the 3 tenths to equal 9 tenths, and finally enough ones to the 2 ones to equal 8 ones. The difference is 6.634.

EXAMPLE 2.

(a)		(b)
		12613
8.273	=	7. ~~2~~~~7~~ ~~3~~
−4.529		−4. 52 9
		3. 74 4

Fig. 56

Upon examining the minuend and the subtrahend, we notice that the minuend has less units of tenths and of thousandths than the subtrahend. We exchange 1 of the ones for 10 tenths and 1 of the hundredths for 10 thousandths. The regrouping or exchange is shown in Fig. 56*b*. Now we perform the subtraction process and derive the difference 3.744. The process of subtraction is the same for decimal fractions as for decimal integers.

8.6 MULTIPLICATION OF DECIMALS

Most people have learned to multiply decimals by mechanically following some rules. They were told to ignore the decimal points and to multiply as if there were no decimal points. Then, after they found the product, they were told to add the number of fractional places in the multiplicand and in the multiplier, and that this sum would indicate the number of fractional places in the product. Thus the decimal point, which was temporarily ignored, was finally recalled and located. The following example illustrates this mechanical process.

EXAMPLE 1.

$$\begin{array}{r} 3.42 \\ \times 2.3 \\ \hline 1026 \\ 684 \\ \hline 7.866 \end{array}$$

If the decimal points are ignored, the exercise is treated as if it were 23×342. Since there are two fractional places in 3.42 and one in 2.3, there should be three fractional places in the product. The decimal point is placed between the 7 and 8.

Multiplication of decimals can, and should, be explained. Every step in the process should be meaningful. The exercise 2.3×3.42 is a statement that we have 2 groups of 3.42 and also 3 tenths of a group of 3.42. We arrange the multiplicand and the multiplier so that the decimal points are in a column, just as in addition and in subtraction. We can even put in the decimal points for the partial products and the final product before any multiplication is actually done, as in Fig. 57*a*.

(*a*)

$$\begin{array}{r} 3.42 \\ \times 2.3 \\ \hline . \\ . \\ \hline . \end{array}$$

(*b*)

$$\begin{array}{r} 3.42 \\ \times 2.3 \\ \hline 1.026 \\ 6.84 \\ \hline 7.866 \end{array}$$

(*c*)

$$\frac{3}{10} \times \frac{2}{100} = \frac{6}{1000}$$

$$\frac{3}{10} \times \frac{4}{10} = \frac{12}{100}$$

$$\frac{3}{10} \times 3 = \frac{9}{10}$$

$$2 \times \frac{2}{100} = \frac{4}{100}$$

$$2 \times \frac{4}{10} = \frac{8}{10}$$

$$2 \times 3 = 6$$

Fig. 57

We first find 3 tenths of 3.42. It is necessary to know that 1 tenth of 1 tenth equals 1 hundredth and that 1 tenth of 1 hundredth equals 1 thousandth. This is, of course, part of the place-value concept, but it can also be developed in the common fraction form. Now 3 tenths of 2 hundredths equals 6 thousandths. We place the 6 in the thousandths place. Then 3 tenths of 4 tenths equals 12 hundredths. We write the

2 hundredths in the hundredths place and exchange 10 hundredths for 1 tenth. Then 3 tenths of 3 equals 9 tenths, and the 1 tenth equals 10 tenths. We exchange them for 1 one. Then we multiply by the 2. Two times 2 hundredths equals 4 hundredths, 2 times 4 tenths equals 8 tenths, and 2 times 3 ones equals 6 ones. We write each of these products in the proper position. The result of each step is shown in Fig. 57*b*. The multiplication in the common fraction form is shown in Fig. 57*c*. The sum of the partial products is 7.866. It was not necessary to formulate any rule about locating the decimal point in the answer because the decimal points were already placed in the proper position, as noted in Fig. 57*a*. Each partial product was written in the proper position at the time it was derived.

The next example follows the same procedure. The decimal points are lined up in Fig. 58*a*. The decimal multiplication is shown in Fig. 58*b*. The common fraction multiplication is shown in Fig. 58*c*.

$$\begin{array}{r} 7.83 \\ \times 4.73 \\ \hline . \\ . \\ . \\ \hline . \end{array} \qquad \begin{array}{r} 7.83 \\ \times 4.73 \\ \hline .2349 \\ 5.481 \\ 31.32 \\ \hline 37.0359 \end{array}$$

(*a*) (*b*)

$$\frac{3}{100} \times \frac{3}{100} = \frac{9}{10000}, \quad \frac{7}{10} \times \frac{3}{100} = \frac{21}{1000}$$

$$\frac{3}{100} \times \frac{8}{10} = \frac{24}{1000}, \quad \frac{7}{10} \times \frac{8}{10} = \frac{56}{100}$$

$$\frac{3}{100} \times 7 = \frac{21}{100}, \quad \frac{7}{10} \times 7 = \frac{49}{10}$$

(*c*)

Fig. 58

Since the decimal points were in position before the multiplication was begun, it was not necessary to ignore and then recall them by some rule. The rule for placing the decimal point in the answer, however, is a good one and should be learned by children. It is awkward to learn the names of the fractional decimal units when there are many decimal places. The procedure described in the two examples can be followed when there are one- or two-place fractional units.

Children may generalize, after some experience, that the number of fractional places in the product is equal to the sum of the fractional places in the multiplicand and the multiplier. The teacher should ask children to explain each step with the decimal points lined up in a column, but the teacher should also encourage the children to discover the generalization, or the rule, for locating the decimal point. Once this generalization is discovered, it can be applied. Then it will no longer be necessary to line up the decimal points.

Children may rationalize the rule in a simple statement that is acceptable to their level. For instance, to multiply by 1 tenth we go to the place to the right of the digit. The decimal place-value system is based on the idea that the first position to the right of a given digit has a place value that is 1 tenth of the place value of the given digit, and that the position that is two places to the right of a given digit has a place value that is 1 hundredth of the place value of the given digit. In 2.3×3.42, we know that the smallest fractional unit of the product will be three places to the right of the ones place. In 4.73×7.83, the smallest fractional unit of the product will be four decimal places to the right of the ones place. In 5.74×8.6325, the smallest fractional unit of the product will be six places to the right of the ones place.

The mathematical explanation for the rule is based on the law of exponents for multiplication. In 2.3×3.42, the 2.3 can be written as 23×10^{-1} and the 3.42 can be written as 342×10^{-2}. In $23 \times 10^{-1} \times 342 \times 10^{-2}$, we first multiply the 342 by 23, no decimal points. Then $10^{-1} \times 10^{-2}$ equals 10^{-3}. We add the exponents. The 10^{-3} tells us that we have three decimal places. In 4.73×7.83, we can write the exercise as $473 \times 10^{-2} \times 783 \times 10^{-2}$. Again we multiply 473×783, numbers without decimal points. But $10^{-2} \times 10^{-2}$ equals 10^{-4}, thus giving us four decimal places in the answer.

The rule for locating the decimal point in the product should follow, but not precede, the meaningful explanations for multiplication of decimals.

8.7 DIVISION OF DECIMALS

The same principles are applied to the division of decimals as to the division of integers. We separate the dividend into groups of equal size. We will consider first the divisor that is an integer, then the divisor that is a decimal fraction, and finally, the divisor that is a mixed number.

EXAMPLE 1.

$$
\begin{array}{rr}
 & 2.87 \\
3 & \overline{)8.61} \\
 & \underline{6} \\
 & 2.6 \\
 & \underline{2.4} \\
 & .21 \\
 & \underline{.21}
\end{array}
\qquad\qquad
\begin{array}{rr}
 & .856 \\
3 & \overline{)2.568} \\
 & \underline{2.4} \\
 & .16 \\
 & \underline{.15} \\
 & .018 \\
 & \underline{.018}
\end{array}
$$

(a) Fig. 59 *(b)*

In Fig. 59*a* we first separate the 8 ones into three equal groups. There are 2 ones in each group. The remainder of 2 ones is exchanged for 20 tenths. Now the 26 tenths are divided into three equal groups. There are 8 tenths in each group with a remainder of 2 tenths. We exchange them for 20 hundredths. Now the 21 hundredths are divided into three equal groups. There are 7 hundredths in each group. Thus we have 2.87 in each of the three equal groups.

In Fig. 59*b* the 2 ones are not enough to separate into three equal groups. We exchange the 2 ones for 20 tenths. Now we separate the 25 tenths into three equal groups. There are 8 tenths in each group, with a remainder of 1 tenth. We exchange the 1 tenth for 10 hundredths and divide the 16 hundredths into three equal groups. There are 5 hundredths in each group, with a remainder of 1 hundredth. This is exchanged for 10 thousandths and the 18 thousandths are divided into three equal groups. There are 6 thousandths in each group. Thus there are 0.856 in each of the three equal groups.

From the point of view of applied mathematics, division of decimals may be measurement division or partitive division. The process described uses the notion of partitive division. We make no distinction between these two concepts with regard to the division process. The proper label, number of groups or size of groups, for the quotient will be determined by the question.

In both exercises the decimal points are kept in a column just as in addition, subtraction, and multiplication. By keeping the decimal points in this manner, it becomes easier to see and to explain each step in the division process. Separating tenths, hundredths and thousandths into groups of equal size is the same as separating tens, hundreds, and thousands into groups of equal size.

```
EXAMPLE 2.   .7)8.344          11.92
                             7)83.44
                               7
                               --
                               13
                                7
                               ---
                                6.4
                                6.3
                                ---
                                 .14
                                 .14
                                 ---

               (a)              (b)
```

Fig. 60

Example 2 differs from Example 1 in that the divisor is a fraction. If we write the indicated division of Fig. 60*a* as a fraction, it would be written as $\frac{8.344}{0.7}$. If we multiply the numerator and the denominator by 10, the new fraction is $\frac{83.44}{7}$. Now Fig. 60*b* is similar to Example 1.

Multiplying dividend and divisor by a power of 10 is the same as multiplying the numerator and denominator of a fraction by the same number. Multiplying a decimal by a power of 10 has the effect of shifting the decimal point as many places to the right as the power of 10. The correct statement is that the numerals are shifted so many places to the left, but the concept of moving the decimal point is so widely held that it becomes advisable to use this idea rather than to change it.

Some educators feel that moving the decimal point really changes the original exercise. Although it is true that 83.44 divided by 7 gives the same result as 8.344 divided by 0.7, these are really two different exercises. They suggest that the decimal points should be kept in their original positions, but that a caret (∧) be used to indicate the new positions of the decimal points after multiplying by the power of 10. This is indicated in Fig. 61.

EXAMPLE 2*a*.

```
                          1 1.92
7)8.344         .7 ∧ )8.3 ∧ 44
                          7
                          ---
                          1 3
                            7
                          ----
                            6.4
                            6.3
                            ----
                             .14
                             .14
                             ---
  (a)                        (b)
```

Fig. 61

EXAMPLE 3.

```
                                   1.15
8.42)9.6874         8.42 ∧ )9.68 ∧ 74
                              8 42
                              ------
                              1 26.7
                                84.2
                              ------
                                42.54
                                42.10
                                -----
                                  .44
   (a)                          (b)
```

Fig. 62

In Fig. 62*a* the dividend and divisor are multiplied by 100 so that the divisor will become an integer. The result is shown in Fig. 62*b*. The explanation for the steps is left to the reader.

8.8 OPERATIONS WITH FRACTIONS IN OTHER BASES

The point in every number base is used to indicate the ones place just as with the decimal system. In 3.42_{five} we have 3 units of ones, 4 units of fifths, and 2 units of twenty-fifths. In proceeding to the right from any given position, each place has a value that is one-fifth of the place value to its immediate left. In 3.42_{eight} we have 3 units of ones, 4 units of eighths, and 2 units of sixty-fourths. In 3.42_{twelve} we have 3 units of ones, 4 units of twelfths, and 2 units of one hundred forty-fourths. In 2.122_{three} we have 2 units of ones, 1 unit of thirds, 2 units of ninths, and 2 units of twenty-sevenths. In 1.1011_{two} we have 1 unit of halves, no units of fourths, 1 unit of eighths, and 1 unit of sixteenths. Thus the place-value concept is followed in each numeration system.

We must be careful in giving the proper name to the point in each number base. It is called the decimal point only in the base ten. It is the quinal point in base five, the octal point in base eight, the duodecimal point in base twelve, the tertial point in base three, and the binal point in base two.

1. *Addition of mixed numbers in other bases.*

(*a*)	(*b*)	(*c*)	(*d*)	(*e*)
Base five	*Base eight*	*Base twelve*	*Base three*	*Base two*
3.41	7.634	8.634	2.11	1.1011
2.31	1.527	5.529	1.21	1.0111
1.	1 1	1	1	1 111
11.22	11.363	11.*e*61	11.02	11.0010

Fig. 63

In adding fractions we add like units, just as with integers. We must remember to exchange the proper number of units for the next larger size unit. In Fig. 63*a* we add 1 unit and 1 unit for a sum of 2 units. Then 4 units and 3 units have the sum 12_{five} units (7_{ten}). We write the 2 units in that column and the 1 of 12_{five} in the column to the left. Now we add 3, 2, and 1 of the same kind of units (ones). Their sum is 11_{five} (6_{ten}).

In Fig. 63*b* we add the 4 and the 7 units. Their sum is 13_{eight} (11_{ten}). In the next column we add 3, 2, and 1 and derive the sum 6. There is no exchange of smaller units for larger units. In the next column to the left, however, the sum of 6 and 5 is 13_{eight} (11_{ten}), and it is necessary to exchange eight units for 1 of the next size. Then the sum of 7, 1, and 1 is 11_{eight} (9_{ten}).

In Fig. 63*c* we add the units in each column. The sum of 4 and 9 is 11_{twelve} (13_{ten}). In the next column the sum is 6. In the next column the sum is e_{twelve} (11_{ten}). The sum of the ones is 11_{twelve} (13_{ten}). The explanations for the steps in Fig. 63*d* and 63*e* are left to the reader.

2. *Subtraction in other number bases*

(*a*)	(*b*)	(*c*)	(*d*)	(*e*)
Base five	*Base eight*	*Base twelve*	*Base three*	*Base two*
10	10	10	10	10 10 1 10
2 $\not{0}$ 11	2 0 11	2 0 11	1 0 11	0 0 0 1$\not{0}$ 0 10
$\not{3}$. $\not{1}$ $\not{1}$	$\not{3}$. $\not{1}$ 1	3. $\not{1}$ 1	$\not{2}$. $\not{1}$ 1	$\not{1}$ $\not{1}$. $\not{1}$ 0 $\not{1}$ 0
−1 4 2	−1. 4 2	−1. 4 2	−1. 2 2	− 1. 1 1 1 1
1. 1 4	1. 4 7	1. 8 *e*	. 1 2	1. 1 0 1 1

Fig. 64

In all five examples in Fig. 64 we resort to the decomposition method. We exchange one larger unit for a number of smaller units, according to the base. In *(a)* we cannot subtract 2 units from 1 unit. We exchange the 1 unit of the next larger size for five smaller units. The 11_{five} represents six units. The difference between 11_{five} and 2_{five} is 4_{five}. In the next column we cannot subtract 4 units from 0 units. We exchange 1 of the larger units for five smaller units. Now we subtract 4_{five} units from 10_{five} units. The difference is 1. Then we subtract 1 one from 2 ones. We use the same digits in *(b)* and *(c)*, but they represent different units. In *(b)* we exchange 1 larger unit for eight smaller units whereas in *(c)* we exchange 1 larger unit for 12 smaller units. The steps are as follows: in *(b)*, $11_{\text{eight}} - 2_{\text{eight}} = 7_{\text{eight}}$ whereas in *(c)* $11_{\text{twelve}} - 2_{\text{twelve}} = e_{\text{twelve}}$. In *(b)* $10_{\text{eight}} - 4_{\text{eight}} = 4_{\text{eight}}$, and in *(c)* $10_{\text{twelve}} - 4_{\text{twelve}} = 8_{\text{twelve}}$. The explanations for the steps in *(d)* and *(e)* are left to the reader.

3. *Multiplication in other number bases.*

Base five	*Base eight*	*Base twelve*	*Base three*
(*a*)	(*b*)	(*c*)	(*d*)
3.42	3.42	3.42	2.12
×2.3	×2.3	×2.3	×1.2
2.131	1.246	. *t*06	1.201
12.34	7.04	6.84	2.12
20.021	10.306	7.646	10.021

Fig. 65

We have the same rule for locating the point in the product for each base as for base ten. The number of fractional places in the product is equal to the sum of the number of fractional places in the multiplicand and the multiplier. We line up the points in a column as was done with the examples in base ten. We can explain each step in the multiplication process. All of the steps in (*a*) will be explained, but it is left to the reader to explain the steps in *(b)*, *(c)*, and *(d)*.

Figure 65*a* is a statement that we have 2 and 3 fifths groups of 3 ones, 4 fifths, and 2 twenty-fifths. Three fifths of 2 twenty-fifths are six (11_{five}) one hundred twenty-fifths. We write the 1 in the one hundred twenty-fifths place and keep in mind the 1 twenty-fifth. Then 3 fifths of 4 fifths are 12 (22_{five}) twenty-fifths. We add the 1 twenty-fifth from the previous step. We write the 3 twenty-fifths in the twenty-fifths place and keep in mind the 2 fifths. Then 3 fifths of 3 ones are 9 fifths, and we add the 2 fifths of the previous step for a total of 11 (21_{five}) fifths. The 1 fifth is written in the fifths place and 10 fifths are exchanged for 2 ones, which are written in the ones place. Now we multiply the 3.42 by 2. Two times 2 twenty-fifths are 4 twenty-fifths, which we write in the twenty-fifths place. Two times 4 fifths are 8 fifths, or 1 one and 3 fifths. We write the 3 fifths in the fifths place and keep in mind the 1 one. Two times 3 ones are 6 ones, and the 1 one make 7 ones, or 1 five and 2 ones. These are written in the proper position. Now we add the partial products, remembering to exchange 5 smaller units for 1 larger unit.

We can ignore the points and multiply as if there were no points. Then we locate the point in the product according to the rule. We rationalize the rule for each base by writing the numbers as integers multiplied by a negative power of the base, as follows:

Base five:
$$2.3 \times 3.42 = 23 \times 10^{-1} \times 342 \times 10^{-2} = 20021 \times 10^{-3} = 20.021.$$

Base eight:
$$2.3 \times 3.42 = 23 \times 10^{-1} \times 342 \times 10^{-2} = 10306 \times 10^{-3} = 10.306.$$

Base twelve:
$$2.3 \times 3.42 = 23 \times 10^{-1} \times 342 \times 10^{-2} = 7646 \times 10^{-3} = 7.646.$$

Base three:
$$1.2 \times 2.12 = 12 \times 10^{-1} \times 212 \times 10^{-2} = 10021 \times 10^{-10} = 10.021.$$

We must remember, of course, that 10_{five} equals 5, 10_{eight} equals 8, 10_{twelve} equals 12, and that 10_{three} equals 3.

4. *Division in other number bases.*

(*a*)	(*b*)	(*c*)
Base five	*Base eight*	*Base twelve*
1.22	1.33	1.49
3)4.23	3)4.23	3)4.23
3	3	3
1.2	1.2	1.2
1.1	1.1	1.0
.13	.13	.23
.11	.11	.23
.02	.02	.00

Fig. 66

In Fig. 66*a* we separate the 4 ones into three equal groups. There is 1 one in each group and a remainder of 1 one. We exchange the 1 one for 5 fifths. Now we divide the 7 fifths into three equal groups. There are 2 fifths in each group and a remainder of 1 fifth. We exchange the 1 fifth for 5 twenty-fifths. We divide the 8 twenty-fifths into three equal groups. There are 2 twenty-fifths in each group and there is a remainder of 2 twenty-fifths.

In Fig. 66*b* we separate the 4 ones into three equal groups. There is 1 one in each group and a remainder of 1 one. We exchange the 1 one for 8 eighths. Now we divide the 10 eighths into three equal groups. There are 3 eighths in each group and a remainder of 1 eighth. We exchange the 1 eighth for 8 sixty-fourths. Now we divide the 11 sixty-fourths into three equal groups. There are 3 sixty-fourths in each group and there is a remainder of 2 sixty-fourths.

In Fig. 66*c* we separate the 4 ones into three equal groups. There is 1 one in each group and a remainder of 1 one. We exchange the 1 one for 12 twelfths. Now we divide the 14 twelfths into three equal groups. There are 4 twelfths in each group and a remainder of 2 twelfths. We exchange the 2 twelfths for 24 one hundred forty-fourths. Now we divide the 27 one hundred forty-fourths into three equal groups. There are 9 one hundred forty-fourths in each group and there is no remainder.

If the divisor is a fraction, we multiply the dividend and the divisor by a power of the base so that the divisor becomes an integer. If we multiply by the base, the effect is to move the point one place to the right. If we multiply by the base squared, we move the point two places to the right. We find the same rule that was applied in the base ten is applied to all bases. We move the points in the dividend and the divisor the same number of places, and the resulting quotient is not changed. We can use a caret to indicate the new position of the point.

```
                                 1.44
Base five:    .4)1.241 = .4 ∧ )1.2 ∧ 41
                               4
                               ---
                               3.4
                               3.1
                               ----
                                .31
                                .31
                                ---

                                 2.50
Base eight: .4)1.241 = .4 ∧ )1.2 ∧ 41
                             1 0
                             ---
                             2.4
                             2.4
                             ---
                              .01
                              .00
                              ---
                              .01

                                   3.70
Base twelve:  .4)1.241 = .4 ∧ )1.2 ∧ 41
                               1 0
                               ---
                               2.4
                               2.4
                               ---
                                .01
                                .00
                                ---
                                .01

                                   2.21
Base three:     .2)1.212 = .2 ∧ )1.2 ∧ 12
                                 1 1
                                 ---
                                  1.1
                                  1.1
                                  ---
                                   .02
                                   .02
                                   ---
```

Fig. 67

The explanation for the steps in each example is left to the reader.

8.9 PERCENT

One of the meanings of the fraction symbol discussed in Chapter 6 is the ratio, or the division comparison between two numbers. The ratio $\frac{8}{5}$ is a statement that 8 is $\frac{8}{5}$ as great as 5. The ratio $\frac{5}{8}$ is a statement that 5 is $\frac{5}{8}$ as great as 8. A ratio has many names, that is, it can be expressed in different ways. Thus when we write $\frac{3}{4} = \frac{6}{8} = \frac{15}{20} = \frac{27}{36}$, we are showing that when we compare 6 with 8, 15 with 20, or 27 with 36, we get the same ratio as when we compare 3 with 4. In other words, 6 is $\frac{3}{4}$ as great as 8, 15 is $\frac{3}{4}$ as great as 20, and 27 is $\frac{3}{4}$ as great as 36. There are, of course, other ratios that are equal to $\frac{3}{4}$. One such ratio is $\frac{75}{100}$. A ratio that is expressed as hundredths has a special name. It is called percent and its symbol is %. We can use the percent sign whenever a number is expressed as hundredths. Thus $0.32 = 32\%$, $0.04 = 4\%$, $0.348 = 34.8\%$, $0.063 = 6.3\%$, $0.004 = 0.4\%$.

Since a percent is a ratio, it is a comparison between two numbers. We call the first number the percentage, and the number we compare it with is the base. The result of the comparison is percent, if it is expressed as hundredths. In $\frac{19}{20} = 0.95$ (95%), 19 is the percentage, 20 is the base, and 95 is the percent. We can generalize all ratios as $\frac{p}{b} = r$, and all percents as $\frac{p}{b} = \frac{r}{100}$.

The r's in the two equations are not the same. An example of $\frac{p}{b} = r$ is $\frac{15}{20} = \frac{3}{4}$, in which $p = 15$, $b = 20$, and $r = \frac{3}{4}$. An example of $\frac{p}{b} = \frac{r}{100}$ is $\frac{15}{20} = \frac{75}{100}$ in which $p = 15$, $b = 20$, and $r = 75$, or $\frac{r}{100} = 75\%$.

Since there are three variables in the ratio (p, b, and r), there are three questions related to percent, sometimes called the three cases of percent.

EXAMPLE 1. What is 36% of 198?

This is a statement that $\frac{p}{198} = 0.36$. Since the quotient tells us how many groups of the divisor are contained in the dividend, we can write the relationship as $p = 0.36 \times 198$. We derive the answer $p = 71.28$.

EXAMPLE 2. 36 is what percent of 198?

This is a statement that $\frac{36}{198} = r$. If we divide 36 by 198, we derive the quotient 0.182 or 18.2%.

EXAMPLE 3. 36 is 9% of what number?

This is a statement that $\frac{36}{b} = 0.09$. We may also express this relationship as $0.09b = 36$. We divide both sides of the equation by 0.09 and derive the answer $b = 400$.

In all three examples the percent can be expressed as a common fraction.

8.10 REPEATING DECIMALS

Since we have two ways of referring to the fraction concept, the common fraction and the decimal fraction, we may want to change from one form to the other. A decimal fraction can always be expressed as a common fraction. Thus 0.4 can be written as $\frac{4}{10}$, 0.32 as $\frac{32}{100}$, 0.387 as $\frac{387}{1000}$, etc. A mixed decimal number can also be expressed as a common fraction. Thus, 2.3 can be written as $\frac{23}{10}$, 3.74 as $\frac{374}{100}$, 5.639 as $\frac{5639}{1000}$, etc.

We can write a common fraction as a decimal fraction if the denominator has the factors 2 or 5 or both repeated any number of times. Thus $\frac{3}{5}$ can be written as 0.6, $\frac{3}{4}$ as 0.75, $\frac{7}{8}$ as 0.875, $\frac{7}{20}$ as 0.35, $\frac{9}{40}$ as 0.225 $\frac{37}{125}$ as 0.296. Such decimals are called terminating decimals.

If we want to write a common fraction whose denominator contains factors other than 2 or 5, we think of the fraction as an indicated division. In changing the fraction $\frac{3}{7}$ to a decimal fraction we divide 3 by 7. The result is not a terminating decimal as shown in the following:

```
     .428571428571
  7)3.00000000000000
     2 8
       20
       14
        60
        56
         40
         35
          50
          49
           10
            7
           30
           28
            20
            14
             60
             56
              40
              35
               50
               49
                10
                 7
                 3
```

We notice that the quotient has a repeating cycle of digits, namely, 428571. The division is not complete for there is a remainder no matter where we stop. Continuing the division would result in another cycle of the digits 428571. Such numbers are called repeating decimals. Instead of repeating the digits, we may indicate the cycle by placing dots over the first and last digits of the cycle. We write $\frac{3}{7} = 0.\dot{4}2857\dot{1}$, $\frac{2}{3} = 0.\dot{6}\dot{6}$, $\frac{1}{15} = 0.0\dot{6}\dot{6}$.

All rational numbers when converted to decimals are either terminating decimals or nonterminating repeating decimals. Although it will not be shown in this book, it can be shown that all decimals that are repeating decimals can be expressed as fractions, or rational numbers. A nonterminating decimal that is not a repeating decimal is not a rational number. Such numbers are called irrational numbers and they will be discussed in Chapter 10.

8.11 TEACHING DECIMALS TO CHILDREN

In order to teach children the extension of the decimal place value system to include fractions, children should first be given the opportunity to experience decimal fractions such as tenths, hundredths, and thousandths. They should learn that a base unit (ones) can be divided into 10 equal parts so that they can experience 0.1 or $\frac{1}{10}$. They should experience $\frac{1}{10}$ of $\frac{1}{10}$, and $\frac{1}{10}$ of $\frac{1}{100}$.

One way of giving children such experiences is to use square paper, or graph paper, that has 10 squares on a side. The large square is the base unit. Children can cut the large square into 10 equal strips. Each strip is $\frac{1}{10}$ of the base unit. Each strip can then be cut into 10 small squares. Each small square is $\frac{1}{10}$ of a strip, and it is also $\frac{1}{100}$ of the large square, the base unit. Then the children can cut each small square into 10 equal rectangles. One rectangle is $\frac{1}{10}$ of a small square, it is $\frac{1}{100}$ of a strip, and it is $\frac{1}{1000}$ of the large square. The children can use the strips, small squares, and rectangles to experience 0.1, 0.2, 0.3, up to 0.9. They see that if they have 10 tenths, they have a base unit. They learn that 0.5 is equal to one-half. They learn the meaning of 0.01, 0.02, 0.03 up to 0.09. They see that when they have 10 hundredths, they can exchange it for 0.1. They learn that 0.47 means 4 strips and 7 small squares, or 0.4 and 0.07.

Another method of showing the relationship of tenths, hundredths, and thousandths is to have the children build a large cube that is 10 cubes by 10 cubes by 10 cubes. It requires, of course, 1000 cubes. After this large cube is set up, children can remove sections from the cube, the base unit. Since there are 10 sections, each section is $\frac{1}{10}$ of the cube. Each section is made up of 10 columns. Each column is $\frac{1}{10}$ of a section, and $\frac{1}{100}$ of the large cube. Each column contains 10 small cubes. One cube is $\frac{1}{10}$ of a column, $\frac{1}{100}$ of a section, and $\frac{1}{1000}$ of the large cube. The children can use this cube to develop an understanding of the exchange rate for the different units, that is, the decimal concept.

These concrete aids will help children to understand the extension of the decimal place-value system to include fractions as well as integers. In the actual process of addition and subtraction of mixed decimals some children will have no difficulty with the process of exchange. The understanding developed with integers will be applied to fractional units. Some children, however, will not find this extension easy to follow. Squares of colored paper can be used with fractional units in the same manner as with integers. Thus 3.87 can be represented by 3 yellow squares, 8 blue squares, and 7 red squares; and 5.46 can be represented by 5 yellow, 4 blue, and 6 red squares. The child sees the need to exchange 10 red squares for 1 blue square, or 10 blue squares for 1 yellow square. The children who operate on the abstract level have no difficulty with the extension of the place-value system. Concrete aids should be available to those children who need them.

8.12 SUMMARY

The concept of a decimal place-value system of notation is complete when fractional units are included with integral units. The idea of exchanging 10 smaller units for 1 larger unit is applied to all decimal units. Thus 10 thousandths equal 1 hundredth, 10 hundredths equal 1 tenth, 10 tenths equal 1 one, 10 ones equal 1 ten, etc.

The ones place is the center of the notation system. This makes the system symmetrical. Thus the thousands place is three places to the left of the ones place and the thousandths place is three places to the right of the ones place, the hundreds place is two places to the left of the ones place and the hundredths place is two places to the right of the ones place, the tens place is one place to the left of the ones place and the tenths place is one place to the right of the ones place. The decimal point is the symbol that indicates the ones place. It is written to the right of the ones place. There are other ways that can be used to indicate the ones place. In England the decimal point is raised a little as in 3·147.

The extension of the decimal place-value system to include decimal fractions can be used in a similar manner with other base systems. In the quinal system 3.24 represents 3 ones, 2 fifths, and 4 twenty-fifths. In the octal system 3.24 represents 3 ones, 2 eighths, and 4 sixty-fourths. In the tertial system 2.2112 represents 2 ones, 2 thirds, 1 ninth, 1 twenty-seventh, and 2 eighty-firsts. In the binal system 1.010111 represents 1 one, no halves, 1 fourth, no eighths, 1 sixteenth, 1 thirty-second, and 1 sixty-fourth. As with the decimal system, the quinal point, the octal point, the duodecimal point, the tertial point, and the binal point is used to indicate the ones place.

The concepts of division, multiplication, subtraction, and addition that were developed with the integral units are applied to fractional units. In addition and subtraction like units are added or subtracted, and when necessary the concept of exchange is applied. In multiplication the rule for locating the decimal point is developed by using the understanding of the multiplication of fractions. In division, the concept of separation into groups of equal size is applied, but it becomes necessary to multiply dividend and divisor by a power of 10 in order to make the divisor a whole number.

At all times the teacher should see that children learn that the basic concepts developed with integers are applied to fractional units. The concept of percent is an extension of the concept of ratio, with the emphasis placed on the ratio expressed as hundredths.

EXERCISES

1. Discuss the role of the decimal point in the decimal numeration system.
2. Perform the indicated operations:

(*a*)	(*b*)	(*c*)	(*d*)
$\begin{array}{r} 3.47 \\ 5.89 \\ +6.73 \\ \hline \end{array}$	$\begin{array}{r} 8.76 \\ -2.98 \\ \hline \end{array}$	$\begin{array}{r} 3.78 \\ \times 2.96 \\ \hline \end{array}$	$.73\overline{)5.964}$

3. Write the following fractions as decimals:

(*a*)	(*b*)	(*c*)	(*d*)	(*e*)	(*f*)
$\frac{9}{16}$	$\frac{73}{80}$	$\frac{37}{160}$	$\frac{5}{32}$	$\frac{113}{200}$	$\frac{189}{200}$

4. Write the following as common fractions:

(*a*) .63 (*b*) .309 (*c*) .743 (*d*) .0009 (*e*) .4003

5. Express each of the following in power notation:

(*a*)	(*b*)	(*c*)	(*d*)
38.649	806.325	4.2007	.00008

6. Express each of the following as if the numbers were made up of hundredths:

(a)	(b)	(c)	(d)	(e)	(f)
.347	.079	2.34	4.625	2	31.2

7. What is the effect when the decimal point is moved two places to the right?
8. What is the effect of moving the decimal point three places to the left?
9. Discuss the merit or lack of merit in the proposal to teach children decimals before common fractions.
11. If a team wins 39 games out of 56 games played, what percent of the games were won?
12. Perform the indicated operations:

(a)	(b)	(c)	(d)	(e)
Base five	Base eight	Base twelve	Base three	Base five
3.24	6.32	4.97	2.12	
1.41	−2.67	5.4*e*	×2.02	.3)1.423
+2.31		+9.*t*4		

13. Find the following:

   (*a*) 37.6% of 8974
   (*a*) 48.7% of 769
   (*c*) What number is .3% of 58?
   (*d*) 87 is 23% of what number?
   (*e*) 71 is what percent of 275?

14. Express the following as decimals:

   (*a*) 3.42_{five}
   (*b*) 5.6_{twelve}
   (*c*) 1.0101_{two}
   (*d*) 7.65_{eight}

15. What explanations are necessary to teach multiplication and division of mixed decimals?

SUGGESTED SUPPLEMENTARY READING

1. Banks, J. Houston, *Learning and Teaching Arithmetic*. Boston: Allyn and Bacon, 1959. Chap. 11.
2. Binter, Alfred R., "Two Ways of Teaching Per Cent," *The Elementary School Journal*, February 1963. pp. 261–265.
3. Buckingham, Burdette R., *Elementary Arithmetic, Its Meaning and Practice*. Boston: Ginn and Company, 1953. Chaps. 10 and 11.
4. Johnson, J. T., "Decimal versus Common Fractions," *The Arithmetic Teacher*, November 1956. pp. 201–203.

5. Jones, Emily, "Historical Conflict—Decimal versus Vulgar Fractions," *The Arithmetic Teacher,* April 1960. pp. 184–188.
6. Kessler, Rolla V., "The Equation Method of Teaching Percentage," *The Arithmetic Teacher,* February 1960. pp. 90–92.
7. Kinney, Lucien B., "Teaching Percentage for Understanding and Use," *The Mathematics Teacher,* January 1958. pp. 38–41.
8. Larsen, Harold D., and H. Glenn Ludlow, *Arithmetic for Colleges.* New York: The Macmillan Company, 1963. Chaps. 8 and 9.
9. Marks, John L., C. Richard Purdy, and Lucien B. Kinney, *Teaching Arithmetic for Understanding.* New York: McGraw-Hill Book Company, 1958. Chaps. 9 and 10.
10. McSwain, E. T., and Ralph J. Cooke, *Understanding and Teaching Arithmetic in the Elementary School.* New York: Henry Holt and Company, 1958. Chaps. 8 and 9.
11. Mueller, Francis J., "The Neglected Role of the Decimal Point," *The Arithmetic Teacher,* March 1958. pp. 87–88.
12. ———, *Arithmetic, Its Structure and Concepts.* Englewood Cliffs, N.J.: Prentice-Hall, 1956. pp. 188–213 and 214–229.
13. Rappaport, David, "Percentage—Noun or Adjective?" *The Arithmetic Teacher,* January 1961. pp. 25–26.
14. Spencer, Peter L., "Do They See the Point?" *The Arithmetic Teacher,* November 1958. pp. 271–272.
15. Spitzer, Herbert F., *The Teaching of Arithmetic.* Boston: Houghton Mifflin Company, 1954. Chap. 8.
16. Wendt, Arnold, "Per Cent without Cases," *The Arithmetic Teacher,* October 1959. pp. 209–214.

Chapter 9 Measurement

9.1 INTRODUCTION

The changing elementary mathematics curriculum described in Chapter 1 reflects the educational philosophy and purpose of teaching mathematics that has developed in recent years. For many years the main purpose of teaching arithmetic was to develop computational skills and to apply these skills to the solution of everyday practical problems. The "new" mathematics reflects a shift in emphasis to teaching basic concepts, the rationale of mathematics, the structure of mathematics. Whereas mathematics, especially arithmetic, was considered to be a tool subject, today's mathematics, including arithmetic, is developed as a logical system.

These new attitudes raise serious questions about the place of measurement in the elementary mathematics curriculum. Measurement has nothing to do with mathematics as a logical system. The basic postulates and structure of arithmetic deal with abstract ideas and are not related in any way to measurement. Why, then, should the curriculum provide time for teaching measurement? Will the topic of measurement detract from the interest in principles? Will the work on measurement hinder the learning of the logical structure of mathematics?

These interesting questions, raised by a number of people, require reflection and reconsideration of the place of mathematics in the education of children. One can dismiss these questions with the generalization that a topic like measurement should be taught because all schools include it in the curriculum. A topic that is so widely considered to be important needs no justification. But this topic can be justified for much better reasons.

The need to develop a new mathematics curriculum for the elementary school does not mean that the old curriculum should be completely discarded. There was an overemphasis in the past on mere computational skills, which resulted in the ability to perform operations, but often without understanding. This does not mean that computational skills are not important. The emphasis on meanings should result in better skills rather than a lack of skills. Without the ability to perform computations, a student will find it difficult to advance in his study of mathematics. Understanding and skill are both necessary.

The emphasis on teaching mathematics as a logical and structured system is necessary for developing mathematicians. There is a danger, however, in overemphasis on abstract logic for all children in the elementary school. Only a very small percent of such children will become mathematicians or scientists. All children need to learn the tools of mathematics that relate to their everyday life. The understanding of the structure of mathematics will help children to understand better the application of mathematics to the technological world in which they live. It should not be an either-or situation, either logical structure or no mathematics. There needs to be a balance between logic and application, between understanding and skill, between the abstract and the concrete.

Measurement is an important part in everyone's life. The child has already had many experiences with measurement before he enters school. When his parents buy him a pair of shoes they are a certain size. Milk is poured out of a quart or half-gallon container. He hears about a pint of ice cream. He learns that he has grown so many inches or that he has gained so many pounds. He rides a sixteen-inch or a twenty-inch bicycle. On a vacation trip the family has driven so many miles. He learns that something is too long or too short. If he has not experienced measurement directly, he hears the people around him mention different kinds of measurements such as miles per gallon or pounds per square inch. Most people are involved with some form of measurement throughout their lives.

Although measurement is concerned with the concrete, man's concern with measurement has often led to the development of mathematics itself. His interest in measurement led to the development of fractions, which resulted in the development of rational numbers. Newton developed the calculus when he tried to calculate the gravitational pull of the earth upon a physical body. Applied mathematics has often led to the development of abstract mathematics.

9.2 THE NEED FOR A UNIT

The term measurement implies that there is something to be measured, that something is related to some unit. To measure is to find the number of units that are contained in the thing that is measured. The measure, or the measurement, is a number that expresses the ratio between the thing measured and the unit. The word "measure" is used as both verb and noun. As a verb it describes the process of finding the number of units contained in something. As a noun it is the number of such units. We measure the length of a room by laying out the units in the length, and we say that 30 units is the measure of the length. In performing the process and in finding the result of the process, we must understand the nature of the unit that is used.

Counting. Counting is the simplest form of measurement. We count the number of children in a room, the number of books on a shelf, the number of cows in a herd, or the number of chickens in a flock. In counting, each object is a unit and the units may have different characteristics. In counting the children in a room, each child is counted as one. Some children are heavier than others, some are taller, some are slower than others. These differences are ignored. Each child, regardless of his weight, height, or speed, is counted as one child. The books on a shelf differ in size, the number of pages, or the color, but each book is counted as one book. In the same manner the farmer counts each cow as one cow and each chicken as one chicken, and he disregards their differences. In counting, the units may or may not be alike.

Linear Measurement. Measurement, other than counting, requires that the same unit be used. This unit is repeated until the object has been measured. If I want to measure the length of a room, I may use a given pencil as my unit. I lay the pencil on the floor at one end of the room and move it continually end to end until I have reached the other side of the room. I may find that the room is 73 pencils long. I may, on the other hand, use a book as my unit and find that the room is 52 books long. Any object may be used as a unit of measurement, but this is not generally practical. It is one thing to find the ratio between a given length and some unit, but quite another thing to communicate the result to other people. Man developed well known units so that everyone using the same language would understand the result. Thus we have units of length such as inch, foot, mile, centimeter, meter, and kilometer. Many units, once popular, have been discarded. We no longer use ells or cubits. We use the name of the unit when announcing the result so that everyone will know what particular unit was used.

Some units have become standard units and are determined by law.

The Congress of the United States has legally defined what a yard is, and it has, of course, prescribed the legal requirements for other units.

Area Measurement. In finding the area of something it is necessary to have an area unit. Generally, area units are squares. We have square inches, square feet, square miles, square centimeters, and square meters. But not all units are squares. The farmer measures his fields in acres, and if he has a very large farm he may measure his fields in sections. An acre was originally a rectangular tract of land 40 rods by 4 rods. Fields were often laid out so that they were 40 rods long and every 4 rods of width represented 1 acre. Fields may no longer be 40 rods long. In this case an acre is 160 square rods. A section is one square mile or a tract of land that contains 640 acres.

A unit for area measurement can also be a circle. In electricity the cross section of a wire is used to determine the resistance of the wire. The circular mil is the area unit for the cross section of the wire. A circular mil is a circle whose diameter is 1 mil, or one thousandth of an inch.

Volume Measurement. The unit for volume is generally a cube. We have cubic inch, cubic foot, cubic centimeter, and cubic meters. Not all volume units are cubes. We are familiar with pints, quarts, and gallons.

Other Measurements. The list of different kinds of measurements is a lengthy one. We measure weight, time, speed, and heat. These are common measures. There are many units used in science that have become somewhat familiar to children who listen to science programs on television. Ergs, foot-pounds, calories, watts, dynes, horsepower, and light years are just a few of the units used.

9.3 UNDERSTANDING THE UNIT

With so many different things to be measured, it is important that measurement should be meaningful to children. The child should become familiar with the kinds of units before he is asked to compute with them. Too often in the past, children were given a list of units and relations between the units. These were tables of measures. Then children were asked to answer questions raised in various exercises. They were asked to convert feet to inches, rods to yards or feet, pecks to bushels, feet to centimeters, and meters to inches. These have too often been meaningless exercises. Dry measure, liquid measure, troy weight, and various units used in commercial enterprises may be too far removed from the child's experience. Pecks, bushels, carats, barrels, long tons, and short tons may be necessary units, but children need experiences with units in order to apply them intelligently. Many people have learned to do such exercises mechanically and without understanding. Units of measurement should be meaningful.

9.4 APPROXIMATE MEASUREMENT

Since measurement is the application of a unit to the object that is measured, the question arises as to whether or not measurement can be exact. If one applies the measurement unit, he finds that some part of the object is left over. Since there is not enough of a remainder, a smaller unit has to be used. This led to the development of fractions. The fractional unit is just as much a measurement unit as the original unit. In measuring the length of a room one may apply the foot unit of measure 8 times and find part of a foot remaining. Then one uses the inch as the measurement unit and finds that there are 5 inches. But will this complete the measure? It is then possible to apply a fraction of an inch as a unit and then a fraction of that fraction, etc. We measure to the nearest foot, the nearest inch, or the nearest fraction of an inch. Measurement is, therefore, approximate. Counting is the only exact measurement because each object is considered as one unit. A count of 8 bottles is an exact measurement, but 8 quarts represents an approximate measure because the unit 1 quart is only approximate. All measurements are numbers that represent an approximate number of units or fractional units.

9.5 PRECISION AND ACCURACY

Since all measurements are approximate, we are interested in the degree of approximation. Standards for measurement have to be established. To understand these standards we use three terms that must be clearly defined. These are error, precision, and accuracy.

Error. If we want to measure the length of something we use a unit of measurement. Let us say that our unit is a foot. This means that we have a stick or a rod that is 1 foot long. It has no divisions on it. Now let us say that this 1-foot rod was used 8 times in this particular measurement and that there was just a little bit remaining. We then say that the object is 8 feet long. But suppose that the object is just short of 8 feet. We would still say that the object measures 8 feet. The measurement 8 feet, therefore, is only approximately 8 feet. Since our foot rod has no divisions on it, we cannot use any fractional unit. By general agreement we allow a margin of one-half a unit. This means that a measurement of 8 feet represents a true measure that is greater than $7\frac{1}{2}$ feet and less than $8\frac{1}{2}$ feet. This margin of plus or minus one-half of a unit is called the margin of error, or just error. The term error does not mean mistake. It is not the result of someone's counting incorrectly or letting the measuring instrument slip, but error is a part of the nature of measurement.

Now suppose that our foot ruler is divided into twelve equal parts, namely, into inches. We may now find that the object we are measuring is 8 feet and 4 inches long. The 4 inches is, of course, not exact. Our true measurement is between 8 feet $3\frac{1}{2}$ inches and 8 feet $4\frac{1}{2}$ inches. Our error is now plus or minus one-half inch.

Now let us suppose that the inches on our ruler were each divided into $\frac{1}{2}$ inches. Our new measurement may be 8 feet 4 inches. The true measurement now lies between 8 feet $3\frac{3}{4}$ inches and 8 feet $4\frac{1}{4}$ inches. Now the error is plus or minus $\frac{1}{4}$ inch or $\frac{1}{2}$ of $\frac{1}{2}$ inch.

If the inches on our measuring stick were divided into tenths, the new measure may be 8 feet 3.8 inches. The true measure lies between 8 feet 3.75 inches and 8 feet 3.85 inches. The error is now plus or minus 0.05 inch, one-half of 0.1 inch.

If the inch is divided into hundredths, the error is plus or minus 0.005 or one-half of 0.01. A measurement of 3.78 inches represents a true measure that is between 3.775 inches and 3.785 inches.

The error, or margin of error, is also called the absolute error. It is always one-half of the smallest unit of measurement.

Precision. Precision refers to the smallest unit of measure. To say that a measurement is 3.748 units is to say that the object contains 3 base units, 7 tenths of a unit, 4 hundredths of a unit, and 8 thousandths of a unit. The smallest measurement unit is 0.001. The absolute error is 0.0005. The smaller the measurement unit the more precise the measurement. Thus 3.7864 is a more precise measurement than 3.786.

Accuracy. Accuracy is a relative error. It is a ratio of the absolute error to the measurement. The relative error is found by dividing 0.005 by 3.48. The relative error is 0.0015. If a measurement is 0.48, the absolute error is 0.005 and the relative error is 0.0105. If the measurement is 0.03, the absolute error is 0.005 and the relative error is 0.166.

In all three of the above measurements the absolute error is the same, namely, 0.005. Therefore, all three measurements have the same precision. But these three measurements have different relative errors. The first measurement, 3.48, is the most accurate because it has the smallest relative error. Precision is determined by the magnitude of the unit of measurement, accuracy is determined by the ratio of the magnitude of the error to the magnitude of the measurement.

Examine the following three measurements: 35 inches, 3.5 inches, and 0.35 inch. The corresponding absolute errors are: 0.5, 0.05, and 0.005. The relative errors are the same for all three measurements. All three measurements have the same accuracy, but the third measurement is the most precise.

Precision is not improved by calculation; it is improved by using more refined measuring instruments. Accuracy is not improved by calculation; it is determined by the measurement and the instrument used in the measurement.

One must be careful to make a distinction between absolute, or abstract, numbers and measurement numbers. The fraction, or rational number, $\frac{10}{16}$ is equivalent to $\frac{5}{8}$. We thus say that the fraction $\frac{10}{16}$ is reduced to $\frac{5}{8}$. This cannot be done with measurement numbers. The measurement $\frac{10}{16}$ inch has an error of $\frac{1}{32}$ inch. The measurement $\frac{5}{8}$ inch has an error of $\frac{1}{16}$ inch. The relative error of the first measurement is $\frac{1}{32} \div \frac{10}{16}$ or $\frac{1}{20}$. The second measurement has a relative error of $\frac{1}{16} \div \frac{5}{8}$ or $\frac{1}{10}$. The first measurement has a greater accuracy than the second measurement. The insistence of many teachers that all fractions must be reduced to the lowest terms makes measurement answers less accurate.

9.6 INDIRECT MEASUREMENT

Some measurements are found directly. We can find the length of a room by counting the number of linear units that are contained in the length. We can weigh an object by putting it on a scale and read the weight, or we can use a balance and count the number of unit weights that balance the object. We can find the area of a rectangle by counting the number of squares that it contains. We can find the capacity of a container by filling it with some liquid and then pour the liquid into unit containers and then count the number of units.

Direct measurement is not always possible. We cannot measure directly the distance of the moon from the earth. It was not possible to measure the heights of the pyramids in Egypt by direct measurement. It would be rather difficult to measure the number of square units in a circular object.

Indirect measurement is the process of deriving the number of measurement units through calculation. This requires the use of formulas such as $A=\pi r^2$, $c=2\pi r$, $v=\frac{1}{3}\pi r^2 h$, or by the use of algebraic or geometric techniques Every branch of science has its own formulas. Once these formulas are known, they can be applied to the solution of specific problems. Since such formulas are numerous, one has to select a few that are within, or can become a part of, the experiences of children.

Proportions. A common method of indirect measurement is the use of proportions. When two ratios are equal they form a proportion. Since $\frac{3}{5}=\frac{6}{10}$, the numbers 3, 5, 6, and 10 are in proportion. We have found in Chapter 7 that two ratios are equal if the product of the means equals the product of the extremes. In our treatment of percent we used the proportion $\frac{p}{b}=\frac{r}{100}$. If geometric figures are similar their corresponding sides are proportional. This is why there is so much interest in similar polygons in plane geometry.

In ancient times proportions were used to calculate the heights of the pyramids. The early geometers found that the length of a pyramid's shadow and the length of any stick's shadow taken at the same time had the same ratio as the height of the pyramid and the height of the stick. They established the following proportion:

$$\frac{\text{The height of the pyramid}}{\text{The length of the shadow}}=\frac{\text{the height of the stick}}{\text{the length of the shadow}}$$

or $\frac{H}{L}=\frac{h}{l}$, where H is the height of the pyramid, L is the length of the pyramid's shadow, h is the height of the stick, and l is the length of the stick's shadow. Since L, h, and l are measurable, H can be calculated.

Similar triangles are used by Boy Scouts to calculate the height of a tree, a pole, or any building. Similar triangles are studied in geometry in a formal manner. Children in the elementary school can study about similar triangles intuitively.

Scale Drawings. Maps and architectural plans are drawn to scale. This is another way of saying that the corresponding parts of the plan and the real object are in proportion. The scale is the ratio. A map is a scale drawing. If 1 inch on a map represents 100 miles, then $2\frac{1}{2}$ inches on the map represent 250 miles.

9.7 OPERATIONS WITH MEASUREMENT NUMBERS

Since all measurements are approximations, how do we evaluate sums, differences, products, and quotients of measurement numbers? We are interested in the errors of such operations. We operate with numbers that report measurements.

Addition. Suppose we were to add several numbers representing measurements such as 3.4 inches, 5.83 inches, 8.7 inches and 7.28 inches. The sum of the absolute numbers is 25.21 inches. One may conclude that the absolute error is 0.005 or one-half of the smallest unit, namely, hundredths. This, however, is not correct. We set up the numbers for addition with the margin of error, as in Fig. 68.

(a)	(b)	(c)
3.4	3.35	3.45
5.83	5.825	5.835
8.7	8.65	8.75
7.28	7.275	7.285
25.21	25.100	25.320

Fig. 68

In Fig. 68*a* we have the four measurements. It is understood that 3.4 represents the true measure that lies between 3.35 and 3.45. The measurements minus the errors are shown in Fig. 68*b*, and the measurements plus the errors are shown in Fig. 68*c*. The sum of the true measures lies between 25.100 and 25.320. If we add the errors of the four measurements (.05, .005, .05, .005) we find their sum is 0.110. Since 25.100 is equal to 25.21 minus 0.110 and 25.320 is equal to 25.21 plus 0.110, we conclude that 0.110 is the error of the sum. We thus see that the error of the sum equals the sum of the errors. The more measurements we add the greater the absolute error of their sum.

Subtraction. Suppose we were to subtract 2.3 inches from 8.74 inches. The difference of the absolute numbers is 6.44 inches. What is the error of this difference? In Fig. 69 we show the difference of the two original measurements, and also the differences of all of the possible subtractions for the true measures.

(a)		(c)		(e)
8.74	8.745	8.735	8.745	8.735
−2.3	−2.35	−2.25	−2.25	−2.35
6.44	6.395	6.485	6.495	6.385

Fig. 69

We find that the largest difference is 6.495, and that the smallest difference is 6.385. Since error is the result of the nature of measurement and not the result of human failing, we must consider the largest error rather than the smallest. For example 6.385 is equal to 6.44 minus 0.055, and 6.395 is equal to 6.44 plus 0.055. The sum of the errors of the two measurements (.005 and .05) is 0.055. We note that the error of the difference is equal to the sum of the errors, the same as for addition.

Multiplication. Suppose we wanted to find the area of a rectangle with width of 2.4 inches and a length of 8.34 inches. The area, found by multiplying the two numbers, is 20.016 square inches. What is the error of this product? Again we examine the possibility for the largest and the smallest products by taking the upper and lower limits of the measurements. The work is shown in Fig. 70.

(*a*)	(*b*)	(*c*)
8.34	8.345	8.335
2.4	2.45	2.35
3 336	41725	41675
16 68	3 3380	2 5005
20.016	16 690	16 670
	20.44525	19.58725

Fig. 70

Since the smallest measurement unit in the original measures is hundredths we round off the answers to hundredths. The three products shown in Fig. 70 are 20.02, 20.45, and 19.59. The margin of error for the product is 0.43. We add 0.43 to 20.02 to derive 20.45, and we subtract 0.43 from 20.02 to derive 19.49. How can we derive the error 0.43 without doing the above multiplication? Let us consider why there is an error in the first place. One of the reasons for the error is that the measure 2.4 represents a true measure that is either greater or smaller than 2.4 by 0.05. Therefore, the error of the product should be 0.05×8.34, but 8.34 represents a true measure that is either greater or smaller than 8.34 by 0.005. Therefore, another error is 0.005×2.4, the error of the product is the sum of these two errors. Upon multiplying the above, we find that the two errors are 0.417 and 0.012, and that the sum is 0.429, which is rounded off to 0.43. We can generalize this as follows:

$$\text{If } P = A \times B, \text{ then } p = a \times B + b \times A$$

In this formula A is one measurement, B the other measurement, P their product, a the error of A, b the error of B, and p the error of the product P. There is a third error, 0.05×0.005, but this was not considered in the total error of the product because this factor is negligible.

An understanding of the error of the product of measurement numbers should eliminate some faulty procedures that are often carried out in schools. If we want to find the circumference of a circle we use the formula $c = \pi d$. What value for π should we use? Is it 3 , 3.14, 3.1416, or 3.1459? We apply the principle that accuracy is determined by the measurement instrument and not by calculation. If the diameter of the circle is measured as 35 units, then π is taken as 3 . If the diameter is measured as 3.43 units, then π is taken as 3.14. If the diameter is measured as 3.4378 units, then π is taken as 3.1416.

Division. To find the rule for determining the error of a quotient, we use the rule for the error of a product. If $Q = \frac{A}{B}$, then $Q \times B = A$. Then $q \times B + b \times Q = a$. From this we can develop the formula $q = \dfrac{a + b \times Q}{B}$. It is understood that a plus or minus precedes the right side of the equation.

9.8 TABLES OF MEASURES

Most textbooks contain tables of various measures and their relationships. There are tables of lengths, weights, capacities, the metric system of measures, etc. There are numerous exercises in which children are asked to convert from one unit to another. It is not our concern in this book to take up these tables. Our concern is with the nature of measurement rather than the actual computations.

9.9 TEACHING MEASUREMENT TO CHILDREN

If children are to learn to solve practical problems involving measurement, they should first have experience with measurement. Children should measure the lengths and widths of the desks, windows, doors, and the floor of the classroom. They should use foot rulers, yard sticks and meter sticks. They should become acauainted with pints, quarts, and gallons by actually pouring water or sand from one container to another. They should experience 1-pound, 2-pound, 5-pound, $\frac{1}{2}$-pound weights, etc.

Children should understand the nature of a unit and the need for regulation or standard units. They may measure the length or width of a room by using their own shoes as units. They repeat the measurement by using different books as units, or sticks of various lengths. They will learn that, although any object may be used as a measuring unit, standard units are better if they want to communicate their results to others.

If children have direct experience with various measurement units, measurement calculations will become meaningful to them. It must be clear, however, that some units of measurement cannot be experienced. It is not possible to experience time. We may notice that the hands of a clock move, but we do not actually experience the passage of time. The thermometer will register the temperature of the room or of water that is being heated, but one does not experience heat as a quantity. Children will learn about the use of many meters that measure quantities, but they must first learn about the nature of the measurement.

Operations with Units. Units are often treated as numbers. This practice may be defended when the nature of the unit is completely understood. The scientist works with different kinds of units and treats them as numbers. He divides and multiplies units in the same way that he divides and multiplies numbers. In the formula $d = rt$, if t is 5 hours and r is 45 miles/hour, then $d = 45\ \frac{\text{miles}}{\text{hour}} \times 5$ hours or $d = 225$ miles. The scientist cancels the hours in the same way that he cancels numbers. This becomes a mechanical process that is too often accompanied by a complete lack of understanding. Some advocate this procedure in finding areas and volumes. This is contrary to the meaning of the mathematical process.

How do we find the area of a rectangle? Do we multiply the length by the width? If the length is 5 units and the width is 3 units, is the area equal to 5 units times 3 units with the result of 15 square units because unit times unit equals square unit just as 5×5 equals 5 squared or 5^2?

Let us examine the rectangle in Fig. 71 that is 5 units long and 3 units wide. We can find the number of area units (squares) by counting them. We find that there are 15 squares in the rectangle. This procedure is not feasible for large rectangles. We notice that the number of square units in one column is 3 and that there are 5 columns or 5×3 square units.

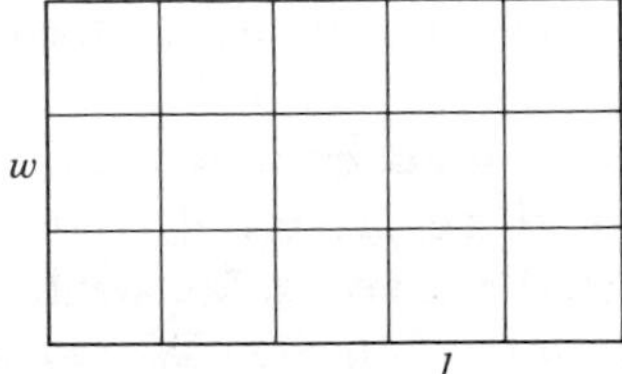

Fig. 71

We thus derive the formula $A = l \times w$. A, l, and w are numbers. A represents the number of area units, l represents the number of linear units in the length, and w represents the number of linear units in the width. But w also represents the number of square units in a column and l represents the number of columns. There is a one-to-one correspondence between the number of square units in one column and the number of linear units in the width of the rectangle. There is also a one-to-one correspondence between the number of columns and the number of linear units in the length of the rectangle. Thus:

$$A = l \times w \text{ square units, or}$$
$$A = 5 \times 3 \text{ square units}$$

We may also express the area as:

$$A = w \times l \text{ square units, or}$$
$$A = 3 \times 5 \text{ square units}$$

In the second formula, l represents the number of square units in one row and w represents the number of rows. Again we have a one-to-one correspondence between the number of square units in one row and the number of linear units in the length, and between the number of rows and the number of linear units in the width. The concept of

$$A = l \times w, \text{ as}$$
$$A = \text{length} \times \text{width, or}$$
$$A = 5 \text{ units} \times 3 \text{ units, or}$$
$$A = 15 \text{ square units}$$

is contrary to the meaning of multiplication.

How do we find the volume of a rectangular box? We really want to know the number of volume units that are contained in the box. Generally the volume units are cubes. Let us examine the box in Fig. 72.

We notice that there are 4 cubes in one column. Since there are 3 columns in one section, there are 3×4 cubic units in one section. Since there are 6 sections, we have $6 \times 3 \times 4$ cubic units. In this manner we develop the formula $V = l \times w \times h$. We have a one-to-one correspondence between the number of cubic units in one column and the number of linear units in the height, a one-to-one correspondence between the number of columns in one section and the number of linear units in the width, and there is a one-to-one correspondence between the number of sections and the number of linear units in the length.

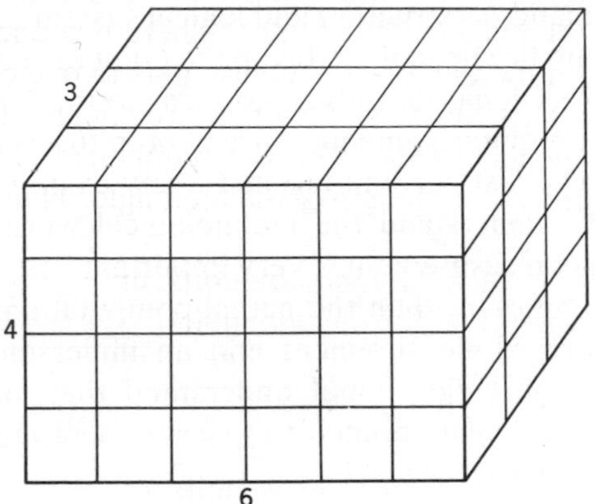

Fig. 72

We may represent the formula for the volume of the box in different ways. A few of these are $V = lhw$, $V = whl$, $V = hlw$, $V = wlh$, etc. Each of these representations should be interpreted differently. The various interpretations are left to the reader. All of the formulas give the same numerical result, because the commutative principle for multiplication applies when we multiply numbers.

Addition of Denominate Numbers. Measurement numbers are often called denominate numbers. The measurements are very often stated in several units. A length may be 4 yards 2 feet and 7 inches, or a weight may be given as 3 pounds 9 ounces. One of the arguments for adopting the metric system is that the units are related to each other in a decimal ratio. Perhaps too many textbooks have too many exercises with denominate numbers. Our interest in denominate numbers is that we can apply the knowledge of various numeration systems. If we add measurements containing yards, feet and inches, we use the base twelve in changing inches to feet and the base three in changing feet to yards. If our measurements contain gallons, quarts and pints, we use the base two in changing pints to quarts and the base four in changing quarts to gallons. If we deal with months, weeks and days, we operate with base seven and base four. If years are also included with months we operate in base twelve. In the past, exercises with denominate numbers may have been boring and often meaningless. With the knowledge of other number bases, children may find exercises with denominate numbers quite interesting.

9.10 SUMMARY

There are differences of opinion regarding the place of measurement in the elementary school mathematics curriculum. From the point of view of mathematics as structure and logical system there is no place for measurement in the curriculum. From the point of view of children's needs there is a very important place for measurement. Children grow up in a world that requires some measurement in their daily existence. Size, weight, speed, cost per unit are just a few examples of common measurements. To understand the technological world in which we live, a knowledge of measurement is very important.

What is more important than the actual computations is the knowledge of the nature of measurement and an understanding of units in measurement. The child should understand that measurement is always approximate. Highly related to measurement are the concepts of error, precision, and accuracy.

How much should be done with tables of measures depends on the community and the needs of the children in that community. One should always keep in mind the basic psychological principle that the units and the exercises that involve various measurements should be meaningful to children.

EXERCISES

1. What are the absolute and the relative errors of the following measurements?

   3.47, 8.624, 0.324, 0.0076, 0.008

2. Arrange the following measurements in the order of precision.

   32.63, 8.62, 1.063, 0.052, 0.0063

3. Arrange the measurements in Exercise 2 according to accuracy.
4. Give five examples of measurement that would be experienced by an elementary school child.
5. Illustrate the difference between a unit in counting and a unit in measurement.
6. Show how you would teach children to understand the nature of a unit.
7. What are standard units and why are they needed? Cite a specific example.
8. What are the probable errors of the sums of the following measurements?

(a)	(b)	(c)
3.41	283	0.006
2.058	5830	0.1034
1.7	904	0.27
0.032	+7000	+1.3
+0.0061		

9. What are the probable errors of the differences of the following measurements?

(a)	*(b)*	*(c)*
3.47	1.079	8746
−1.2	−.1234	−2380

10. What are the probable errors of the products of the following measurements?

(a)	*(b)*	*(c)*
34.62	8.784	0.384
×3.2	×2.3	×0.032

11. Make up three exercises that illustrate indirect measurement and discuss how you would teach them to children.

SUGGESTED SUPPLEMENTARY READING

1. Banks, J. Houston, *Learning and Teaching Arithmetic*. Boston: Allyn and Bacon, 1959. Chap. 12.
2. Bell, Clifford, Clela D. Hammond, and Robert B. Herrera, *Fundamentals of Arithmetic for Teachers*. New York: John Wiley and Sons, 1962. Chaps. 15 and 16.
3. Botts, Truman, "Linear Measurement and Imagination," *The Arithmetic Teacher,* November 1962. pp. 376–382.
4. Buckingham, Burdette R., *Elementary Arithmetic, Its Meaning and Practice*. Boston: Ginn and Company, 1953. Chaps. 13–20.
5. Christofferson, H. C., "Meanings in Multiplication," *The Arithmetic Teacher,* April 1959. pp. 148–151.
6. ———, "Multiplication Socialized," *School Science and Mathematics,* October 1959. pp. 532–539.
7. Churchill, Eileen M., *Counting and Measuring*. Toronto: University of Toronto Press, 1961. Chap. 7.
8. Crumley, Richard D., "Unifying Ideas in the Arithmetic Curriculum," *School Science and Mathematics,* May 1958. pp. 341–346.
9. Grossnickle, Foster E., and Leo J. Brueckner, *Discovering Meanings in Arithmetic*. New York: Holt, Rinehard, and Winston, 1959. Chap. 14.
10. Holder, Lorena, "Measurements – A Skit by Eighth Graders and Their Teacher," *The Arithmetic Teacher,* October 1955. pp. 86–90.
11. Jenkins, Jan, "Teaching Concepts of Linear Measurement," *The Arithmetic Teacher,* October 1957. pp. 182–183.
12. Larsen, Harold D., and H. Glenn Ludlow, *Arithmetic for Colleges*. New York: The Macmillan Company, 1953. Chaps. 10 and 11.
13. Marks, John L., C. Richard Purdy, and Lucien B. Kinney, *Teaching Arithmetic for Understanding*. New York: McGraw-Hill Book Company, 1958. Chap. 11.

14. McSwain, E. T., and Ralph J. Cooke, *Understanding and Teaching Arithmetic in the Elementary School.* New York: Henry Holt and Company, 1958. Chap.10.
15. Mueller, Francis J., *Arithmetic Its Structure and Concepts.* Englewood Cliffs, N. J.: Prentice Hall, 1956. Chap. 6.
16. Parker, Helen C., "Teaching Measurement in a Meaningful Way," *The Arithmetic Teacher,* April 1960. pp. 194–198.
17. Payne, Joseph N., and Robert C. Seeber, "Measurement and Approximation," *The Growth of Mathematical Ideas Grades K–12.* Twenty-Fourth Yearbook, The National Council of Teachers of Mathematics. Washington, D.C.: The National Council of Teachers of Mathematics, 1959. Chap. 5.
18. Rappaport, David, "Units in Measurement Should be Meaningful," *School Science and Mathematics,* March 1960. pp. 202–206.
19. Ringenberg, Lawrence A., "The Area of a Rectangle," *The Mathematics Teacher,* May 1963. pp. 329–332.
20. Sachs, Jerome M., Ruth B. Rasmusen, and William J. Purcell, *Basic College Mathematics.* Boston: Allyn and Bacon, 1960. pp. 84–97.
21. Sanford, Vera, "Standard Time," *The Arithmetic Teacher,* December 1959. pp. 322–323.
22. Spitzer, Herbert F., *The Teaching of Arithmetic.* Boston: Houghton Mifflin Company, 1954. Chap. 9.
23. Swain, Robert L., *Understanding Arithmetic.* New York: Rinehart and Company, 1957. Chap. 11.

Chapter 10 Algebra

10.1 INTRODUCTION

Some form of algebra has always been a part of the elementary school curriculum. Children have learned to use formulas to find area, volume, distance, interest, etc. Since formulas have letters that represent numbers, children have had some experience with so-called literal numbers. In the formula $A = lw$, l represents the number of linear units in the length, w represents the number of linear units in the width, and A represents the number of area units in the rectangle. Some children have also been exposed to simple equations using x and y.

This is a somewhat superficial view of algebra. It involves a series of mechanical operations in which all letters except one are replaced by numerals, and the result of the operations is the replacement value for the remaining letter. This kind of manipulation, however, does not teach children the underlying basic principles of algebra. Children also fail to understand the relationship between arithmetic and algebra. They merely learn to replace a letter by a numeral. The new elementary school mathematics curriculum emphasizes meaning, understanding, structure, and theory. Many of the principles of arithmetic are also applied in algebra. Children thus learn the relationship between arithmetic and algebra. Both are logical systems with defined and undefined terms and postulates. In both disciplines valid conclusions are derived by means of a logical procedure or proof.

Algebra is a complex subject. Many books have been written on various levels of development of this field of mathematics. It would be very difficult to give a complete treatment of algebra in one chapter, and it is not the purpose of this book to do this. Since this book is concerned with the mathematics curriculum for the elementary school, this chapter will be only a very simple introduction to algebra. Only simple ideas that can become a part of the elementary school curriculum will be presented. The bibliography at the end of this chapter contains references for a more exhaustive treatment of algebra for the interested reader.

It is customary for many authors to begin with listing the properties of a field and then showing that the system of rational numbers constitutes a field. Other number systems are analyzed to determine whether they meet the field postulates. The aim in the following section is to avoid being extremely formal, but rather to mix some formal definitions and postulates with an informal explanation that an unsophisticated reader can follow with little difficulty.

Since natural numbers and rational numbers have already been treated in previous chapters, we proceed immediately to the discussion of irrational numbers.

10.2 IRRATIONAL NUMBERS

Suppose we wanted to find the solution for $x^2 = 2$; does the set of rational numbers contain elements that will make this sentence true? We find that there is no rational number whose square is 2. In many parts of mathematics a similar need arises for numbers that are not rational numbers. Such numbers are called irrational numbers. Examples of irrational numbers are : $\sqrt{2}$, $\sqrt{3}$, $\sqrt{5}$, and π. Such numbers are not considered appropriate for introduction to elementary school children. Elementary school teachers, however, should know of their existence and how and why they were created. If we try to express rational numbers as decimals, we find that they are either terminating decimals or nonterminating decimals, and that the nonterminating decimals are repeating decimals. Thus $\frac{1}{8} = 0.125$ is a terminating decimal, and $\frac{1}{7} = 0.142857142857142857\ldots$ is a repeating nonterminating decimal. An irrational number such as $\sqrt{2}$ can be approximated as a decimal number to any number of places, but there is no repeating cycle of numbers as with rational numbers. The interested reader may find a number of books that discuss rational and irrational numbers more fully.

The number line has been used on several occasions in this book to represent numbers. We began with the natural numbers which were represented by points that were evenly spaced. The numbers represented the distances from the starting point. The fractions were represented by points that were between the points representing the natural numbers. A question is raised as to how many points lie between two integral points. There are an infinite number of such points. Suppose we placed this infinite set of points between two integral points, will our line be a solid dense line? The answer is no. If all rational points were placed on the number line, there would still be space between these points. This space is taken up by the irrational numbers. We do not prove this, we merely accept it. In drawing the graphs of relations, discussed in later sections, the inclusion of irrational numbers with the rational numbers enables us to draw solid lines.

10.3 NEGATIVE NUMBERS

Suppose a storekeeper starts the day with a certain amount of money in his cash register. If a customer comes into the store and buys something for \$5, the storekeeper has \$5 more than he had at the beginning of the day. Let us suppose, on the other hand, that a bill collector enters the store instead of a customer. If the storekeeper pays a \$5 bill, he has \$5 less than he had at the beginning of the day. After each transaction the storekeeper may determine whether he has more money or less money than he had at the beginning of the day. Any amount more than the original amount of money is called a positive number, such as $+5$. Any amount less than the original amount is called a negative number, such as -5.

On the number line we designate the numbers to the right of 0 as positive numbers and the numbers to the left of 0 as negative numbers. We also designate a direction to the right as the positive direction and to the left as the negative direction.

By means of the number line we can determine the sum of any two signed numbers (positive and negative numbers). Thus we can show that $+5+(+3)=+8$, $+5+(-3)=+2$, $-5+(-3)=-8$, $-5+(+3)=-2$, $+5+(-8)=-3$, and that $-5+(+8)=+3$. We use arrows to show both direction and quantity in the following manner:

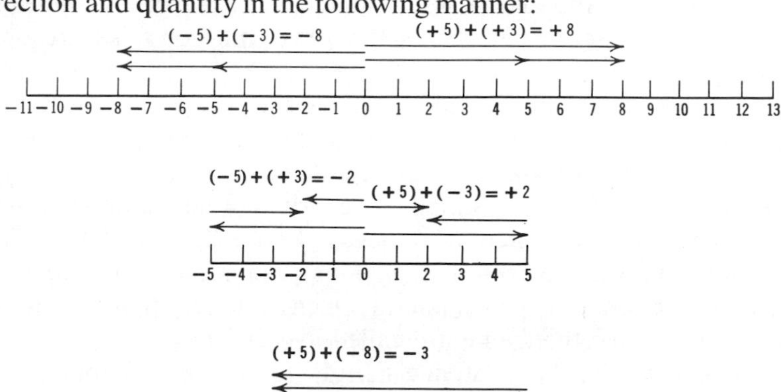

The set of positive numbers and the set of negative numbers, together with zero constitute the set of integers.

10.4 THE REAL NUMBER SYSTEM

All of the numbers that we have discussed can now be considered as belonging to the set of real numbers. Rational numbers and irrational numbers are subsets of the set of real numbers. The set of integers is a subset of the set of rational numbers. The set of natural numbers is a subset of the set of integers.

10.5 SENTENCES

Just as there are sentences in the English language, there are sentences in mathematics. A sentence contains a subject and a predicate. "Jimmy sits in the front row" is a sentence. It may be true or it may be false. If Jimmy sits in the front row, the sentence is true. If Jimmy does not sit in the front row, the sentence is false. Likewise, $5+3=8$ is a sentence. It may be restated to read as follows, "The sum of 5 and 3 is 8." This is a true mathematical sentence. On the other hand, $4+2=7$ is also a mathematical sentence, but it is a false sentence. A sentence that is either true or false is called a closed sentence.

Open Sentences. Some sentences are neither true nor false. If we write, "$\boxed{}$ sits in the first row," we cannot tell whether this sentence is true or false until we write some name in the frame. If we write the name Mary in the frame, we can then determine whether the sentence, "Mary sits in the first row," is true or false. In like manner, the mathematical sentence $\boxed{}+5=9$ is neither true nor false. If we write the numerals 1, 2, 3, 5, or 6 in the frame, the sentence is false in each case. However, if we write the numeral 4 in the frame, the sentence is true. Sentences that are neither true nor false are open sentences.

Identities. Some mathematical sentences are always true, no matter what numeral is written in the frame. Let us consider the sentence $3\cdot(\square+2)=3\cdot\square+6$. We agree that the same numeral must be placed in the same kind of frame. Suppose we write a 4 inside of the frame. The mathematical sentence now reads $3\cdot(4+2)=3\cdot 4+6$. This sentence is true since $3\cdot 6=12+6$. This sentence will be true if we write a 5 or a 6 or a 1, or any numeral. Open sentences that are true for all replacements for the frame are called identities.

The Universe. In the sentence $\square+4=6$, the only replacement for the frame that will make the sentence true is 2. In the sentence $4<\square<8$, we may write 5, 6, or 7 in the frame if we want true sentences. We sometimes have only one replacement that will make a true sentence while at other times we may have more than one replacement that will make a true sentence.

If in the sentence, $4 < \square < 8$, we replace the frame by $5\frac{1}{2}$, $5\frac{1}{3}$, $6\frac{2}{3}$, or $6\frac{3}{5}$ each sentence is true. Do we, or do we not, include fractions? If we limit our replacements to the set of positive integers we get one set of answers. If we permit the use of rational numbers we get a different set of answers. We agree, therefore, to describe the replacement set, from which we select our numbers, that will make a sentence true. We call this replacement set the *universe of discourse* or just *universe*.

How do we answer the question for what numbers is $\square < 3$ a true sentence? If $U = \{\text{non-negative integers}\}$, then 0, 1, and 2 are correct answers. If $U = \{\text{positive rational numbers}\}$, then our answer is an infinite set of rational numbers. If $U = \{\text{integers}\}$, we get different answers than when the universe is limited to the non-negative integers. The universe may be the set of rational numbers or the set of real numbers. In each case we get a different set of answers. We must always relate the solutions to the universe.

10.6 EQUATIONS

An equation is a mathematical open sentence. We solve the equation when we find the set of elements from a given universe that will satisfy the equation, that is, the set of elements for which the sentence is true. This set is called the solution set. The universe, or replacement set, will determine whether an equation has a solution set that is empty, or whether the solution set does contain some elements.

Let us consider the equation $\square + 8 = 5$. The solution set is empty if the universe is the set of natural numbers. If $U = \{-2, -1, 0, 1, 2\}$, the solution set is empty. If $U = \{\text{integers}\}$, the solution set is $\{-3\}$.

In the equation $\square \cdot \square = 9$ the solution set is $\{3\}$ if the universe is the set of natural numbers, and it is $\{3, -3\}$ if the universe is the set of integers.

Variable. A variable is a symbol used to denote any element of a specified set. A frame is a placeholder for the numeral that makes a sentence true. It has been customary to use x or y or any other letter to represent a variable. Thus we write $x + 8 = 5$ or $x^2 = 9$.

10.7 CONDITIONS

If we have a universe, or replacement set, we may select those elements that meet certain conditions. If the universe is the set of integers from -10 to $+10$, what is the set of elements greater than 7? The solution set is $\{8, 9, 10\}$. We describe it as follows:

$$U = \{\text{integers from} -10 \text{ to} +10\}$$
$$\{x|x > 7\} = \{8, 9, 10\}$$

The vertical line is read "such that." $\{x|x > 7\}$ is read as, "the set of all x's such that x is greater than 7." If we want the set of all x's less than -6, we write $\{x|x < -6\} = \{-7, -8, -9, -10\}$. We may have more than one condition. Suppose we want the set of all x's greater than 1 and less than 6, using the same universe. We write $\left\{x|x > 1 \wedge x < 6\right\} = \{2,3,4,5\}$. The symbol $\wedge$ is read "and".

We thus have a universe U, a variable x, and a condition or several conditions. The variable x is a placeholder for the elements taken from U that fulfill the condition. If $U = \{\text{rational numbers from} -10 \text{ to} +10\}$, then $\{x|x > 7\}$ is an infinite set of elements such as 7.1, 7.03, 7.48, 8.2, 8.009, 9.672, 9.0382, etc.

The number line can be used effectively to show the solution set. If U is the set of integers from -5 to $+5$, the elements that are greater than -2 and less than 3 are shown on the number line with rings around them, Fig. 73.

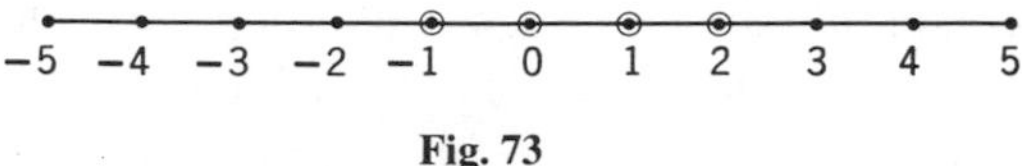

Fig. 73

If the universe is the set of real numbers, the solution set for the above is shown as a heavy line in Fig. 74.

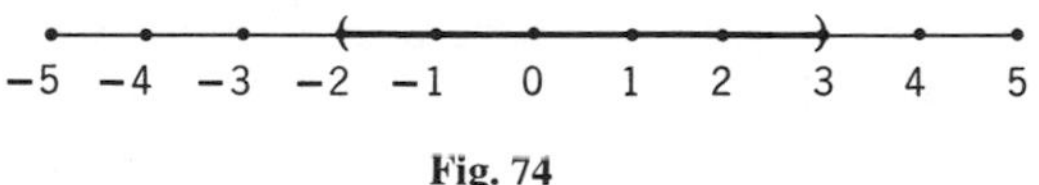

Fig. 74

It is necessary to come to some agreement as to whether or not we include the endpoints. In this book we will use an arc to show that the endpoint is excluded. Thus

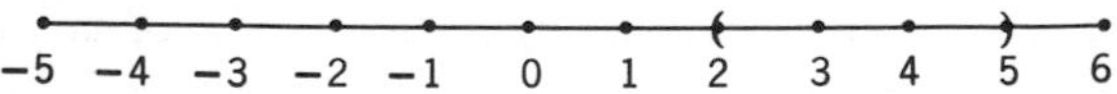

The endpoints 2 and 5 are excluded. If we do not have the arcs, then the endpoints are included. Thus

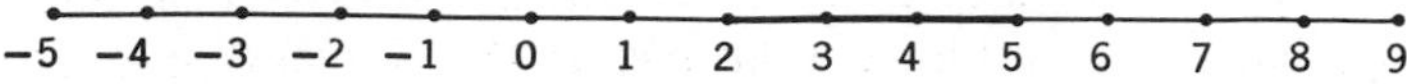

10.8 THE NUMBER PLANE AND COORDINATE GEOMETRY

Just as the number line has been used as a set of points that represents numbers for one variable, the number plane is a set of points that represents ordered pairs of numbers. The distances are counted from a pair of perpendicular lines or axes. x is the distance of a point from the y-axis, and y is the distance of that point from the x-axis. The number pair (3,2) is represented by a point that is 3 units to the right of the y-axis and 2 units above the x-axis.

If $A = \{\text{integers from } -10 \text{ to } +10\}$ and $U = A \times A$, then $\{(x, y)|y = 2x + 1\}$ is the set $\{(-5,-9), (-4,-7), (-3,-5), (-2,-3), (-1,-1), (0, 1), (1, 3), (2, 5), (3, 7), (4, 9)\}$. The solution set is composed of 10 number pairs which are represented by the 10 points in Fig. 75. If, however,

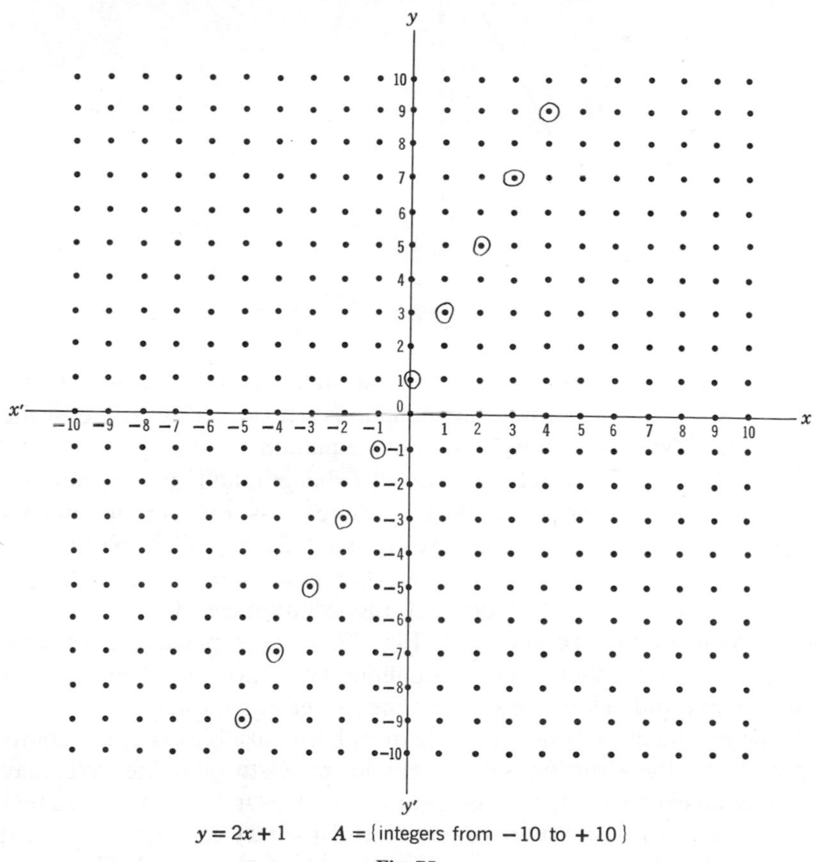

$y = 2x + 1$ $A = \{\text{integers from } -10 \text{ to } +10\}$

Fig. 75

we let A be the set of real numbers from -10 to $+10$, the solution set is an infinite set of points represented by the line segment in Fig. 76.

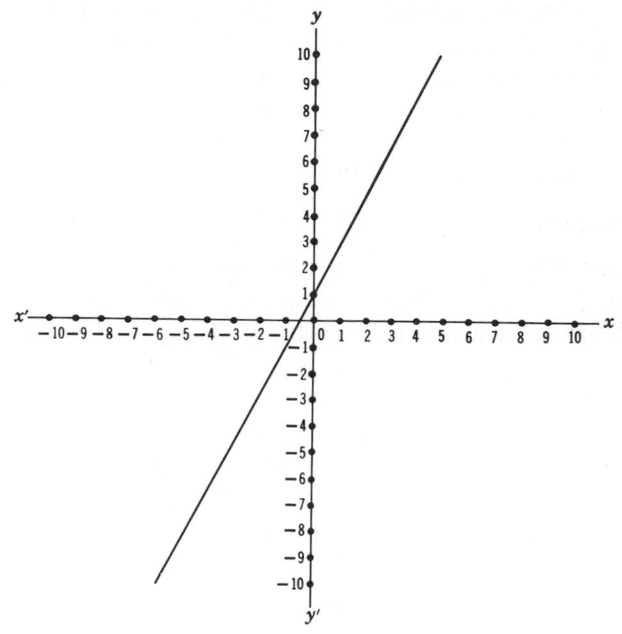

Fig. 76

The equations whose graphs are straight lines are called linear equations. It can be shown that equations whose variables are in the first degree (the exponent is 1) are linear equations.

Inequalities, or inequations, can also be graphed on the number plane. In the first example above, where A is the set of integers from -10 to $+10$, we have the relation $y > 2x+1$. The solution set is represented by the points above the points for $y = 2x+1$. The points below $y = 2x+1$ represent the solution set for $y < 2x+1$. Both sets of points are shown in Fig. 77. If we replace the set A by the set of real numbers, the inequalities are represented by the half planes above and below the straight line for the equation.

If the exponent of either variable or of both variables is 2, the points representing the solution set do not lie in a straight line. We may consider an exception to this generalization. If $x^2 = 0$ it is assumed that we can replace y with any number. Thus if $x = 0$, y can equal 1, 2, 3, 4, $-1, -2, -3$, etc., regardless of our replacement for y, $x^2 = 0$. The points in this example do lie in a straight line, namely, the y-axis. We will consider in this book only those relations that contain both variables.

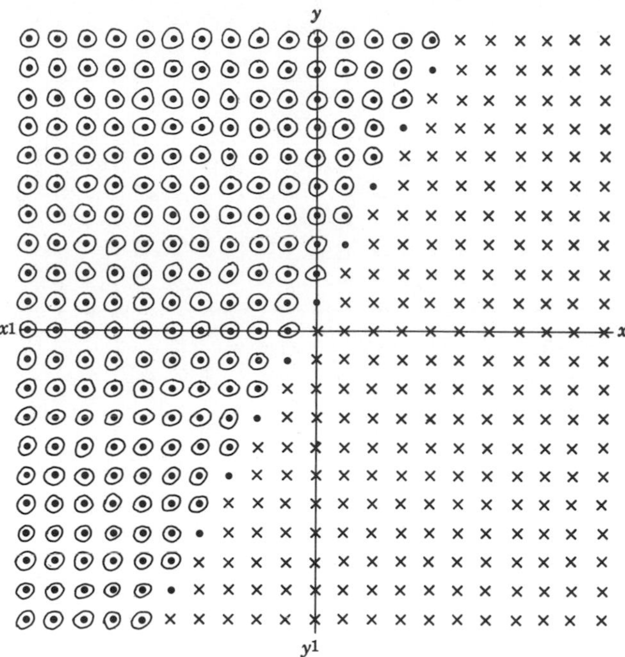

Fig. 77

Equations in which the exponent for either or both variables is 2 are called quadratic equations. Let $A = \{\text{integers from } -10 \text{ to } +10\}$, $U = A \times A$, and $y = x^2 - 5$. $\{(x, y) | y = x^2 - 5\}$ is the set $\{(0, -5), (1, -4), (2, -1), (3, 4), (-1, -4), (-2, -1), (-3, 4)\}$. These points are shown in Fig. 78. If A is the set of real numbers from -10 to $+10$, the points representing the solution set form a curve as in Fig. 79.

It is not the purpose of this book to give an extended treatment of relations and functions. The interested reader will find that many of the references listed in the bibliography at the end of this chapter contain fuller and more extensive treatments of relations and functions. It is the author's purpose to introduce the reader first to the idea of conditions involving one variable and then to relations involving two variables. An interest in relations leads to the concept of ordered pairs of numbers. The representation of ordered pairs of numbers by points in a plane leads to the development of coordinate geometry.

The concept of ordered pairs of numbers has been applied by most elementary teachers in teaching geography. A point on the globe represents a given latitude and a given longitude. In this chapter the concept of ordered pairs of numbers is applied to equations and inequalities.

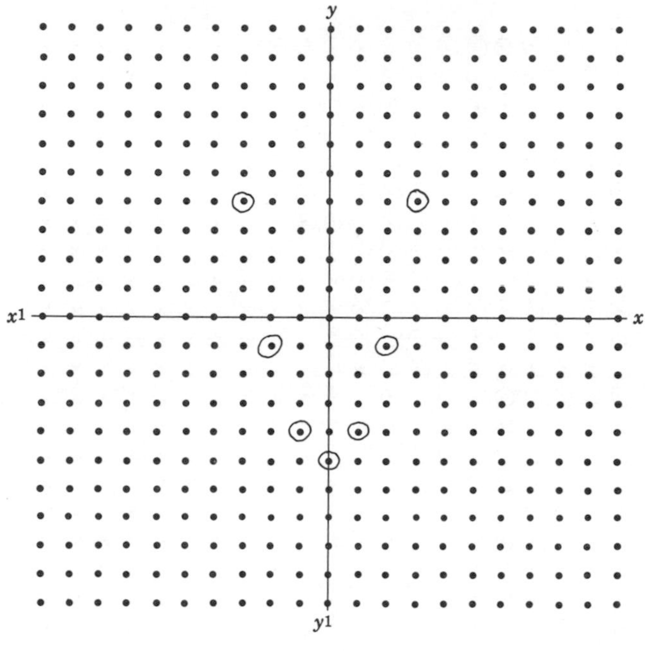

Fig. 78

10.9 TEACHING ALGEBRA TO CHILDREN

Since algebra is a formal logical system, there is great danger that the teacher who attempts to teach algebra in the elementary school will become formal in his approach. A formal approach should be avoided. This does not mean that children should not be taught to develop deductive techniques in deriving conclusions. Children should be led to discover relationships, patterns, and to formulate generalizations. Children may express these generalizations in language that is suitable to them rather than in the strict mathematically precise language. It takes time and maturity to refine the mathematical ideas into the mathematician's sophisticated language. The discovery of mathematical ideas should be an enjoyable experience to children.

Children can be encouraged to develop the postulates of algebra described in this chapter. They can list true mathematical sentences.

At first they will use number sentences such as $4+3=7$, $8-2=6$, and $3\times4=12$. Then they can be asked to write open sentences. They will write such sentences as $\square+3=9$. Then they can be asked to

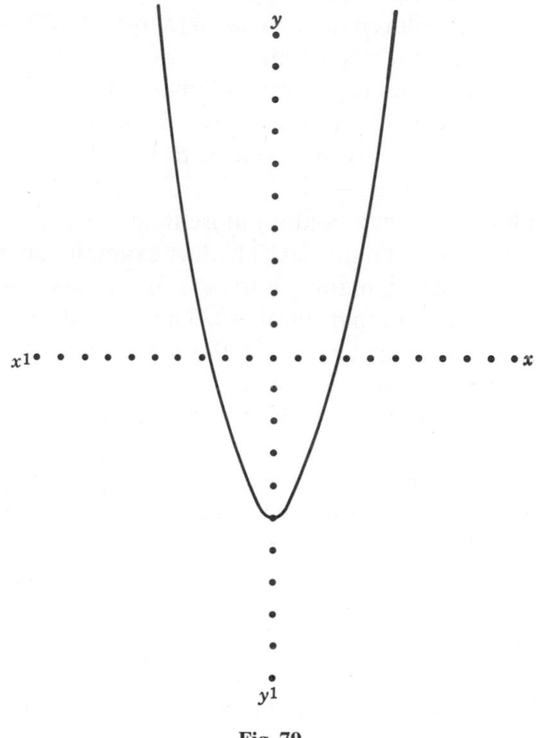

Fig. 79

write identities. They can write such sentences as $\square+5=5+\square$, or $3\cdot\square=\square\cdot3$. The aim is to have them write identities that are more general, that is, to include other identities. Thus children can be challenged to develop the identity $\square+\triangle=\triangle+\square$ as more general than $\square+7=7+\square$. In this manner the associative and commutative properties for addition and multiplication and the distributive property can be developed and discovered by children themselves.

The number line is an effective tool for learning the properties of natural numbers. It is also an effective instrument to show the need for fractions. The cricket jumps from 0 to 9 in two equal jumps. It becomes obvious to children that he lands, after his first jump, on a point that is half way between 4 and 5. But the number line becomes of special importance in the development of negative numbers. The children may be asked the following question, "If a cricket starts at point 9 and makes three jumps to the left, each jump 4 spaces long, where does he land?" The children may create terms of their own to describe the negative numbers. They may call them "other side numbers" or "left numbers" or "below numbers." These names should be accepted by the teacher until the children become used to the idea. Then the teacher may inform the children that such numbers are called negative numbers.

Children are introduced to closed and open sentences. They may be given several sentences and asked to give the numbers that will make the sentences true. They are introduced to the idea of a solution set. Examples: $5+\square=9, \square\cdot\square=16, 4<\square, \square<6, 5\cdot\square=17$. They will learn that a solution set may contain more than one element. The need for a universe may be brought out. The last example has no solution if the universe is the set of natural numbers, but it has a solution if the universe is the set of rational numbers. The second example has one solution if the universe is limited to the set of positive integers and two solutions if the universe is the set of integers.

Children can be introduced to the number plane, first to the quadrant that contains only positive values for x and y. The variables x and y should not be used at first. We can use the $\square$ to represent the horizontal distances and the $\triangle$ to represent the vertical distances. We can begin with the following: $\triangle=\square+2$. Now the solution set contains number pairs. Agreement can be established that the number in the square is listed first and the number in the triangle is listed second. They will suggest number pairs such as (1, 3), (2, 4), (3, 5), (7, 9), and (10, 12). These number pairs can then be plotted as points on the number plane. The various functions that can be studied are determined by the children. Coordinate geometry can be fun for children, but it should not become too involved too soon.

EXERCISES

1. Give an example that demonstrates the associative property for addition of rational numbers.
2. Give an example that demonstrates the associative property for multiplication of rational numbers.
3. Give an example that demonstrates the commutative property for addition of rational numbers; for multiplication of rational numbers.
4. If $A=\{-4,-3,-2,-1,0,1,2\}$ and $B=\{3,4,5,6,7,8\}$, list the elements of $A\times B$ that involve only negative numbers.
5. Use the universe of Exercise 4 and list the solution set for $y=2x+5$.
6. Use the universe of Exercise 4 and list the solution set for $y=x^2+3$.
7. If $A=\{0, 1, 2, \ldots 10\}$ and $U=A\times A$, what is the solution set for $y>3x+2$?
8. Given the universe of Exercise 7, what is the solution set for $y=2x-3$?

9. If $U = \{-3, -2, -1, 0, 1, 2, 3, 4, 5\}$, what is the solution set for $x > 2$?
10. Given the universe of Exercise 9, what is the solution set for $x^2 > 2$?
11. Discuss the need for a universe in the solution of equations.
12. Given U as the set of real numbers, draw the graph for the equation in Exercise 5.
13. Draw the graph of the equation in Exercise 6, given the set of real numbers for the universe.
14. Show that $(-3) + (-5) = -(3 + 5)$.
15. Show that $(+8) + (-2) = +6$ and that $(-8) + (+2) = -6$ by applying the definitions and postulates for negative numbers.
16. Graph the results of Exercises 5, 6, 7, 8, 9, and 10 as points on a number plane.

SUGGESTED SUPPLEMENTARY READING

1. Allendorfer, C. B., and C. O. Oakley, *Principles of Mathematics,* New York: McGraw-Hill Book Company, 1955. Chaps. 2–5.
2. Beberman, Max, and Bruce Meserve, "The Concept of a Literal Number Symbol," *The Mathematics Teacher,* January 1954.
3. Bell, Clifford, Clela D. Hammond, and Robert B. Herrera, *Fundamentals of Arithmetic for Teachers.* New York: John Wiley and Sons, 1962. Chap. 19.
4. Davis, Robert B., *Axioms for Arithmetic and Algebra.* Syracuse, N. Y.: Madison Project, Syracuse University, 1962.
5. ———, "The 'Madison Project' of Syracuse University," *The Mathematics Teacher,* November 1960. pp. 571–575.
6. ———, "The Madison Project: Algebra In Grades 3–9." *Frontiers of Elementary Education,* Vol. VII. Syracuse University Press, 1961. pp. 56–59.
7. ———, *Matrices, Functions, and Other Topics.* Syracuse, N.Y.: Madison Project, Syracuse University, 1963.
8. Dienes, Z. P., *Building Up Mathematics.* London: Hutchinson Educational, 1960. Chaps. 4 and 5.
9. Evenson, A. B., *Modern Mathematics: Introductory Concepts and Their Implications.* Chicago: Scott, Foresman, and Company, 1962. Chaps. 4–6.
10. Fujii, John N., *An Introduction to the Elements of Mathematics.* New York: John Wiley and Sons, 1961. Chaps. 8–10.
11. Gray, James F., *Sets, Relations, and Functions.* New York: Holt, Rinehart, and Winston, 1962.
12. MacLane, Saunders, "Algebra," *Insights into Modern Mathematics.* Twenty-Third Yearbook, The National Council of Teachers of Mathematics. Washington, D.C.: The National Council of Teachers of Mathematics, 1957. Chap. 5.
13. Maria, May H., *The Structure of Arithmetic and Algebra.* New York: John Wiley and Sons, 1958.
14. May, Kenneth O., and Henry Van Engen, "Relations and Functions," *The Growth of Mathematical Ideas, Grades K–12.* Twenty-Fourth Yearbook, The National Council of Teachers of Mathematics. Washington, D.C.: The National Council of Teachers of Mathematics, 1959. Chap. 3.

15. Meserve, Bruce E., "New Trends in Algebra and Geometry," *The Mathematics Teacher,* October 1962. pp. 452–457.
16. Meserve, Bruce E., and Max A. Sobel, *Mathematics for Secondary School Teachers.* Englewood Cliffs, N.J.: Prentice-Hall, 1962. Chaps. 6–9.
17. Mueller, Francis J., "Building Algebra Readiness in Grades Seven and Eight," *The Arithmetic Teacher,* November 1959. pp. 269–273.
18. Page, David A., *Number Line, Functions, and Fundamental Topics.* Urbana, Illinois: University of Illinois Arithmetic Project, 1961.
19. Parsons, Cynthia, "Algebra in the Fourth Grade," *The Arithmetic Teacher,* February 1960. pp. 77–79.
20. Sawyer, W. W., "Algebra in Grade Five." *The Arithmetic Teacher,* January 1960. pp. 25–27.
21. Sloan, Robert W., *An Introduction to Mathematics.* Englewood Cliffs, N.J.: Prentice-Hall, 1960. Chap. 4.
22. Standish, Henry, "Seventh Graders Volunteer for After-School Classes in Algebra," *The Mathematics Teacher,* December 1960. pp. 640–643.

Chapter 11 Geometry

11.1 INTRODUCTION

In the traditional mathematics curriculum geometry was the first mathematics course in which students learned about postulates, theorems, and deductive proof. Algebra, on the other hand, was the problem solving course in which students learned to set up equations and to solve them. In the "new" mathematics curriculum algebra, and to some extent arithmetic, has been treated as a postulational system with formal proofs of theorems. Some have even justified the place of geometry in the curriculum purely on the teaching of the nature of proof rather than on the subject matter itself. Since children now learn a great deal about systematic derivations of logical conclusions in their study of algebra, what role should geometry play in the elementary school mathematics curriculum?

As has been pointed out in Chapter 1, many of the new mathematics programs give a more prominent place to geometry in the elementary school than had been done in the past. Some formal geometry is being taught to some children in the primary grades. What distinguishes the new approach to the teaching of geometry from past methods is the effort to relate geometry to algebra and arithmetic so that common ideas and concepts run through all of them. The concept of set has become the principle that unifies arithmetic, algebra, and geometry.

Children are now exposed to more precise definitions than in the past. Some terms, however, are accepted without any attempt to define them. Euclid attempted to define all geometric terms. He did not succeed because in his definitions he used terms that he did not define. It has become evident that all logical systems must have some undefined terms. These are sometimes called primitives.

In teaching geometry to elementary school children teachers should resist the temptation to become too formal. There should be a balance between formal and intuitive approaches to the learning of geometry. In this chapter some of the new ideas in geometry will be presented and suggestions for teaching them to children will be offered.

11.2 NONMETRIC GEOMETRY

Nonmetric geometry deals with relations rather than with measurement. In order to understand these relations it is necessary to understand a number of geometric concepts. Some of these will be clearly defined, others merely described.

Point. A point is not defined. We think of a point as having a position on a line, a plane, or in space. We cannot see a point. We represent a point by means of a dot, and we frequently name the point by means of a capital letter. This physical representation of a point is necessary in order to communicate our ideas about a particular position.

Line. If there are two points, as in Fig. 80, it is possible to follow several paths from point A to point B. One of these paths is a straight line. Straight line is not defined. However, we have an intuitive knowledge of what a straight line is. If we fold a sheet of paper, the edge along the fold represents a straight line. If we stretch a string, it represents a straight line. If we look at an object, we think of the line of sight between the object and our eye as a straight line. Whenever we use the word line, we mean it to represent straight line. A path other than a line is a curve.

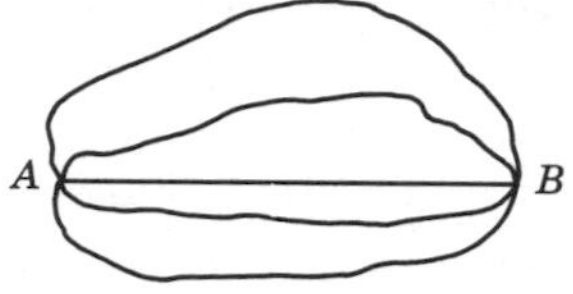

Fig. 80

A line can also be considered as an infinite set of points. We assume that between any two points there always exists a third point. We also think of a line as having no limit. A line, like a point, cannot be seen. We represent a line by a drawing with a pen or a pencil but we understand that the physical drawing is not the real line. Since a line has no limit, we can represent only a portion of a line on any sheet of paper. The arrows at both ends of the drawing indicate that the line can be extended in both directions. We can name a particular line by a small letter on the line or by naming any two points on the line.

In Fig. 81 we have the line m or the line AB. In order not to repeat the word line too often, we place a line segment with arrows at both

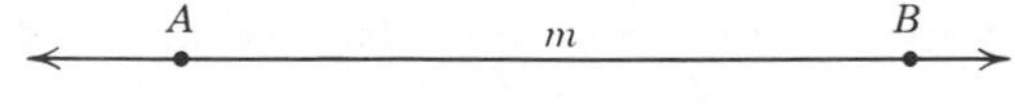

Fig. 81

ends over $\overleftrightarrow{AB}$. If there is only one point, it is possible to draw many lines through that point (see Fig. 82*a*). If there are two points, ex-

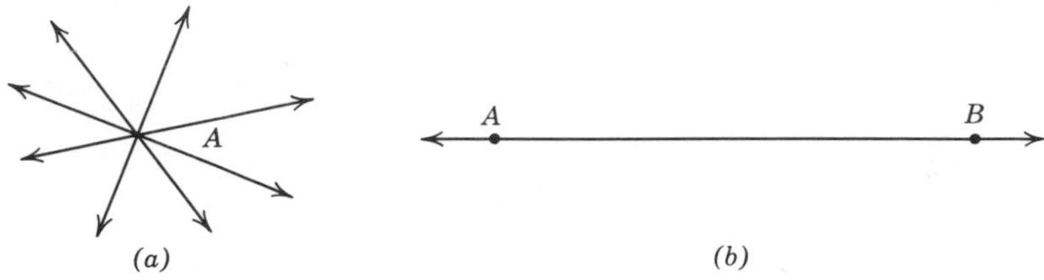

Fig. 82

perience shows that only one line exists between those two points (see Fig. 82*b*). We conclude that two points determine a line.

Ray. We may want to consider only that portion of the line shown in Fig. 83, which is a half-line, or ray. In order to name the ray, a second

Fig. 83

point such as B is used. We distinguish line AB from ray AB by drawing arrows at both ends to indicate a line and an arrow at one end to indicate a ray; thus $\overleftrightarrow{AB}$ and $\overrightarrow{AB}$. The line $\overleftrightarrow{AB}$ is identical to line $\overleftrightarrow{BA}$, but ray $\overrightarrow{AB}$ is not the same as ray $\overrightarrow{BA}$. To indicate a line any two points of the line may be used. To indicate a ray, the endpoint comes first and then any other point on the line may be used.

Line Segment. A segment is a portion of a line. Let us examine the line AB in Fig. 84. If we start with point A and consider the portion

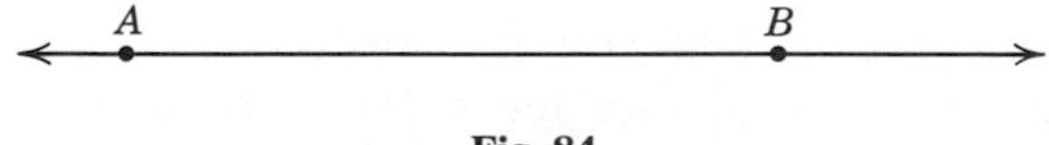

Fig. 84

of $\overleftrightarrow{AB}$ to the right of A, we have the ray $\overleftrightarrow{AB}$. A ray is a set of points just as a line is a set of points. A ray is a subset of a line. Now if we consider the portion of line $\overleftrightarrow{AB}$ that is to the left of B, we have the ray $\overleftrightarrow{BA}$. The two rays $\overrightarrow{AB}$ and $\overrightarrow{BA}$ overlap. The portion of the line between A and B is called a line segment or segment. We represent it without the arrows in this manner, $\overline{AB}$. Whereas a ray has one endpoint, a line segment has two endpoints. We now redefine a line segment as the intersection of two rays, or $\overline{AB} = \overrightarrow{AB} \cap \overrightarrow{BA}$.

Angle. Let us consider two distinct rays that have the same endpoint. In Fig. 85 there is the ray $\overrightarrow{AB}$ and the ray $\overrightarrow{AC}$. The two rays form an angle.* Since A is the endpoint for both rays that form the angle, we

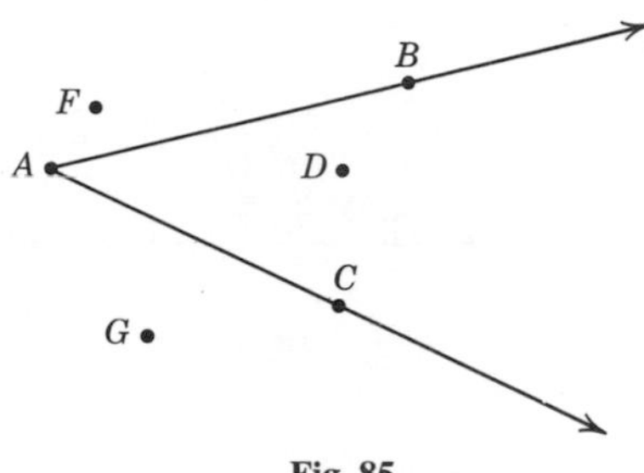

Fig. 85

name the angle by placing the letter A in the middle between two other letters that represent a point on each ray. We name the angle in Fig. 85 as $\angle BAC$. Angle BAC is identical with $\angle CAB$. An angle can be defined as the union of two rays. Thus $\angle BAC = \overrightarrow{AB} \cup \overrightarrow{AC}$. An angle has an interior and an exterior. In Fig. 85 point D is in the interior of $\angle BAC$ whereas points F and G are exterior to $\angle BAC$.

Simple Closed Curve. If we start at a certain point and follow a path that ends at the starting point, we trace a closed curve. If the curve does not cross itself at any point, it is a simple closed curve. In Fig. 86 there are several closed curves; (*c*), (*d*) and (*e*) are simple closed curves, but (*a*) and (*b*) are not.

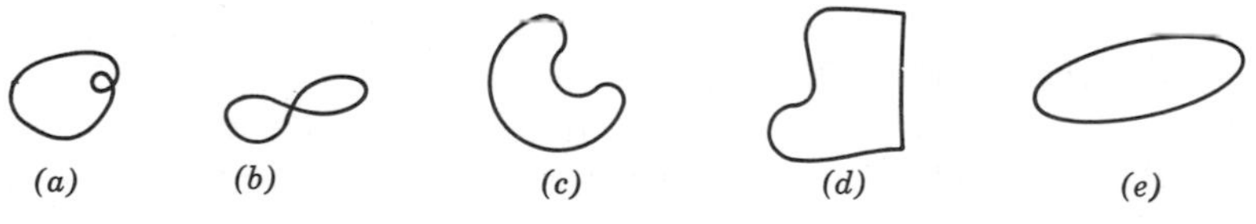

Fig. 86

Polygons. A polygon is a simple closed curve bounded by line segments. It is the union of line segments. A triangle is the union of three line segments, a quadrilateral, of four, a pentagon, of five, and a hexagon of six. The endpoints of the line segments are called vertices

*It is required, of course, that A, B, and C be non-collinear, that is, that the three points do not lie in the same line.

of the polygons, and the polygon is named by the vertices. In Fig. 87 we have the triangle ABC, the quadrilateral $ABCD$, the pentagon $ABCDE$, and the hexagon $ABCDEF$. The $\triangle ABC$ is $\overline{AB} \cup \overline{BC} \cup \overline{CA}$. The quadrilateral $ABCD$ is $\overline{AB} \cup \overline{BC} \cup \overline{CD} \cup \overline{DA}$.

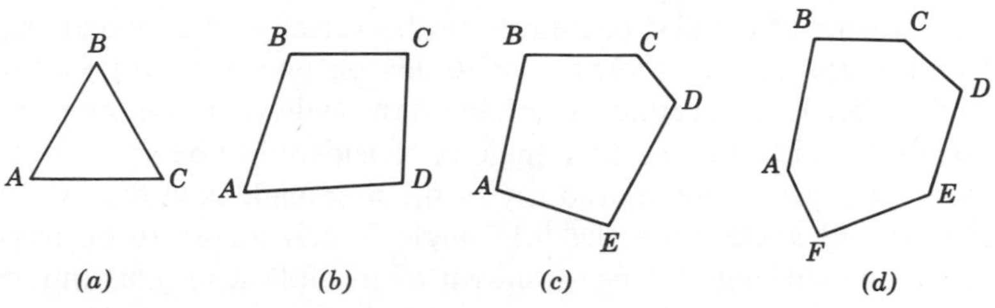

Fig. 87

Circle. A circle is a simple closed curve, all of whose points are the same distance from a given point called the center. Figure 88 shows a circle with the center P. Some line segments have special significance.

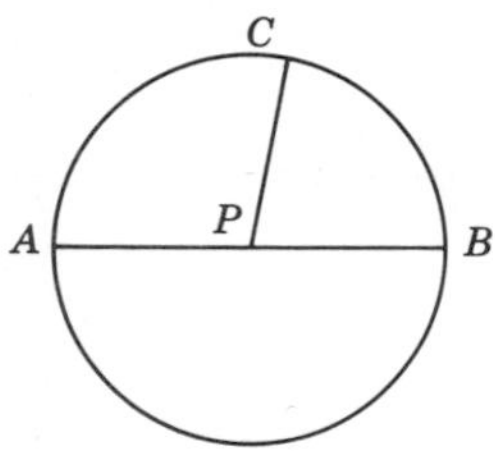

Fig. 88

Thus the line segment from the center to the circle is called the radius. $\overline{PC}$, $\overline{PA}$, and $\overline{PB}$ are examples of a radius. If a line segment has two endpoints on the circle and it also contains the center, this line segment is called the diameter of the circle. $\overline{AB}$ is an example of a diameter.

11.3 METRIC GEOMETRY

The reader may be interested in making comparisons between line segments or between angles. In comparing two line segments, we may find that they have the same length or that one is longer than the other. A compass may be used to compare lengths of line segments. Since the word equal in mathematics means identical, two line segments are said to be congruent ($\cong$) if, and only if, they have the same length.

If we are interested in the specific lengths of line segments, we are concerned with measurement. For this we need a unit. Any given line segment may be used as a unit. If a given unit is laid end to end until the line segment is covered, we have the measure of the line segment. Children can use different lengths as units, but they soon learn that a standard unit is best for purpose of communication. Thus we use an inch or a centimeter as measurement units.

Angles can also be compared. Suppose two angles are placed so that the vertex of the first angle lies on the vertex of the second angle and one of the rays of the first angle lies on one of the rays of the second angle. If the second ray of the first angle is in the interior of the second angle, then the first angle is considered to be smaller than the second angle. If the second ray of the first angle is in the exterior of the second angle, then the first angle is considered to be larger than the second angle. This is shown in the following illustrations:

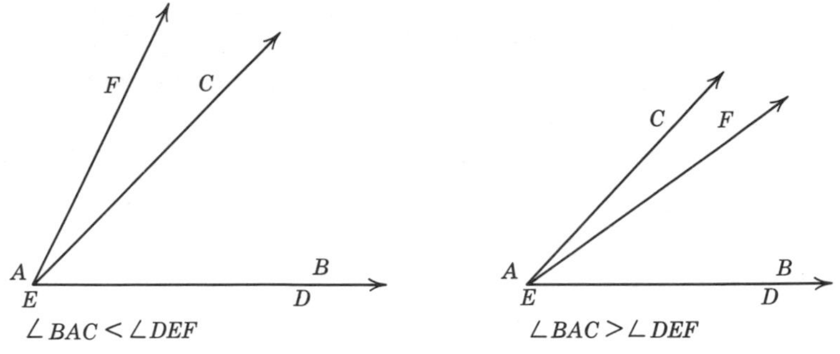

Fig. 89

If we fold a sheet of paper and then fold it a second time so that the two parts of the original crease lie on the same line, we have a right angle. This angle can be used as a model to compare angles. If an angle is greater than a right angle, it is an obtuse angle. If it is smaller than a right angle, it is an acute angle. One can measure an angle more specifically if he has a given angle as a unit. A protractor is an instrument to measure angles. If a semicircle is divided into 180 congruent arcs, each arc determines an angle having a measure of one degree. The degree is generally the standard unit for measuring angles. A different unit for angle measurement, called a radian, is used in mathematics quite frequently, but it is generally not studied in elementary schools. A right angle has a measure of 90 degrees or 90°. Angles that have the same measure are called congruent.

Once units of measurement have been established, we can construct line segments of a given size and also angles of a given size. Circles can be compared according to the length of the radius. Triangles, rectangles and other polygons can be examined from the point of view of the lengths of the sides or the areas of the polygons.

11.4 TEACHING GEOMETRY TO CHILDREN

Children should be given the opportunity to learn about geometry intuitively. This can be accomplished best by means of constructions. After they have become familiar with many of the concepts of geometry they may begin to prove theorems formally. Children can be trained to handle a straightedge,* ruler, compass, and protractor correctly. They learn to derive some generalizations from their constructions.

Children can be asked to make a dot on a sheet of paper to represent a point. Then they are asked to draw a line through that point. Can they construct a second line through that point? A third line? How many lines can they draw through the one point? Then they are asked to mark two points. How many lines can they draw through two points? How many paths can they draw through two points? Children thus learn that two points determine a line.

What happens if they have three points? All three points may lie on the same line. Suppose that only two of the three points lie on one line. How many lines can they draw, using two points each time? Is a simple closed curve formed? How many angles are formed? Given four points, no three of which are on one line, how many lines can be drawn? How many simple closed curves are formed? How many angles are formed? If there are five points or six points, how many lines can be drawn?

For all of the examples cited above, we can ask how many rays can be formed or how many line segments can be drawn. Since lines, rays, line segments, and angles are sets of points, what are the various intersections of two sets or the union of two sets? The union of several sets?

Circles of various radii are drawn. The circles may have the same centers or they may have different centers. What are the intersections of two circles? We may have some points in the interior of the circle and some points in the exterior. Line segments are drawn from the center to all of these points. How do these line segments compare in length with the radius of the circle?

Children can be taught to construct line segments that are congruent to a given line segment or angles that are congruent to a given angle. They can be taught to bisect line segments, to bisect angles, and to draw perpendiculars to given line segments.

*A straightedge is an instrument whose edge is a portion of a straight line. It has no markings on it. A ruler is a straightedge that has markings on it showing equal-line segments.

Children are asked to construct squares, rectangles, equilateral and isosceles triangles. They can then be asked questions about the lengths of the diagonals of a rectangle or of a square. They learn that the diagonals of a rectangle are congruent and that they bisect each other. They learn that the opposite sides of a rectangle are congruent. They measure the angles of an equilateral triangle, of an isosceles triangle, and of a scalene triangle. They learn that the sum of the degree measures of the angles of any triangle equals 180°. They draw two intersecting lines and measure the angles formed. They discover that the opposite angles are congruent.

The Hawley and Suppes material contains many geometry exercises for children in the primary grades. Experience has shown that primary grade children can learn a great deal about geometry if given the opportunity. The SMSG material for fourth, fifth, and sixth grades contains several units on geometry. More and more textbooks published commercially contain geometry that is presented from the new point of view.

Formal proofs of geometry can be presented to children in the elementary school when they are ready for it. They may begin by accepting as postulates that two triangles are congruent if the corresponding sides are congruent, and if the two triangles have two sides and the included angles congruent, and if the two triangles have two angles and the included sides congruent. They can then be motivated to prove some of the constructions that they have already learned to do. They may be encouraged to formulate generalizations of their own.

Formal proof requires a set of definitions and postulates. Most children in the elementary school are not quite ready to develop deductive proofs from a set of postulates. Such postulational geometry should be postponed until the high school years. There is always the danger that postulational geometry taught to all children in a class will result in the memorizing of rules and in the use of mechanical steps without real understanding. Postulational geometry is not included in this book. Instead the emphasis is on intuitive geometry. Children should be encouraged to discover many geometric relationships. Some may even be able to formulate their findings into generalizations. Care should be taken by the teacher to see that all of this is done inductively.

Some coordinate geometry is discussed in Chapter 9. How much coordinate geometry should be taught in the elementary school? This depends on the children in the class. Children may learn to graph a function such as that described by $y = 2x + 3$. They may learn that the graph is a straight line whose slope is 2 and that the line crosses the y-axis at (0, 3). Children may learn to generalize that all linear equations may be expressed as $y = mx + b$, that the line crosses the y-axis at $(0, b)$, and that the slope of the line is m. Children may also learn about negative slopes. There is, however, great danger that children will be exposed to a logically structured geometry before they are ready. This type of coordinate geometry is also omitted from this book.

Research evidence is needed to determine how much postulational geometry and how much coordinate geometry should be incorporated into the elementary school mathematics curriculum. Until this is determined by experimental means, each school will formulate its own mathematics curriculum and each teacher will determine how much of this material should be taught in his classroom. The teacher should always observe sound pedagogical and educational principles based on good learning theory.

11.5 SUMMARY

In the past, geometry had been taught as a formal system of definitions, postulates, constructions, and theorems. Formal proof was stressed at all times. Today, algebra has become the subject of a formal system of postulates, definitions, and deductive proof. Many of the involved theorems of geometry have become simple exercises in coordinate geometry. Children are now learning geometry intuitively. By means of constructions they discover for themselves many of the relations in geometry. An effort is made at all times to relate arithmetic, algebra, and geometry. The concept of set makes it possible to unify these three subjects. This is not to imply that the three subjects do not have distinct characteristics of their own.

EXERCISES

1. Draw four points A, B, C, and D, no three of which are on the same line. Draw lines connecting two of the points. Name all the lines you can draw. Name all the rays. Name all the angles formed.
2. Mark three points on the same line. How many different rays can you name? How many different line segments can you name?
3. Draw a triangle. Measure each side. How does the sum of the measures of any two sides compare with the third side?
4. Draw a triangle and extend one side in only one direction. How does the measure of the exterior angle compare with the measures of the interior angles? With the sum of the measures of two interior angles?
5. Draw two points A and B. With A and B as centers and a radius that is

greater than the distance AB, construct two circles. Do these circles intersect? In how many points? Draw line segments from A to the points of intersection, from B to the points of intersection, and from A to B. How many triangles are formed? What kind of triangles are they? What can you conclude about the two triangles?

6. Repeat Exercise 5, but this time use a radius that is equal to the distance AB. What kind of triangles are formed? Why?
7. Mark two dots, A and B, on a sheet of paper. Draw a circles through A and B. Can you draw a second circle through A and B that is different from the first one? Can you draw a third circle? A fourth? Where do the centers of these circles lie?
8. Construct an isosceles triangle. Draw a perpendicular from the endpoint of the two congruent sides to the third side. What does the perpendicular do to the third side? What does the perpendicular do to the angle formed by the two congruent sides?
9. Draw a triangle. From each vertex draw a perpendicular to the opposite side. What conclusion can you draw about the three perpendiculars?
10. Draw a triangle. Draw a segment from each vertex to the midpoint of the opposite side. These segments are called medians. What conclusion can you form about the three medians?
11. Draw a triangle. Construct a perpendicular bisector to each side of the triangle. What conclusion can you form about the three perpendicular bisectors?
12. Draw a triangle. Bisect each angle. What conclusion can you form about the three angle bisectors?
13. Draw any quadrilateral. Find the midpoint of each side. Draw line segments connecting these midpoints. What conclusions can you form?
14. Discuss the concept of set in the changing concepts of geometry.
15. Some educators agree that primary grade children can learn a great deal of geometry but question the advisability of teaching young children geometry. Discuss the pros and cons of this question.
16. The geometry of space was not discussed in this chapter. How would you expose children to three dimensional space?
17. How would you introduce children to simple proofs?
18. What is the relationship between concepts in geometry and measurement exercises such as areas, perimeters, circumferences, etc?

SUGGESTED SUPPLEMENTARY READING

1. Bell, Clifford, Clela D. Hammond, and Robert B. Herrera, *Fundamentals of Arithmetic for Teachers*. New York: John Wiley and Sons, 1962. Chap. 21.
2. Brumfiel, Charles F., et al., *Principles of Arithmetic*. Reading, Mass.: Addison-Wesley Publishing Company, 1963. Chap. 16.
3. Brune, Irvin H., "Geometry in the Grades," *The Arithmetic Teacher*, May 1961. pp. 210–219.
4. ———, "Some Geometric Ideas for Junior High School," *The Mathematics Teacher*, April 1963. pp. 620–626.

5. Denmark, Thomas, and Robert Kalin, "Suitability of Teaching Geometric Construction in Upper Elementary Grades—A Pilot Study," *The Arithmetic Teacher,* February 1964. pp. 73–80.
6. Goldmark, Berniece, "Geometry in the Primary Grades," *The Arithmetic Teacher,* April 1963. pp. 191–192.
7. Hawley, Newton, and Patrick Suppes, *Geometry for Grades,* Books 1 and 2, Teachers Manual. San Francisco: Holden-Day, 1961.
8. Keedy, Mervin L., *A Modern Introduction to Basic Mathematics.* Reading, Mass.: Addison-Wesley Publishing Company, 1963. Chap. 14.
9. Lamb, Pose M., "Geometry for Third and Fourth Graders," *The Arithmetic Teacher,* April 1963. pp. 193–194.
10. Meder, A. E., "What Is Wrong with Euclid?" *The Mathematics Teacher,* December 1958. pp. 578–584.
11. Meserve, Bruce E., "New Trends in Algebra and Geometry," *The Mathematics Teacher,* October 1962. pp. 457–461.
12. Rutland, Leon, and Max Hosier, "Some Basic Geometric Ideas for Elementary Teachers," *The Arithmetic Teacher,* November 1961. pp. 357–362.
13. School Mathematics Study Group, *Mathematics for the Elementary School,* Teachers Commentary. Yale University, 1961.

Chapter 12 Problem Solving

12.1 INTRODUCTION

Problem solving has been discussed in several chapters of this book. The purpose of this chapter is to discuss and to analyze the factors that are basic to the development of the ability to solve problems. The question of problem solving receives a prominent place in every book on methods of teaching mathematics. A number of articles on problem solving have been published in various educational journals. There is general agreement that problem solving is difficult. There also appears to be general agreement that schools have not been too successful in training children to solve problems.

Some educators believe that mathematics is a tool to be used in solving practical problems of everyday life. This view holds that social utility is the main purpose for studying mathematics. Others believe that mathematics is principally applied to the solution of science problems. This view considers mathematics to be applied science. A third view is that problem solving is synonymous with learning itself, that all learning is problem solving. The mathematician who believes in pure mathematics as opposed to applied mathematics also regards problem solving very highly, but his interpretation of a problem is different from the one held by the others.

Recognizing the importance of problem solving in the educational development of children many writers have offered suggestions that will help children learn to solve problems. Children are advised to read carefully, to search out the information and the thing that is sought, to try to diagram the situation, and to set up the proper equation. They often suggest clues for the search. All of these suggestions are worthwhile, but children still find problem solving a difficult task.

An analysis of the nature of problem solving should convince one that the teacher cannot teach children to solve problems. Problem solving is an internal intellectual experience. The teacher who is aware of the nature of problem solving will strive to conduct his class in such a manner that children will have the opportunity to develop this ability. The teacher is the resource person, the guide, the one who selects the activities, the one who challenges the children, and the one who skillfully motivates children to work according to their abilities. But problem solving is at all times an internal experience.

12.2 WHAT IS A PROBLEM?

There are many interpretations of what a problem really is. Some consider any verbal statement to be a problem. This distinguishes a problem from a mere exercise. As long as the question is stated in words, this is considered to be a problem. This is an artificial distinction. If the child is asked to find the product of 8 and 5, this is called an exercise. If the child, on the other hand, is asked to find the area of a rectangle whose length is 8 units and whose width is 5 units, this is called a problem. Both of these are in reality exercises. Verbal statements are too often the excuse for exercises.

Some teachers consider a problem to be a situation to which the answer is not immediately apparent. According to this interpretation the necessary computation is not indicated but must be determined by the child. In an exercise the child is told what mathematical operation he must perform, but in a problem he must figure out what operation or operations are necessary to derive the solution. This is a somewhat narrow interpretation of a problem.

Some teachers distinguish between an exercise and a problem by the complexity of the situation. If it is easy, it is an exercise. If it is difficult, it is a problem. This, too, is an inadequate definition of a problem.

Of the many interpretations of a problem, the one given by McSwain and Cooke is the most helpful in the analysis of problem solving. According to them, "A problem is a particular situation in which a person encounters a blocking of mental and/or physical action in reaching a desired goal."* This definition emphasizes two concepts, blocking and a goal. Before a child can have a problem he must have a desired goal. If he wants to achieve a goal but something prevents him from achieving it, he has a problem. If he does not have a goal he has no problem. The verbal statement in a textbook should present a problem

*E. T. McSwain and Ralph J. Cooke, *Understanding and Teaching Arithmetic in the Elementary School.* New York: Henry Holt and Company, 1958. p. 285.

that the child wants to solve but to which he cannot find an immediate answer. This inability to find the answer when he desires to find the answer constitutes the problem. The apathy toward much of mathematics that is displayed by many children comes from the fact that the children do not really desire to find the answer; that this is not their goal.

The above definition of a problem emphasizes the need for proper motivation so that the child's goal will be the same as the school's. Let us examine a typical exercise found in many textbooks. Johnny sells 21 papers on Monday, 28 on Tuesday, 25 on Wednesday, 18 on Thursday, and 19 on Friday. What is the average number of papers that Johnny sells a day? Now the child who reads this exercise may not be interested in Johnny's success in selling papers. This is not a problem for the child in the classroom unless he is interested in finding the answer. A child may be bored with classroom exercises and refuse to do them. He may be punished for not doing the assignment. His problem then becomes one of avoiding punishment, not solving problems of mathematics.

Many textbooks in the past contained numerous exercises about taxes, insurance, installment buying, and stocks and bonds. Such problems were considered necessary in order to prepare children for future social needs. But are such exercises important to children? Is solving such exercises a part of children's desired goals? Unless children are motivated so that they are interested in finding the answers to such questions, these are not problems to them.

Some children find many verbal statements difficult because they have reading difficulties. They may have the mathematical skills to find the correct answer, but they do not understand what is asked. These are not mathematics problems, they are reading problems. Verbal statements should be phrased in language that children understand. It is only when the child understands what he reads and wants to find the answer to a question but does not know how to find the answer, that he has a real problem.

If a verbal statement is so perplexing to a child that he decides that there is no use in even trying to find the answer, he no longer has a problem. He may have had the desired goal, to find the answer, but if the perplexing situation makes him discard the goal he no longer has a problem. Teachers often assume that if exercises are assigned to children they will accept them as problems. This may be true in many instances, but there are also many instances where children do exercises only to please the teacher.

It becomes quite evident that very few exercises in textbooks are real problems. Real life problems are seldom found in the classroom. The verbal exercises are still exercises. It becomes necessary to present simulated problems in textbooks or in the classroom. These are exercises that children are willing to accept as if they were real problems. If verbal statements are to be accepted by children as problems, that is, if finding the answers are desirable goals, certain conditions have to be met. The statements should be meaningful to children. They should represent situations that come within children's experience. The mathematical skills necessary for a given solution should be those that children have mastered. If children do not have the necessary skills, they will give up.

It must be understood that meaningful experiences do not necessarily mean social experiences found outside the classroom. Children who have studied negative numbers will accept problems that involve negative numbers. Operations with negative numbers or the graphing of functions may be meaningful experiences to children even if they do not relate them to a practical situation. Abstract number relations may be more acceptable to children as problem situations than the so-called practical problems.

12.3 WHO IS THE PROBLEM SOLVER?

The problem solver is the one who has the problem. If a child is confronted with a situation whose solution is not immediately apparent, and he wants to find that solution but cannot, he has a problem. Since he is frustrated by his inability to find the solution to his problem, he may seek some help. If he asks his teacher for help and his teacher shows him how to find the answer, has the child solved the problem? It is evident that, in this case, the child has not solved his problem. The next time he is faced with a similar situation he will have the same difficulty. Showing or telling the child the answer will merely supply the child with the answer, not help him to solve problems. The child who finds the answer by himself or follows a teacher's suggestion discovers relationships that will enable him to apply to similiar situations. In short, the only problem solver is the one who has the problem.

12.4 TRAINING CHILDREN TO SOLVE PROBLEMS

We often encounter statements about teaching children to solve problems. We cannot teach children to solve problems in the same sense that we teach children to multiply fractions or to multiply two numbers. Since the one who has the problem is the problem solver, he must find the solution himself. He cannot be taught to solve problems;

he learns to solve problems. The child develops the ability to solve problems.

The teacher's role is to provide the proper classroom situations that enable children to learn how to solve problems. The teacher motivates and challenges all children to work according to their abilities. The teacher selects the exercises and makes sure that the children have the mathematical skills necessary to find the correct solutions. The teacher can help children to develop problem-solving techniques.

12.5 EMPHASIS ON MEANINGS

Children who have learned mathematics mechanically without understanding the basic principles and concepts will find problem situations difficult to solve. Children who have been given rules to follow do not develop individual judgment. On the other hand, children who have learned to generalize have an understanding of mathematical relationships that can be applied to other situations. It is the ability to apply generalizations to different situations that forms the basis for problem solving. Children who have been encouraged to make their own discoveries are being trained for problem solving.

Some teachers demand that all children do exercises in the same way. They fear that children will be confused if they learn that there are different ways of deriving answers. Rather than confusing children, learning different ways to derive answers will develop independent thinking. Teachers should always encourage children to look for different ways of finding the answer. If a child derives the answer to a particular exercise, the teacher may ask the class if any one did it a different way. Children will not hesitate to show the class their way. If there are two different methods, is it possible that there is a third or even a fourth way? Children who are motivated to look for different ways of finding answers further their knack for making discoveries and sharpen their ability to probe into new areas. It is this ability to investigate new areas of learning that constitutes the basic factor called problem solving.

12.6 PROVIDING FOR INDIVIDUAL DIFFERENCES

It is an accepted fact that children differ in their capacity and rate of learning. This means that what is a problem to one child may not be a problem to another child. Teachers who know the children in their class know just what abilities children have. They know which children are on the operational level of learning, which are on the generalization level, and which children are capable of rationalization. Such teachers challenge children according to their ability and present children with the kind of exercises that they can do.

Teachers who are aware of the various abilities of the children will strive to differentiate the assignments so that the slower children will not be frustrated and the capable children will not be bored. Such an environment will enable children to make progress from easy assignments to more difficult ones.

Time is an important factor in problem solving. Children who work at a slow rate need, and should be given, more time. The teacher must have patience with the slow learner. Children look upon the teacher as their chief resource person. They seek help from the teacher. The teacher should refrain from telling children what to do but should guide the children to make their own discoveries. If a teacher shows impatience with children they will hesitate to ask her for help, and this will prevent establishing the kind of morale in the classroom that is conducive to problem solving.

The teacher selects the exercises. As children experience the thrill of success they are ready to tackle more difficult exercises. Children are thus motivated to accept the more difficult challenges. This principle that applies to slow learners also applies to the rapid learners. The teacher selects the exercises that will challenge the rapid learners, but the challenge must be based on the child's ability to meet it.

12.7 THE EQUATION AND PROBLEM SOLVING

Students readily admit their difficulty with word problems. This stems from their inability to set up the proper equations. Although they have learned to solve equations, many have not learned to establish equations. A verbal problem represents some action. The equation describes this action with mathematical symbols. The words are replaced by symbols. Although some words may be necessary to make English sentences grammatically correct, they may not be needed in the equivalent mathematical sentence.

Children must learn to read a sentence and see the sense of it. The action described in a verbal statement is generally represented in a mathematical sentence as a mathematical operation. Quantitative expressions contain numbers that are represented by numerals. In setting up the equation that describes the action, it is often necessary to use a placeholder for the numerals. At first children use frames for place holders because they can understand that a numeral can fit into the frame. After they understand the use of the placeholder they learn to use a letter as the placeholder for a numeral.

The ability to write mathematical equations to replace verbal statements is developed slowly. Children can learn to do this even in first grade, if the verbal statements are meaningful to them. In several chapters of this book suggestions were given to train children to write equations for stories and to write stories to fit equations. Simple statements are given at first and then more complicated situations are presented, but teachers should always keep in mind that the verbal statements should be based on children's experiences and meaningful situations. Single operations are indicated at the beginning, but a combination of operations are required for more complicated situations.

Children are often told to look for cue words in order to write the proper equation. Reliance upon cue words may often prove to be a handicap. Some cue words may indicate addition when subtraction is really meant. Examine the following example. John has 8 toys. His friend brought him some toys. Now John has 13 toys. How many toys did his friend bring? Does the child add or subtract in order to find the answer to the question. The child must recognize that John's toys and his friend's toys are combined into one set. This indicates the addition operation. Now the child writes the equation $8+\square=13$. The child can find the answer by subtracting 8 from 13. He can also find the answer by adding the required amount to 8 in order to derive the sum 13.

12.8 ORAL EXERCISES

A number of mathematics educators suggest oral exercises as a means of developing the ability to solve problems. They call such exercises mental arithmetic. This is an inaccurate term. All arithmetic is mental. Since operations are performed with numbers, these operations are mental. Written exercises are also mental. In written exercises the child performs the operations in his mind and records the result of the mental operations. Written exercises are just as much mental arithmetic as unwritten or oral exercises.

Oral exercises are good training for developing problem solving abilities. In order to do an exercise without the aid of paper and pencil we must be able to visualize the whole operation. This requires a good understanding of mathematical relationships. The more complicated the operations that a child can perform without the aid of paper and pencil, the better prepared that child will be for problem solving.

12.9 PROBLEMS WITHOUT NUMBERS

Many textbook writers include mathematical problems that do not contain numbers. These are statements of situations in a generalized form that do not contain specific numbers. Children explain the general relationships involved and the operations that are necessary in order to find the specific answers. An example of a problem without numbers is the following: How do you find the percent of increase in the population of a city from one year to another? Children may reason that to find the amount of increase one subtracts the population of the first year from the second year. Then this number is divided by the population during the first year. This can be done better with mathematical symbols. If x represents the population the first year and y represents the population the second year, the percent of increase is $\frac{y-x}{x}$.

12.10 GAMES AND PUZZLES

No chapter on problem solving can be considered complete without some consideration of number games and puzzle-type problems. These have always been strong and effective devices to motivate children to an interest in mathematics. Very often when there is a lull in classroom activities or when general interest in school work has become weak, the teacher presents the class with a puzzling number situation. The reaction is usually quick. The teacher who has a bag of tricks can use them at the appropriate time to arouse interest and to stimulate further interest in mathematics. Care must be taken to select the games that require mathematical understanding for their solution. Too often children are presented with games that have very little mathematical import. The teacher should select those puzzle-type problems that help strengthen the understanding of basic concepts in mathematics. It is also advisable to select the kind of mathematical puzzle that will lead children to create their own puzzles.

Three Men in a Hotel. Three men rented a room in a hotel and paid the $30 that the manager requested. After the men went to their room the hotel manager decided that he had overcharged the men. He called over the bellboy and gave him $5 to return to the three men. The bellboy thought that it would be difficult to divide $5 equally among three men. He therefore pocketed $2 and returned $3 to the men with the explanation that they had been overcharged for the room. The $27 that the men paid for the room and the $2 kept by the bellboy add up to only $29. What happened to the missing dollar? This question puzzles college students as well as elementary school children. The answer to the question is that the wrong numbers were added. The $2 kept by the bellboy is included in the $27 and should, therefore, not be added to the $27. The correct equation is $27 (paid for the room) = $25 (paid to the manager) + $2 (kept by the bellboy).

Think of a Number. There are many types of number games that begin with, "Think of a number." Think of a number. Double it. Add 5. Multiply the result by 5. Give me your answer and I will tell you what your number was. Subtract 25 from the answer. The result is 10 times the original number. This can be represented in equation form as follows:

	Let $x =$ the number	Step 1
Double the number	$2x$	Step 2
Add 5	$2x+5$	Step 3
Multiply by 5	$10x+25$	Step 4

This number game can be varied by adding 6, 7, 8 or any number in Step 3. Then we subtract 5×6, 5×7, 5×8, or 5 times the number added from the final answer.

This number game can also be made more complicated in the following manner: Think of a number. Double it. Add 5. Multiply the answer by 5. Add any number from 1 to 9. Now give me your answer. Subtract 25 from the answer. In the number left, the number in the one's place is the number from 1 to 9 that was added. The rest of the digits represent the original number. If the child says that his answer is 91, subtract 25. The result is 66. The original number is 6 and the number added in the last step is also 6. If the answer given is 123, subtracting 25 yields 98. The original number is 9 and the number added in the last step is 8. The children are eager to give their answers. The teacher subtracts 25 mentally from each answer and then is able to announce the two numbers used by the child. Often the child will say that the teacher did not give the correct answers. In that case have the child retrace his steps. He will find that he made an error. The algebraic explanation is as follows:

	Let $x =$ the number	Step 1
Double the number	$2x$	Step 2
Add 5	$2x+5$	Step 3
Multiply by 5	$10x+25$	Step 4
Add a number 1–9	$10x+25+a$	Step 5

Subtracting 25 from the final answer gives $10x+a$. Multiplying the number x by 10 moves the digits one place to the left. The one's place is occupied by a, the number added in Step 5.

The following is another number game. Think of a number. Add 3. Multiply the answer by 2. Add 2. Divide the answer by 2. Subtract the original number. The answer is 4. Children want to know why this is so. The algebraic explanation is:

	Let $x=$ the number	Step 1
Add 3	$x+3$	Step 2
Multiply by 2	$2x+6$	Step 3
Add 2	$2x+8$	Step 4
Divide by 2	$x+4$	Step 5
Subtract original number	4	Step 6

The important thing in all of the above examples is to have children learn to set up the equation as representative of the action taking place. Children should learn to use a placeholder for the number. This placeholder is a frame at first and then a letter such as x or y. When children learn to solve such puzzles by using the equation method, they develop a better understanding of mathematics. They also learn how to solve mathematical problems.

Guess the Number. Think of any number from 0 to 127. Allow me seven questions that you must answer by yes or no and I will tell you what your number is. This can be done if we think of numbers in the binary numeration system. Let us say that the number is 100. The highest binary digit in numbers from 0 to 127 is 64. My first question is, "Is the number greater than 63?" The answer, of course, is yes. Therefore I know that the number contains 1 sixty-four. Now I add 32 to the 63 and my second question is, "Is the number greater than 95?" The answer, of course, is yes. Therefore I know that the number contains at least 1 sixty-four and 1 thirty-two. My third question is, "Is the number greater than 111?" $(95+16)$. The answer, of course, is no. Mentally I have the following digits of the incomplete number: 1100000. My fourth question is, "Is the number greater than 103?" $(95+8)$. The answer is no. I still have the digits 1100000. The fifth question. "Is the number greater than 99?" $(95+4)$. The answer is yes. The incomplete number is now represented as 1100100. The sixth question. "Is the number greater than 101?" $(99+2)$. The answer is no. Since the number is greater than 99 and not greater than 101, it is either 100 or 101. The seventh question. "Is the number greater than 100?" $(99+1)$. The answer is no. Since the number is greater than 99 and not greater than 100, it must be 100. Any number from 0 to 63 should be guessed in 6 questions because the highest binary digit is 32, or 2^5, or in the sixth place. Any number from 0 to 255 should be guessed in 8 questions because the highest binary digit is 128, or 2^7, or the digit in the eighth place in the binary place-value numeration system.

X *Guess the Number.* Guess any number from 1 to 15. We think of all the fifteen numbers as written in the binary system. List all the numbers that have a digit in the ones place in the first column, all the numbers that have a digit in the twos place in the second column, all the numbers that have a digit in the fours place in the third column, and all of the numbers that have a digit in the eights place in the fourth column. The following is the complete table:

1	2	3	4
1	2	4	8
3	3	5	9
5	6	6	10
7	7	7	11
9	10	12	12
11	11	13	13
13	14	14	14
15	15	15	15

Let the child indicate the columns that contain his number. Write a 1 in each column in reverse order and a 0 for the column not mentioned This will give the binary numeral which must be translated into the decimal system. If the child says that his number is in columns 1 and 4, we write 1001 and recognize the number 9. If he says that the number is in columns 2, 3, and 4, we write 1110 and recognize the decimal number 14. Let children discover that the binary numeration system is used.

The Counterfeit Coin. A man has 12 coins of the same denomination, one of which is a counterfeit coin. We will assume that the counterfeit coin is lighter than the other coins and we will assume that all of the good coins are exactly the same weight. If we have a balance scale, how can we find the counterfeit coin in three weighings? Children will discover the trick. Separate the coins into 3 sets of 4 coins each. Place one set of coins on one side of the balance scale and a second set on the other side. If the two sets balance each other, we know that the counterfeit coin is in the third set. Now separate the four coins of the third set into two sets of two coins each. Place them on the balance scale. One of the sets will be the lighter one. Balance the two coins on the scale for the third weighing and determine which is the lighter coin. If the counterfeit coin is in one of the two sets of the first weighing then select the lighter set and proceed as before.

The same procedure is followed if it is known that the counterfeit coin is the heavy coin. If it is not known whether the counterfeit coin is heavier or lighter, a fourth weighing is necessary.

12.11 SUMMARY

Problem solving is an important part of mathematical learning. It is not a skill that can be taught children in the same way as mathematical operations or computations. Problem solving is an internal psychological process. The teacher can help the child develop this ability by providing a wholesome classroom atmosphere that is conducive to such learning. The teacher must recognize the needs of every child as well as the particular abilities of the children. If children are encouraged to make generalizations by their own discoveries of mathematical relations rather than to follow rules presented by the teacher, those children will be better prepared for problem solving. If the work in a classroom is paced so that each child works according to his own rate of learning, children will be better prepared for problem solving. If children are taught mathematics in a meaningful way so that they understand the structure and basic postulates and concepts of mathematics, they will be better prepared for problem solving. If children are given the opportunity from the very beginning to write equations for verbal statements, they will be better prepared for problem solving. If children are presented with situations that come within their experience, and are therefore meaningful, they will be better prepared for problem solving. Finally, if teachers will be patient with children and refrain from showing or telling them but let them work out their own solutions even if it takes more time, then children will be better prepared for problem solving.

EXERCISES

1. If it takes 6 minutes to saw a log, how long will it take to saw a log into 4 pieces?
2. A child took 15 cents to buy one 10-cent candy bar and one 5-cent candy bar. When he arrived at the store, he found that there was a sale. The 10-cent candy sold for 5 cents and the 5-cent candy sold for 3 cents. In how many different ways can the child spend all or part of the 15 cents?
3. A little theatre contains 100 seats. Adult tickets sell for \$5 each, and children's tickets sell for 50 cents each. How many tickets of each kind have to be sold so that 100 tickets bring in \$100?
4. What is the answer to Exercise 3 if adult tickets are reduced to \$3?
5. Find the product 37×48 without using pencil and paper. Explain how you derived your answer.
6. Estimate the product $9\frac{1}{4} \times 19\frac{5}{6}$. Explain how you estimated your answer.
7. A teacher presented the following question to the class, "If I live 5 miles from school, how long will it take me to drive home?" Discuss the possible reactions of children to this question.

8. A teacher presented the following exercise to the class, "A man bought a truck for $2900. How long will it take him to pay for the truck?" Discuss the possible reactions of children to this question.
9. What value is there in posing questions to children like those in Exercise 7 and Exercise 8?
10. Examine an arithmetic textbook and select three exercises that represent the kind of experiences that elementary school children would have experienced.
11. Make up five exercises that are problems without numbers.
12. Discuss the difference, if any, between a problem and a puzzle.

SUGGESTED SUPPLEMENTARY READING

1. Alexander, Vincent E., "Seventh Grader's Ability to Solve Problems," *School Science and Mathematics,* November 1960. pp. 603–606.
2. Banks, J. Houston, *Learning and Teaching Arithmetic*. Boston: Allyn and Bacon, 1959. Chap. 13.
3. Brownell, William A., "Problem Solving," *The Psychology of Learning,* Forty-First Yearbook, Part II, National Society for the Study of Education. Chicago: University of Chicago Press, 1942. Chap. 12.
4. Burch, Robert L., "Formal Analysis as a Problem-Solving Procedure," *Journal of Education,* November 1953. pp. 44–47.
5. Buswell, Guy T., *Patterns of Thinking in Solving Problems*. University of California Publications in Education, Vol. 12, No. 2. Berkeley and Los Angeles: University of California Press, 1956. pp. 63–148.
6. Flournoy, Frances, "Developing Ability in Mental Arithmetic," *The Arithmetic Teacher,* October 1957. pp. 147–150.
7. ———"Providing Mental Arithmetic Experiences," *The Arithmetic Teacher,* April 1959. pp. 133–139.
8. Grossnickle, Foster E., "Verbal Problem Solving," *The Arithmetic Teacher,* January 1964. pp. 12–17.
9. Grossnickle, Foster E., and Leo J. Brueckner, *Discovering Meanings in Arithmetic*. New York: Holt, Rinehart, and Winston, 1959. Chap. 13.
10. Hall, Jack V., "Mental Arithmetic: Misunderstood Terms and Meanings," *The Elementary School Journal,* Vol. 54, 1956. pp. 349–353.
11. Henderson, Kenneth B., and Robert E. Pingry, "Problem-Solving in Mathematics," *The Learning of Mathematics, Its Theory and Practice,* Twenty-First Yearbook, The National Council of Teachers of Mathematics. Washington, D.C.: The National Council of Teachers of Mathematics, 1953. Chap. 8.
12. Koenker, Robert H., "Twenty Methods for Improving Problem Solving," *The Arithmetic Teacher,* March 1958. pp. 74–78.
13. Manheim, Jerome, "Word Problems or Problems with Words," *The Mathematics Teacher,* April 1961. pp. 234–238.
14. Marks, John L., C. Richard Purdy, and Lucien B. Kinney, *Teaching Arithmetic for Understanding*. New York: McGraw-Hill Book Company, 1958.
15. McSwain, E. T., and Ralph Cooke, *Understanding and Teaching Arithmetic in the Elementary School.* New York: Henry Holt and Company, 1958. Chap. 11.

16. Pace, Angela, "Understanding and the Ability to Solve Problems," *The Arithmetic Teacher,* May 1961.
17. Petty, Olan, "Non-Pencil-and-Paper Solution of Problems," *The Arithmetic Teacher,* December 1956. pp. 229–235.
18. Sawyer, W.W., "Tricks and Why They Work," *Enrichment Mathematics for the Grades,* Twenty-Seventh Yearbook, The National Council of Teachers of Mathematics. Washington, D.C.: The National Council of Teachers of Mathematics, 1963. Chap. 12.
19. Schaaf, William L., "A Realistic Approach to Problem-Solving in Arithmetic," *The Elementary School Journal,* May 1946. pp. 494–497.
20. Sobel, Max A., "Providing for the Slow Learner in the Junior High School," *The Mathematics Teacher,* May 1959. pp. 347–353.
21. Spitzer, Herbert F., *The Teaching of Arithmetic.* Boston: Houghton Mifflin Company, 1954. Chap. 6.
22. Spitzer, Herbert F., and Frances Flournoy, "Developing Facility in Solving Verbal Problems," *The Arithmetic Teacher,* November 1956. pp. 177–182.
23. Thorpe, Cleata E., "Those Problem-Solving Perplexities," *The Arithmetic Teacher,* April 1961. pp. 152–156.
24. Van Engen, H., "Twentieth Century Mathematics for the Elementary School," *The Arithmetic Teacher,* March 1959. pp. 71–76.

Chapter 13 *Evaluation*

13.1 INTRODUCTION

Evaluation is important because everyone who participates in an educational project is rightly concerned about its successful outcome. The superintendent of schools is concerned about the overall program of the school system. The principal wants to know how effective his school's program is. The teacher is interested in the progress that he is making in teaching the school's curriculum for that grade.

Evaluation is a continuous process that attempts to answer three questions. What are the goals? Are the goals being achieved? Are the goals being achieved in the most effective manner? The answers to these questions determine whether a curriculum should be modified and to what extent. If the goals are not achieved, why not? Is it necessary to make some changes in order to effectuate the program? If the goals are achieved, are they worthwhile goals? Can the school set higher goals? Consideration of these questions determines whether goals should be maintained, modified, or discarded.

Although these questions are important for all schools, they are not the concern of this book. We are interested only in the mathematics program of the elementary school. The mathematical concepts and understandings that children should learn have been described in the preceding chapters. This chapter is devoted to the methods that a teacher can use to determine how well the children have learned these concepts.

13.2 THE NATURE AND PURPOSE OF EVALUATION

To many teachers evaluation is synonymous with testing. Every student has experienced numerous tests throughout his school life.

Although testing is an important aspect of evaluation, it is not the only means, and often it is not the best means of evaluating a pupil's progress.

To many teachers evaluation is synonymous with grading. The office demands a grade for each pupil, and the parents expect grades for their children. Teachers fulfill these demands by testing children and by assigning grades that are based on the test results. Although grades are an inevitable part of most schools, evaluation goes much further than the assigning of grades.

Since the teacher is concerned with education of each child, he is interested in the progress made by each child. The teacher wants to know if the children in the class have achieved the goals which were established for that class. Those children who have not made sufficient progress need help from the teacher. Perhaps they need concrete aids or different aids. Perhaps the teacher should use different teaching techniques. The children who have made sufficient progress in their understanding of mathematical concepts should be challenged by more difficult situations. *The purpose of evaluation is to promote learning.*

Although tests generally reveal a child's ability to perform computational skills, the ability to perform these skills is no longer the main goal of the mathematics program. Children are encouraged to discover generalizations and mathematical relationships. Children are expected to learn the structure of mathematics and to apply their knowledge to problem situations. To measure children's progress in understanding, the teacher finds tests to be inadequate. He finds it necessary to use other techniques than testing. Teachers learn that a variety of techniques is more effective than a reliance on one technique, mainly tests.

13.3 PAPER-AND-PENCIL-TYPE TESTS

The most common means of testing children is to administer a paper-and-pencil-type test. Everyone who goes to school experiences this type of test. A student is given a set of exercises or questions, and he answers them on paper. There are many variations of this type of test. There may be true-false, multiple choice, or completion tests as well as a request to do all the computations on the answer sheet. Sometimes the answer sheet is such that the student punches holes out. All of these tests are based on the same techniques, questions, and written answers.

1. *Teacher-made tests.* The most common paper-and-pencil-type test is one made up by the teacher. The teacher has taught the chil-

dren some mathematics. Have they learned it? Have the goals been achieved? The teacher is the best judge of what learning situations have been presented in the class. The teacher wants to have immediate evidence of the progress made by the children. The teacher will generally include only those items that have been covered in class. The teacher may also include some completely new items in order to test children's ability to apply knowledge to new situations. The teacher learns how effective the teaching has been. It is a test of the teacher as well as the child. The teacher learns which children have not learned a given process. The teacher will use the test results to help children in those areas that they need help. If many children have not succeeded in learning a given skill, the whole class has to be retaught.

If used properly, teacher-made tests are important tools in the evaluation process. It may be important to know which children have high ability and which have low ability. If tests are used for the sole purpose of assigning marks to children then they do not promote learning. The children with high ability will receive the high grades, and the children with low ability will receive low grades. Will it help children make progress if they receive the same grade year after year? Achievement in learning, rather than grades, should be the main purpose for testing.

The child who has missed certain exercises knows that he needs improvement in those areas. Properly administered, tests should be welcomed by children. Children will become eager to take tests if they know that tests will be used to measure their progress rather than to give them grades. Used for this purpose, children will measure their progress according to their own standard rather than the standard established by other children. Competition for grades may be a stimulus for greater effort for some children, but competition as a steady diet soon loses its effect. Competition for grades very often upsets the wholesome classroom situation that promotes learning and often proves to be a frustrating experience to many children.

2. *Textbook tests.* Most textbooks include a number of tests, both chapter tests and semester tests. They have the advantage over teacher-made tests because they are usually made by experts. Not every teacher knows how to construct a good test that is meaningful to children and that tests the understanding of the mathematical vocabulary and concepts. The textbook authors generally set up norms for their tests, based on a larger sample and wider application than a single teacher's class. These norms are often translated into grade levels. The teacher who uses the textbook tests has a better instrument to measure a child's progress. If a child scores a 6.3 grade level at the beginning of a

semester and a 7.1 grade level at the end of the semester, the teacher knows that this child has improved 0.8 grade in one semester.

The textbook tests are often more varied than teacher-made tests. Some are overall achievement tests, some are readiness tests, and some are diagnostic tests. Textbook tests, however, have one disadvantage as compared to teacher-made tests. The teacher knows the children and the community in which the children live. The teacher can select examples that are closer to the children's experiences. Textbook tests are applied to children in many states, and the examples selected by these authors have a tendency to be less personal than those selected by teachers.

3. *Departmental tests.* A departmental test is the combined effort of teachers who pool their ability. Since these teachers are aware of the goals for the particular school or the particular school system, such tests are a better means of evaluating progress in achieving these goals than the textbook tests. These tests are constructed by several teachers who may be teaching the same grade in a particular school or in several schools of the system. Since most teachers have a tendency to emphasize in their teaching those concepts that they understand well and to neglect the areas in which they feel less secure, they will construct tests that will reflect this attitude. The teacher who feels insecure with percent will not spend sufficient time with percent, even though the curriculum calls for this topic. The departmental tests will alert teachers to the need for treating each topic adequately.

Departmental tests serve a useful function, but they may be misused. If they are used solely to grade the children then they no longer have the effect of promoting learning. They may be used by some principals to grade teachers. This may result in making teachers insecure, and the teachers may resort to teaching test material rather than promoting mathematical understanding. There are many factors that should be considered in interpreting the results of achievement tests. The teacher whose class has scored low on a test may have done a more effective teaching job than the teacher whose class scored high on the test. If these tests are administered to children in several schools, the schools may be judged by the results of the tests. It is unfair to judge the schools for the same reason that it is unfair to judge the teachers.

These tests, when used properly, will indicate what kind of help children need. This will promote learning. When teachers pool their abilities, they will produce more challenging exercises for the more advanced students and more effective exercises for the less advanced students.

4. *Standardized tests.* Standardized tests have become very popular in the last few decades. Based on a large sample that is nationwide, the norms established for these tests have wider applicability than textbook tests or departmental tests. Since these norms are truly national norms, teachers using such standardized tests have the most effective instrument for measuring the progress made by each individual child. Whereas most tests indicate a child's ability to get correct answers, the number of correct answers achieved on a standardized test are translated into grade scores.

It is often important to rank a child's accomplishment in mathematics in relation to other children in the country. We can determine if a child ranks in the upper fifth, tenth, or half of the grade population or if another child ranks in the lower fifth, third, or fourth of the grade population. Standardized tests are means of ranking children according to ability.

The very strength of standardized tests is also their weakness. Since they are based on results of testing children in different geographic locations, cultures, and experiences, these tests may reflect lower norms than would result from testing children in selected areas. The standards established in some schools are higher than those in other schools. Some educators may be too easily satisfied by children's achievement that is measured by standardized tests. Children who rank in the 80th percentile may be capable of doing much better work than the rank indicates.

A more serious criticism of standardized tests is based on the scores and what they reflect. In administering standardized tests we must follow instructions precisely and use the answer key without any modification. Failure to do so invalidates the norms. An answer is either right or wrong. One child reads the exercise, understands what he reads, translates it into mathematical symbols, makes the proper substitutions, performs the calculations, but makes a slight error. He gets no credit for his effort. A second child reads the same exercise and is completely baffled. He does not even attempt to do the exercise. He also gets no credit. Both children receive the same treatment, no credit. Yet one child has done considerable thinking as a result of his understanding whereas the other child has done no thinking. It is evident that the first child is penalized because the test does not allow for any partial credit. The score indicates the ability to obtain the correct answer rather than mathematical understanding.

13.4 OTHER EVALUATION TECHNIQUES

The paper-and-pencil-type tests are important evaluation tools, but they do not meet the needs for complete evaluation. The new elementary school mathematics programs emphasize understanding. The general criticism of all paper-and-pencil tests is that they measure computation skills. To measure understanding other techniques have to be developed. Some leading educators believe that it is not possible to measure understanding by means of paper-and-pencil tests. They consider understanding to be an internal psychological process that requires other tools and techniques. Although it is true that paper-and-pencil tests measure computational skills, efforts have been made to devise paper-and-pencil tests that do measure understanding.*

1. *Recitation.* Teachers have always used the recitation as a means of evaluating children's understanding. Children put exercises on the blackboard and explain how they obtained their answers. The oral recitation reveals what the child is thinking. The teacher asks questions to make sure that the child really understands what he is doing. How the child responds to the questions gives the teacher a better opportunity to judge what the child knows than if the child merely records a correct answer on a standardized test.

The teacher will also be in a better position to determine whether the child is ready for more challenging situations.

2. *Observations.* The teacher observes children working at their seats. Some children do not recite well, even though they do have understanding. At their seats they feel more comfortable and are more confident in their response to the teacher's questions. The teacher observes the children at their work, notes the manner in which they attack problems, and also the kind of exercises they select. Since the children are working at their own level, the teacher can evaluate each child.

3. *Individual conferences.* Teachers have found this method very effective for measuring understanding as well as for diagnosing pupil difficulties. In a personal interview the teacher has the opportunity to ask the child questions and to rephrase the questions in order to make sure that the child really understands the questions. The teacher picks an example and notes how the child answers it. He modifies the example slightly or radically, according to need, and observes the child's new reactions. He selects different questions and examples for different children. The personal conference is a private matter between the child and the teacher. Its purpose is to diagnose children's degree of understanding or lack of understanding.

*David Rappaport, *Understanding Meanings in Arithmetic—A Diagnostic Test.* Chicago: Science Research Associates, Inc., 1959.

4. *Criticism of non-paper-and-pencil evaluation techniques.* Teachers tend to prefer the paper-and-pencil tests because they are objective techniques. It is easy to mark such tests because answers are either right or wrong. It is easy to assign a child a grade by averaging test scores. The teacher is impersonal in marking test papers. This attitude on the part of teachers reflects their emphasis on grades. Those teachers who are concerned about children's mathematical understanding do not rely on the easily scored objective tests.

The objection to the non-paper-and-pencil techniques described above is that they are subjective. The teacher's observation of children's reactions to particular questions are, of course, highly subjective. But they are not used to determine children's grades. The main purpose is to help children where they need help and to determine what kind of challenges to present them, the fast learners and the slow learners. Many teachers prefer the subjective techniques but find them time consuming. The personal interviews may have to be carried out infrequently, but when they are held they are effective.

13.5 ANECDOTAL RECORDS

Anecdotal records have been an important part of a school's records. Some of these are health records of sickness, innoculations, and health examinations. Some of these are educational records of I.Q. tests and various standardized tests and achievement tests. Anecdotal records can be kept by individual teachers on small file cards on which is recorded the child's name, date, and a description of any particular observation made by the teacher. Suppose a child has demonstrated unusual insight in solving a particular problem. This is recorded on the card. If a child demonstrates complete lack of understanding, this is also recorded on a card.

These anecdotal entries are recorded only when the occasion arises. Some teachers have the misconception that an anecdotal record must be made for each child every day in every subject. This would result in insignificant entries. They should be rare and meaningful descriptions of a child's behavior. Anecdotal records kept over a long period of time will show the actual progress that children make in their knowledge of mathematics. Anecdotal records are not, however, the sole method nor a complete method of evaluating children's learning.

13.6 GENERAL PRINCIPLES OF EVALUATION

The teacher is interested in seeing what progress children make in their learning of mathematics. The teacher wants to help each child according to his needs and ability. There are a number of objectives that the teacher has established. It is important for the teacher to know whether these aims have been achieved. Different tools or techniques are used to determine the results for particular goals. Children are expected to learn mathematical skills and their applications. These are best measured by the teacher-made tests or by textbook tests. Standardized tests are often good measures of children's progress in computational skills. Children are expected to learn the basic principles and concepts that constitute the logical mathematical system. These understandings are best measured by observation and individual conferences.

Teachers have learned to use a variety of evaluation techniques. The more techniques and tools that a teacher uses the better able he is to get a picture of the child's mathematical learning. No attempt should be made to rely on only one tool. The teacher uses as many techniques as possible. Sometimes the teacher may have only test scores for evaluating learning. As the opportunities present themselves, teachers use the subjective techniques. These are refined as the teacher has more experiences with such methods. Evaluation is a continuing process and is never complete. Evaluation is a two-way process that affects both the children and the teacher. As a result of evaluation the teacher re-examines his own methods of teaching.

QUESTIONS FOR DISCUSSION

1. In a certain school the principal administers all arithmetic tests, which he keeps in his office. Discuss the pro and con of such a practice.

2. "The only purpose of testing is to determine grades for children." Discuss this statement.

3. Standardized tests are the best tests because they are based on the result of testing many children in many sections of the country. Discuss this point of view.

4. A principal made the following statement, "I do not care if children do not understand the reason why, as long as they get the correct answers." Discuss this attitude.

5. "No person can really understand another person, so why try to measure understanding?" Discuss this statement.

6. Since all textbooks contain tests, the teacher need not be concerned about constructing his own tests. Discuss this statement.

7. Why do some teachers object to conferences with children as a means of evaluating children's learning?

8. Of what value are exercises without numbers?

9. Examine a standardized arithmetic test and analyze its good and bad features.

SUGGESTED SUPPLEMENTARY READING

1. Brueckner, Leo J., "Evaluation in Arithmetic," *Education,* January 1959. pp. 291–294.
2. Glennon, Vincent J., "Testing Meanings in Arithmetic," *Arithmetic 1949,* Supplementary Educational Monograph No. 70. Chicago: University of Chicago Press, 1949.
3. Grossnickle, Foster E., and Leo J. Brueckner, *Discovering Meanings in Arithmetic.* New York: Holt, Rinehart, and Winston, 1959. Chap. 15.
4. Harvey, Lois F., "Improving Arithmetic Skills by Testing and Reteaching," *The Elementary School Journal,* March 1953. pp. 402–409.
5. Koenker, Robert H., "Measuring the Meanings of Arithmetic," *The Arithmetic Teacher,* February 1960. pp. 93–96.
6. Marks, John L., C. Richard Purdy, and Lucien B. Kinney, *Teaching Arithmetic for Understanding.* New York: McGraw-Hill Book Company, 1958. Chap 13.
7. McSwain, E. T., and Ralph J. Cook, *Understanding and Teaching Arithmetic in the Elementary School.* New York: Henry Holt and Company, 1958. Chap. 12.
8. National Council of Teachers of Mathematics, *Evaluation in Mathematics,* Twenty-Sixth Yearbook, Washington, D.C.: The National Council, 1961.
9. Rappaport, David, "Testing for Meanings in Arithmetic," *The Arithmetic Teacher,* April 1959. pp. 140–144.
10. Shane, Harold G., and E. T. McSwain, *Evaluation and the Elementary Curriculum.* New York: Henry Holt and Company, 1951. Chap. 8.
11. Spitzer, Herbert F., *The Teaching of Arithmetic.* Boston: Houghton Mifflin Company, 1954. Chap. 12.
12. ———, "Testing Instruments and Practices in Relation to Present Concepts of Teaching Arithmetic," *The Teaching of Arithmetic,* The Fiftieth Yearbook, Part II, The National Society for the Study of Education. Chicago: University of Chicago Press, 1951. Chap. 10.
13. Sueltz, Ben A., Holmes Boynton, and Irene Sauble, "The Measurement of Understanding in Elementary School Mathematics," *The Measurement of Understanding,* Forty-Fifth Yearbook, Part I, The National Society for the Study of Education. Chicago: University of Chicago Press, 1945. Chap. 7.
14. Weaver, J. Fred, "Big Dividends from Little Interviews," *The Arithmetic Teacher,* April 1955. pp. 40–47.

INDEX